Modern Science
and
Human Freedom

Modern Science
and
Human Freedom

By David L. Miller

AUSTIN

University of Texas Press

To Mary
and Reese

Acknowledgments

MY INTEREST in the main ideas in this work developed as a graduate student at the University of Chicago, where I was privileged to study under the late George Herbert Mead. Although some of the major thoughts that are presented here existed in embryonic form at that time, I do not wish to suggest that Professor Mead would agree with my further expansion of them, nor should he be held responsible for any of the final conclusions that I have drawn.

Without a research grant from The University of Texas Research Institute during the spring semester of the 1955–56 academic year, and without release from all teaching duties and committee responsibilities during that period, this book would not have been completed.

DAVID L. MILLER

Austin, Texas

Contents

PART II

THE ETHICAL BASES OF FREEDOM

Illustrations

The Physical Bases of Science

CHAPTER I

Basic Problems

THE PEOPLE of Western culture are greatly disturbed. They do not know where to place their loyalties. Furthermore, although they give lip service to freedom and claim to fight wars under her banner, education in the classroom has led many to believe that all things, including man's thinking and behavior, are completely determined by forces over which, finally, men have no control.

This psychological disturbance over loyalties stems from the fact that Western men, after two thousand years of inner struggle, have not yet reconciled the Greek tradition with the Hebraic-Christian tradition. Our sense of law and order, necessity and determinism, logic and repetition, came from the Greeks. Our sense of freedom and creativity, responsibility and choice, individual worth and uniqueness of character, came from the Hebraic-Christian tradition. Recently the Greek components of our culture, logic, reason, and determinism, have been carried over from the physical sciences into the social sciences. Social scientists want to be "scientific" in the physicochemical sense of the term. Not only that, but many of them think of social science as directly opposed to traditional theology and religion, including that part which proclaims the determination of history through purposive behavior.

Consequently, for the Westerner the question of loyalties is taking this form: Shall we be scientific or religious? However, the real question should be: Under the impact of science and the theory of evolution, how are the two great traditions of our culture to be reconciled?

To be disloyal to the basic tenets of the Hebraic-Christian tradition is to forsake freedom, responsibility, and the hope of improving the world through human effort controlled and directed by ethical considerations. To forsake the Greek tradition means throwing science to the winds and giving up the means of accomplishing ends accepted on ethical grounds. The question is not who is right, the Greeks *or* the Hebraic-Christians. Take either component away from Western culture and the values we now subscribe to would be abandoned.

I am of the opinion that science is not a way of life. It is not a substitute for the basic values men cherished and aspired to even before the dawn of science. Science is a means, an indispensable means, of accomplishing goals and preserving cherished values assented to on ethical grounds.

Neither science, logic, nor reason can guarantee future security. To live is to take a chance with the future; to live is to live dangerously. Ethical choice always involves a choice of departure from past and present routine, habitual, fixed ways of behaving. Such choice, or self-determination, is possible only because history is irrepeatable, one-directional, noncyclical and, consequently, neither strictly logical nor repetitious. Choice, therefore, is creative and unpredictable.

I hope to show how it is possible for men to be free, how the theory of biological evolution supports the theory of freedom, and how science as a means to ends increases our freedom. Through an analysis of the meaning of evolution it will be possible to explain that neither thinking nor science is for its own sake but, rather, each is for the sake of practice necessary for changing the status quo and for shaping the environment in accordance with the hopes of men.

Logical positivists have had considerable influence on contemporary philosophy. Their main effort is directed against the belief in metaphysics, against the belief in unobservables, and, finally, against ethics as a respectable, cognitive discipline. Positivists are thoroughgoing actualists maintaining, finally, that if anything whatsoever is to have status (ontological status) it must be sensed. Their position leads to a feeling of insecurity. Men can depend only on things that exist and persist independent of men. If men are convinced that unobservables do not exist and have no status whatsoever, they will be haunted by a feeling of futility. Under the influence of positivism, Humean skepticism tends to give way to nihilism.

I am a realist in the sense that I believe in the objective existence of unobservables as well as possibilities and potentialities. And although all unobservables can be known only in relation to sense experience and behavior, they are by no means reducible to or identical with the latter.

Behaviorists have gone too far in identifying psychological, symbolic processes with overt, observable behavior. Operationalists have made the same mistake by identifying the meaning of terms with the act of measuring their referents. Pragmatists have left the erroneous impression that the referents of all signs and symbols are located in the act (of achieving goals). They suggest that life, and values, exist for the sake of action.

Yet each of these contemporary philosophies contains an important truth. Basically it is this: Sense experience and human behavior are necessarily involved in a scientific understanding of any object. But instead of showing the relationship of experience and behavior to unobservables and to the possible, these philosophers have defined the real in terms of the former and, through this act of definition, they deny the reality of the latter at the expense, finally, of freedom and ethical choice.

I am a naturalist in the sense that I believe that symbolic processes, reflective thinking, mind, and human freedom emerged in a natural way in accordance with the general theory of evolution. Yet each is an emergent, qualitatively and irreducibly different from the conditions for its emergence. Naturalism does not mean that all that is real can be expressed in quantitive terms. Qualities, too, are objective, not subjective. There is not *more* in the universe because of evolution; the world is different qualitatively, and qualities are nonadditive.

The problem of freedom, creativity, and responsibility entails also the problem of individualism. The fact that psychologists can condition lower animals to behave in predictable ways suggests that human beings, too, are conditioned to act as they do by environmental factors, and that the freedom spoken of in prescientific days has no meaning. I believe that it is impossible, in a democracy, for anyone to determine completely the behavior of another. There will never be a dictatorship by scientists regardless of how much they know. It would be contradictory to assume that the behavior of the nonscientist is wholly conditionable but that the behavior of the scientist is not. In a democracy there will never be superconditioners. Individuals are individuals simply because of the freedom they have and because of the responsibility they assume.

In *Individualism Old and New,* John Dewey points out that the old, medieval, prescientific concept of the individual does not fit the requirements of an individual in the modern world and that a new concept is sorely needed. Dewey is correct, and what is most needed is a concept of man and the individual which is in accordance with the tremendous political, economic, and moral responsibilities placed upon him in modern society. Because of science and our greater understanding of the physical world, changes in our tradition have been introduced at an ever increased rate. The basic problem for the individual is not that of keeping pace with these changes. Rather it is that of entering into the constructive business of directing and controlling them, and this is nothing other than directing and controlling science and its application toward the accomplishment of goals not furnished by science. Our chief problem today is the ethical one of selecting and agreeing on the goals selected, and not the lack of means for the accomplishment of these goals. The Greek dimension of Western culture, reason and pure science, may be of assistance in formulating goals, but their final formulation requires a creative act of mind. A knowledge of the world of fact, regardless of how much reasoning is applied to it, is not sufficient to present us with goals to which we give assent and on which we are willing to spend human effort.

The basic tenet of the Hebraic-Christian tradition is expressed poetically in the messianic hope, but when expressed prosaically it amounts to the belief that men, through human effort controlled by the highest ideals society can offer, are capable of continually improving their lot, and that, therefore, history is not a monotonous, repetitious affair. This is, of course, contrary to the Greek view that the forms of things are fixed and that time is cyclical. Consequently, the Hebraic-Christian part of our tradition, not the Greek, supports the theory of evolution and graciously approves of the theory that the individual has within himself, as a free moral agent, the authority to control his behavior and that he must assume full responsibility for doing so. The growth and development of individuals and of society is manifested in the development of pure science and in its application toward the accomplishment of ideals. Yet the motivation and justification for pure science is found only in its application which in turn is justified by goals selected on ethical grounds. The Greek dimension of our culture, pure science, without goals would be stagnant, and knowledge would then be for its own sake without extraneous ends to justify it. On the other hand, ends and the hopes of man, furnished by the Judaic-Christian movement, without the means of attaining them would remain mere ideals, pictures of realizations seen from afar and enjoyed vicariously.

The terms "modern science" and "human freedom" depend on each other for their full meaning. Each in itself is an abstraction, and both belong to the process whereby men, through a scientific understanding, use natural objects to effect ends that could not be realized without the exercise of freedom in which the behavior of men is determined by the symbolic process and choice.

Modern science is distinguished from ancient and medieval science chiefly by the fact that (1) it is experimental and (2) it is, consequently, justified on practical grounds. Experiments require *controlled conditions,* and this implies the ability of man to alter certain factors in the environment "at will," or in accordance with "free choice." Furthermore, generalizations made from a limited number of experiments (in the laboratory) can be justified only by the assumption that laboratory conditions are fair samples of conditions existing in nature outside laboratories. From this assumption it follows easily that the same kind of control and exercise of freedom that takes place in the laboratory by an experimenter may be exercised in the world of ordinary affairs.

It is indeed strange that anyone would argue, on the basis of experimental science, that every phenomenon is completely determined and that, consequently, choice and freedom are empty terms without referents. This is not only strange but contradictory, for an experiment itself presupposes the ability of the experimenter to change and control conditions so that the results would not be what they are without his intervention. Also, since "controlled conditions" implies the ability to substitute one set of conditions for another, it follows that if control is possible, no particular phenomenon must occur at a particular time. If controlled conditions are impossible, then experiments are impossible, and the laboratory technique of discovering the facts would be self-contradictory. Hence, the modern scientific method, which everyone seems willing to accept, makes sense only if we grant the existence of the freedom of man.

Once the freedom implied by experimental science is acknowledged, it will be clear that the more we learn through science the less, proportionately, will men be able to predict distant future events, contrary to present almost universal belief. The reason for this unpredictability of events of the distant future is that men, through the exercise of freedom and choice, will, from time to time, through the application of scientific knowledge, determine in minute detail what in fact does happen. If men were able to control the weather, it would, for ten years following, say, be less predictable than if it were uncontrollable. Eclipses of the moon are far more predictable than economic depressions or the price of cotton.

In prescientific days human freedom could mean little more than giving assent to ends and expressing preferences and intentions. Modern freedom implies both the selection of particular ends or goals among alternative possible ones and, through scientific knowledge, regimenting natural processes directly or indirectly through the actual manipulation of physical objects in order to actualize these selected goals.

Chapter II, which deals with the problem of unobservables, defends the realist's contention that unobservables exist and that they constitute the objects of knowledge and the aim of cognition. Unless there exists a world of objects and processes quite independent of sensations and our perceptions of them, freedom would be impossible, for there would be nothing on which men could depend as they make plans and try to control the spatiotemporal order of events. Men's perceptions and sensations are sporadic and intermittent, but at all times the physical world will lend itself to being manipulated by human hands. For centuries physicists have expressed belief in the independent existence of the physical world in their conservation theories, as exemplified by the theory of the conservation of momentum (Descartes), force (Leibnitz), mass (Newton), or mass-energy (contemporary physicists, after Einstein). In controlling the order of events men do not handle and manipulate sensations and perceptions. Instead, they manipulate physical objects, not perceptions, and an intelligent handling of them presupposes a scientific understanding of them. Freedom and control, therefore, are possible through a knowledge of unobservables—electrons, atoms, and physical objects whose essential characters cannot be expressed in terms of sensations and perceptions, which are relative to human beings.

The interpretation of modern science and freedom presented in this book requires a clearer exposition of the meaning of understanding and explanation than has been given to date. To say merely that understanding consists of a comprehension of phenomena, objects, and natural processes is insufficient, for it could lead easily to the conclusion that scientific knowledge is for its own sake, or possibly to the conclusion that the aim of pure science is to furnish a metaphysical understanding of what is ultimately real. I contend that scientific understanding is for the sake of practice, by means of which men determine not only which events shall take place but where and when. The pragmatists are correct in their insistence that a scientific understanding of phenomena is for the sake of intelligent practice. We should be quick to add, however, that both an immediate appreciation of phenomena, with their immediately attached values, and the immediate aesthetic experience constitute the "cash value" of living, and that neither is reducible to, nor can it be expressed in terms of, practice. Bergson, in particular, emphasizes that scientific understanding is completely divorced from a metaphysical understanding of things. Those who claim that there is only one kind of understanding are, in effect, trying to assimilate ends to means, and in so doing tend to deny the existence of freedom (emphasized in the Judaic-Christian tradition) by using the Greek method to show that the results of an act are determined by previously existing conditions, even as the conclusion of a syllogism is determined by its premises.

Men are free in a different sense from lower animals, and a significant question concerns how human freedom came into existence. In Chapters IV and V, I have explained the significant meaning of evolution and shown how, through the theory of evolution, the emergence of human freedom is accounted for from the naturalistic standpoint. The emergence of freedom is preceded by the emergence of language, on which it depends. Language implies the ability of one organism (self, person) to evoke in itself (implicitly at least) by use of signs the same response that it elicits in other members of society having that same language. Since, then, language can emerge only at the human social level, the kind of freedom which language makes possible emerged in human animals only.

Above all things evolution implies the emergence of genuinely new forms of things. In this sense the past, the conditions for the emergence of novelties, is qualitatively unlike these novelties. Hence, the type of creativity involved in evolution is analogous to creative intelligence whereby new concepts emerge and new ends are envisaged with correspondingly new means of achieving them. This creativity of mind is a case wherein intelligence enters into the creative advance of nature. New ideas originate in the minds of individuals. There is no corporate mind, no general will. Individuals are not only the source of new ideas but they, not society, are free and each must assume responsibility for his behavior.

Contrary to the medieval view, man is not free from the world and from laws of nature. Rather he is free in the world to the extent that he can use his environment and laws to effect new orders. Chapters VI and VII explain the nature of laws with the view that man must understand and depend on them if he is to exercise the kind of freedom and responsibility which society demands of him in a scientific age.

Regardless of the motivation for learning, whether it is from idle curiosity or a desire to alleviate needs through practical information, once men know, freedom and responsibility are increased accordingly. Unless they have the knowledge and the material means to control contagious diseases, men cannot be held morally responsible for their presence. The same applies to flood, famine, suffering, and other misfortunes. Through the development of science and an understanding of laws many of the so-called "acts of God" have come within the control of man. Consequently, to the extent that man has such control he must assume responsibility previously assigned to God alone. No wonder an entirely new concept of the individual, of his freedom, and his responsibility is required, consonant with a scientific understanding of the natural order through a knowledge of the laws of nature.

Because of the innovation of science, the very meaning of knowledge itself has changed. A scientific understanding of phenomena necessarily involves practice controlled by the symbolic process and motivated by symbols of goals to be effected through practice. Modern man has learned to depend on himself and to be self-dependent to the extent that he can depend on the stability of nature known through law. Upon the presence of a lawful order, not its absence, depends his freedom and the nerve of his responsibility.

No distinction between pure and applied science was made prior to the Renaissance and the explicit acknowledgment of the value of experiments in determining the truth value of statements about the world of fact. Early modern scientists, such as Galileo, Stevinus, Huygens, and Hooke, were purportedly interested only in pure science—in knowing the basic laws of nature, without any intention of changing the status quo. The basic question then and today is: Who in our society has the authority to decide how science is to be applied? Shall it be the scientist, the clergyman, the businessman, or shall basic decisions be made by laymen as voting citizens?

In Chapter VIII, I have shown that the distinction between pure and applied science rests on the supposition that neither science nor the pure scientist is responsible for choosing ends to be attained by applying the scientific method. In a democracy the choice of ends is made by ordinary citizens acting in the capacity of citizens, whatever their profession might be. But before fundamental knowledge or basic research can be applied, a choice of ends must be made; and if choice were unnecessary, there would be no distinction between pure and applied science.

Those who believe that science is self-regulative and that it finds expression in technology, despite human institutions and the intervention of men, are simply mistaken. The claim that pure science by its own impetus leads automatically to its own application without human choice is based on the hidden assumption that the Hebraic-Christian dimension of Western culture can be assimilated to the Greek dimension—that the teleological, purposive factors of human behavior are altogether subjective and completely extraneous in the sense that they are causally unrelated to the way in which science is applied. Those who believe science is self-perpetuating must come ultimately to the conclusion that man is like all other physical objects, devoid of the capacity to direct himself and to create ideas, symbols for possible future objectives, that can in any way direct the course of events. For them it is either all Greek or all Christian—a deterministic order or a mystical confusion.

I defend the view that there is both determinism and human freedom, that freedom means self-determination—a directing of one's behavior and, thereby, the course of events on the basis of a selection of the goals sought and, consequently, a selection of the stimuli to which the organism responds in order to attain these goals. I have no intention of defending the theology of the Western world. I wish to defend that part of the Hebraic-Christian tradition which emphasizes the freedom of man and individual responsibility, and which has been challenged by modern science through the Greek thesis that all things are completely determined. Modern scientists have concluded that all determinations are due to efficient causes alone, and that, consequently, final causes, purposes, are inoperative. Had they confined their theory of efficient causes to the physical world excluding men, they would have been correct. But the inclusion of man himself, by psychologists, anthropologists, and sociologists, means the complete annihilation of purpose, freedom, and human responsibility.

In our sober moments we know that civil liberties, individual freedom, and political freedom constitute our basic values. We will go to war and sacrifice millions of lives and kill other millions in order to defend and preserve these values. In fact we will use every scientific means at our disposal to repel those who transgress against them. How utterly irrational it would be to conclude that (1) science teaches us that the expense of human effort in its minutest detail is determined by physicochemical, electrical forces over which man has no control and (2) all motivation of man is furnished gratis by factors in his environment.

As I see it, the most severe personal problems of our generation are concerned with the responsibility of society to the individual and of the individual to society, with the entailed problems of determination and freedom. Science has given these problems an entirely new twist. Does scientific theory entail the conclusion that man is a victim of his environment instead of its master? Is the individual, as opposed to environment, culture, and tradition, instrumental in determining the direction of change? I contend that the individual is the source of new ideas, new theories, by which significant changes are introduced in society. The theory of evolution along with many facts supports this view. In fact the theory of evolution is essential in explaining the origin of freedom, contrary to the view that it implies an all-inclusive determinism.

If one is to have faith in applied science he must have faith also in the intelligence and freedom of men to direct and control it. As a corollary, if one believes freedom in the modern scientific era is a value, he must accept scientific knowledge as a necessary means for exercising it.

CHAPTER II

Do Unobservables Exist?

Scientific Realism vs. *Positivism*

IN THIS CHAPTER I shall defend the thesis that unobservables, imperceptibles have *real* existence and that they can be referred to cognitively, that we can know their logical structure, and that they are objects of knowledge—a part of the aim and end of cognition. For unobservables to have real existence means that they either occupy space at a time or have ontological status, in contrast to systemic existence, which means that they are mere shorthand expressions serving conveniently to refer to objects that can be directly observed.

This is, frankly, the position of a realist so far as the objective status of the world is concerned, and it denies that the full aim and end of cognition is found in sensibilia, sense data, or in what can be perceived. It represents a sort of bifurcation of the referents of cognition. There are perceptibles as well as imperceptibles, and both are necessary to science. Without perceptibles one could not know imperceptibles and without imperceptibles and a knowledge of them, men could not control perceptibles. But men of science and action rely, finally, on an imperceptible order as they make predictions and exercise their freedom in shaping the course of history.

The reason for the revolt against the belief in unobservables is interesting. Basically, it is a protest against the belief in supernatural entities and causes and against traditional theology. If unobservables are allowed, where will we draw the line? Unless the line is sharp and clear all sorts of occult powers, good and evil spirits, and entelechies are likely to creep into science. The positivists are willing to go the whole way in their rebellion against unobservables. Their motive is good enough as they try to unroll the carpet for science and the scientific method. The difficulty is that they go too far. As a consequence the object of knowledge is stripped of all cognitive and logical content except what is furnished by the mind. Were this interpretation correct, it would mean that the rational character of scientific statements about the world of fact could not be attributed to the external world or to physical objects. Sensibilia only could be said to be the objects of knowledge. This would imply that order, since it cannot be observed and inspected, cannot come from nature, but is furnished by mind.

Poincaré and Mach are both considered members of the positivist camp. Poincaré held that the general principles of science and, consequently, all laws of nature are nothing but conventions. Accordingly, it is as easy to "prove" one set of conventions by experience as any other. This implies that experience cannot be used as a basis for knowing anything about unobservables or about a world that exists independent of sensations.

Mach took a different approach in his revolt against metaphysics. He claimed that laws of nature and all general principles are nothing but shorthand expressions, abbreviated descriptions, of observed phenomena or perceptions. The basis for accepting one such description instead of another is the efficiency and economy with which it can be applied, but there is no objective basis beyond economy for testing the truth value of statements.

In *Materialism and Empiriocriticism*,[1] Lenin rejects Mach's philosophy of sensations on the ground that it leads to idealism—a subjective idealism similar to Berkeleianism. The members of the Vienna Circle also took cognizance of the subjective idealistic implications of the thesis that all meaningful statements must refer to experienceable objects or observables alone. Consequently, Carnap suggested the language of physics or what later was known as the doctrine of physicalism. Carnap's doctrine is misleading and not altogether forthright. For

[1] See Emile Burns, *A Handbook of Marx* (New York, Random House, Inc., 1935), pp. 635 ff.

just as Mach's sensationalism clearly suggests subjective idealism, so physicalism suggests materialism. The switch to "physicalism" betrays the positivists' bent toward a naturalistic or materialistic metaphysics. Furthermore, Carnap was not successful in liquidating psychological (spiritual) terms, such as blue, sweet, sour and substituting physical terms in their stead. Rather he held on to the old terminology of Mach and Berkeley and baptized them in the name of physicalism.

The rebellion against metaphysics and against the belief in the existence of unobservables, carried on by Comte, Poincaré, Mach, and by the more recent logical positivists, is also a rebellion against the epistemology of rationalism with its entailed metaphysics. The rationalist held that the objects of knowledge are unobservables and, more specifically, the logical, communicable structure of unobservables. Sensations were considered subjective for the simple reason that they cannot be communicated by one person to another, and they are incommunicable because they have no logical structure; i.e., they are not measurable.

Hume showed that we cannot start with sensations alone and, by strict implication, arrive at the logical structure of unobservables (the causes of sensations). Hume's skepticism lay in the fact that he could not know, on the basis of sensations alone, whether there are unobservables or not. The positivists have turned this skepticism into a dogma. They arbitrarily claim that knowledge and the objects of knowledge are confined to what can be sensed. To argue from this claim leads to the conclusion that unobservables cannot be known. But positivists add a metaphysical tenet; namely, unobservables do not exist, and if they did it would be meaningless to say so. This tenet cannot be derived from Hume's philosophy.

The positivists' denial that the rationalistic object of cognition can be attained by way of sensations and perceptions leads them to the conclusion that the communicable dimension of meaningful statements and words—since they do not (à la Hume) refer to unobservables—must refer to observables alone. The relationships between observables are "philosophical relations," but are resolvable into sensations or perceptions if they make sense. Hence, the positivists "solve" the problem of empiricism, inherited from rationalism, namely, the problem of arriving at the object of knowledge (not sensations) by way of sensations, by claiming that the rationalists were completely mistaken in the first place, and that the real objects of knowledge are observables.

Philipp Frank asks, "How does it come about that we assign to bodies imperceptible as well as perceptible properties?"[2] His answer is that we do it in order to save the traditional law of causality, which he believes has no legitimate meaning. For example, if two pieces of iron look alike, weigh the same, and a steel nail will move toward one, but not the other, we assign to the first an imperceptible property, magnetism, and say that the magnetism attracts the nail. "By the word 'state' one understands the perceptible properties of a system of bodies, plus a series of fictitious properties, of which so many are included that the same states are always followed by the same states."[3] In this manner Frank, with other positivists, argues not only that imperceptibles or unobservables have no *cognitive* meaning but that they are fictitious or have no objective status whatsoever.

F. S. C. Northrop writes, "Neither the electron or molecule nor their collision is directly inspected. All that can possibly be inspected are what the senses convey to us, and these are ineffable, sensuous qualities, that is, aesthetic objects; they are not scientific objects."[4] I agree with Northrop that both postulated, unobservable entities and the "aesthetic continuum" are necessary for science and that both have objective status; neither is fictitious. Whether aesthetic objects are scientific objects need not concern us here.

If there is one thing all contemporary philosophers of science agree to, it is that observation and sense data are indispensable to science. To speak loosely, they are the "cash value" of science. This, however, is far from agreeing that observables or sense data constitute the sole object of knowledge. Nor can anyone prove by any manner or means that if sense data constitute the object of knowledge, unobservables are fictitious or do not exist. The chief difference between David Hume and contemporary logical positivists is Hume's skepticism. As a skeptic Hume doubted that a knowledge (certainty) of causes (impercepti-

[2] Philipp Frank, *Modern Science and Its Philosophy* (New York, George Braziller, 1955), p. 56.

[3] *Ibid.,* p. 57.

[4] F. S. C. Northrop, *The Logic of the Sciences and the Humanities* (New York, The Macmillan Company, 1947), p. 120.

bles) could be attained either by recourse to impressions and ideas or through pure reason. The logical positivists, unable to suffer the skepticism of Hume, especially when it came to glorifying science and accepting its fruits, flatly define the objects of knowledge as observables (sense impressions); and from their own definition they draw the simple conclusion that unobservables are fictitious. They conclude that since the objects of knowledge are sense impressions and since the only referents of scientific (meaningful) statements are sense impressions, we cannot speak meaningfully of unobservables. Finally, they draw the false conclusion that unobservables do not exist. There is nothing skeptical about this.

Of course, if we agree with the positivist's definition of "meaningful statement," then it follows that we cannot, through cognitive statements, refer to unobservables. It does not follow that unobservables do not exist. If by definition positivists have shown that their philosophy leads to the conclusion that unobservables cannot be talked about and do not constitute the referents of meaningful statements, they have shown also the inadequacy and inexpediency of their philosophy.

There is something wholesome about Hume's skepticism. At least he refused to settle for the Lockian-Berkeleian thesis that impressions (sensations, ideas) can bring us to the object of cognition and knowledge. He refused to say that impressions *are* the objects of knowledge, and he left open the gate for other possibilities. The positivists in their hasty distaste for metaphysics ("superstition") settle for a dogma. They say in effect, "The only way to prove that unobservables exist is to *reduce* them to observables; since this is impossible in principle, unobservables do not exist."

From the standpoint of strict implication, observables do not imply unobservables. But neither does a present sense datum imply a future one, or one contemporaneous with it, for that matter. Does the color of the book strictly imply the distant, touchable object? The question, How does it come about that we assign imperceptible properties to bodies? is closely allied to the question, How does it come about that we assign, say, hardness to the visible but distant object? Hume showed that no single impression or idea strictly implies any other. Yet he tried to account for the stubborn fact that a lively idea is inevitably *associated* with a present impression. And although he defines "cause" in phenomenalistic terms, he speaks of the "vivacity" and "liveliness" of ideas, and claims that the association of ideas is due to "custom" or "habit" and a "gentle force," of which the latter is certainly one of the occult powers of which, in Hume's system, there can be no knowledge. It is as difficult to hold ideas and impressions together by a "gentle" force as it is to hold the order of impressions together by necessary connections. Especially so since the gentle force of which Hume speaks is, after all, subjective, and must according to positivists and operationalists, go the way of all metaphysics. So the question, Why attribute imperceptible properties to bodies? has its analogue: Why did Hume resort to "gentle force" and to "occult" psychological tendencies in trying to account for the belief in causes?

Scientific Evidence for Unobservables

Is there any evidence for unobservables, such as neutrinos, genes, ideas, a past, the insides of bodies, and electromagnetic fields? This question has two parts. The first; Does "evidence" have any meaning, or can anything be "evidence" for the existence of some other thing? Of course, evidence is not proof, and if something, c, is evidence for something else, e, this does not mean that c strictly implies e. From the standpoint of strict implication, the color "of a book" is no better evidence for the touchability of the book than it is for the existence of molecules in the book. We can get no other kind of certainty (nor a greater degree of it) for our belief that one impression will be followed by another, than for our belief in the existence of unobservables—causes. In Hume's attempt to define "cause" phenomenalistically, he says, "a cause is an object precedent and contiguous to another, and so united with it, that the idea of the one determines the mind to form the idea of the other, and the impression of the one to form a more lively idea of the other."[5] Here we have a formal definition of cause, and we still have left over the problem of whether or not there are any causes. Are any ideas and impressions in fact related in the manner stipulated by the definition? Also, must they be so related, or can we, by use of the Humean "imagination" separate them? We will find that

[5] See Hume's *Treatise*, ed. by L. A. Selby-Bigge (London, Oxford University Press, 1951 [reprint]), p. 170.

it is as difficult to find *evidence* for causes defined purely phenomenal-istically as metaphysically, for strict implication is lacking in both cases. Just as it is impossible to determine the existence of unobserv-able causes by strict implication and by definition, so it is with phe-nomenal causes.

Do neutrinos exist? Philip Morrison's article explains carefully the evidence for the existence of the neutrino.[6] The firm belief in its ex-istence is based on faith in the law of the conservation of energy. But he is careful to explain that he does not *mean* by "neutrino" some fic-titious entity that saves the conservation law, nor is this law conclusive evidence for its existence. Rather, a group of Los Alamos investigators, Clyde L. Cowan, Jr., Francis B. Harrison, and Frederick Reines, are trying to "capture" the neutrino, i.e., they want to have evidence for it entirely apart from the conservation law. They want something similar to the "click" made by an electron on the Geiger counter, or something similar to the "track" of the electron in the Wilson cloud chamber. If they find such evidence it will be clear that the meaning of "neutrino" is not identical with its measurement. Nor will its meaning be confined to what it does. If they ever hear the click they will not identify the neutrino with it, for the click will come and go; the neutrino, if we grant the continued existence of an external world, will not.

Bridgman says, "From the operational point of view it is meaning-less to separate 'nature' from 'knowledge of nature.' "[7] If this were true, then, combined with his operationalism, "unobservables" could have no referents, nor, in fact, could "nature." A more accurate way of speaking would then be, "knowledge is knowledge," but there will be no such thing as knowledge *of* anything, to say nothing of "nature." This view, closely allied with the positivists' view that statements about imperceptibles are meaningless, amounts to identifying all meanings with operations, or with what is experienced directly, if not with the experience itself. The full meaning of neutrino, then, would be identi-cal with the method of measuring it. Probably the click of the neutrino, even as the track of the electron, might be considered a part of its meaning provided we state what operations are performed in getting

---

[6] In *Scientific American,* CXCIV, No. 1 (January, 1956), 59–68.

[7] P. W. Bridgman, *The Logic of Modern Physics* (New York, The Mac-millan Company, 1928), p. 62.

the click, in which case the word "neutrino" would be a shorthand expression for all operations in connection with neutrinos.

Although quite often the presence of an unobservable object is suspected because of certain disturbances and uncalculated effects, there are always alternative checks which in many cases give further evidence for the existence of the object in question. If we start with the germ theory of diseases and later detect a new disease, medical scientists would not argue that germs are present just to save the germ theory. Nor would they mean by "germs are present" the symptoms of the disease. They would try to isolate the germs, and, if they succeeded, their evidence would not be identical with the disease itself. In fact, in practically every case in which the existence of unobservables as well as observables is suspected, indirect and alternative checks are introduced.

I agree that all theories, all unobservables, and all imperceptibles can be known only by way of observables, but if "evidence" has any meaning, then observables are evidence for unobservables even as they are evidence for other observables. My main protest against the doctrine that unobservables cannot be referred to meaningfully and that they do not exist is that such a doctrine does not and cannot give proper recognition to the temporal character of nature, that, strictly speaking, it must hold that the referents of all terms are the immediately sensed objects, and that, finally, the objective world consists of a set of temporally and spatially disconnected things. If there is an observable flash of light at p and later an observable flash of light at p', some distance from p, can we assume that something happened at each and every point between p and p', even if it were not observed? If something happened, not observed, could what took place be exhausted in principle by observables? I think not.

Do genes exist? Are they observable? Geneticists would never have arrived at the concept of "gene" had they not noticed recurrent patterns in different offspring of the same parents. It is obvious that "gene" does not mean the offspring, though at first the offspring contained the sole evidence for the existence of genes. Yet evidence is not that for which it is evidence; the offspring are not genes. "Gene" has at least two separate meanings: the function and also the chemical structure. Its function is "to determine" the form of the offspring.

Chemically it consists of nucleic acid in the form of a coiled or double chain composed probably of thousands of links.[8] Its basic meaning, of course, is the manner in which it determines the offspring (both its genotype and its phenotype), but this meaning is not the offspring, and certainly no one could hope to observe in a present the referent of a term which referent includes past events and events separated in space and time. What a gene does cannot be seen in a microscope or by any other means. A microscope will reveal the chromosome, the *locus* of the gene, the mechanism by which genes determine the form of the offspring, but neither the final chemical composition nor the function of the gene can be observed. Yet the gene has meaning, and no geneticist doubts its existence. Genes cause certain observable effects, the forms. To identify the meaning of "gene" with what is strictly observable would lead us to give up trying to isolate the mechanism for its functioning or to control the offspring by genetic means.

We must agree in every case that "evidence" is confined to observables, but that for which something is evidence may not be observable, even in principle. To believe that observables can be evidence for other observables but not for unobservables is a confusion due possibly to the mistaken belief that evidence can strictly imply something beyond itself and, to be specific, that it can strictly imply observables. Evidence is what convinces a person of the existence of something other than itself, but conviction should not be mistaken for either proof or strict implication.

From this fact several things follow, one of which is that no one can prove by observables that unobservables do not exist nor, consequently, can one prove that unobservables have no referents. If, however, one were to *define* evidence as that which can indicate the existence of observables only, then it follows that there can be no evidence for unobservables. Such an inadequate definition is often taken for proof of the nonexistence of unobservables, a "proof" derived from the suppressed assumption that men can settle questions about matters of fact by definitions. Men do not believe in the existence of unobservables because of what is strictly implied by experience or observation. As Hume indicated, from the standpoint of strict implication, neither ex-

[8] See H. J. Muller, "Life," in *Science*, CXXI, No. 3132 (January 7, 1955), 1–9.

perience nor pure reason can justify the belief in unobservables. (Neither can they justify a belief in their nonexistence.) Rather, the belief in unobservables is the basis for intelligent practice controlled by symbols for ends not yet experienced—many may never be experienced—whereas the absence of a belief in unobservables leads to a skepticism in which a present object could never, on purely intellectual grounds, hold the promise of a future end, for one would not think in terms of the grounds for ends and could not, therefore, justify a practice necessary to effect them.

The basic question is: Which is the better or the best way to think about the world or any part of it? To look at nature from any point of view whatsoever and to say it is good, means that it is good either in itself or as a means to something else. If we can agree that science is a means to ends freely chosen by men, then its justification is found in the ends. If a belief in unobservables leads to the improvement of science as a means, that is justification enough. The positivist, like the realist, believes his way of looking at things is better for science, but since philosophies cannot be proven or disproven, neither positivist nor realist can prove his point of view. Some men may find one philosophy satisfactory, at least for a time, while other men must turn to another philosophy. I submit that realism is more satisfactory and more complete than positivism principally because it accounts for the continuity of events, makes room for explanation (thereby showing the integral relationship between past, present, and future), and develops in a society the confidence that it can achieve goals. The teleological factor is sorely neglected by positivists. Science does not exist for the sake of prediction and description; rather it is a means for the accomplishment of ends selected on nonscientific grounds. But a philosophy of science that does not evaluate science with reference to its main function is inadequate.

Are Statements about Unobservables Meaningful?

Can unobservables be referred to? Can the meaning of unobservables be communicated by one person to another by scientific symbols; in other words, Are unobservables objects of cognition? Newton says, "The quantity of matter is the measure of the same." But he does not argue that *matter* is the measure of itself. This applies to many other things also—intelligence, anxiety, fear, time, and, of course, all unobservables; there is a difference between what they are and the measure of them. The operationalists, positivists, and thoroughgoing behaviorists want to identify what a thing is with the measure of it. After more or less defining terms operationally, this same group claims that its definitions are adequate and exhaustive; for instance, that the operational meaning of "intelligence" is the only meaning intelligence has or can have; that any other meaning attributed to it is fictitious. Which is to say, all that exists is measure; not *the measure of* something.

John B. Watson denied the existence of thinking as something unobservable. He called it "sub-vocal behavior," and held that all thinking could be detected by instruments (only). No doubt a Watsonian behaviorist would have to carry a measuring instrument with him to know whether or not he was thinking. To be certain of the accuracy of the instrument, he could attach a lie-detecting machine to it. The only difficulty: there would be no one to read the instruments.

A. S. Eddington says, "The whole subject-matter of exact science consists of pointer readings and similar indications."[9] I take it that these are readings of pointers whose existence is not questioned but accepted by every scientist.

There are not only readings in every measurement made by scientists, but the readings refer to something not read. The wave length of green light (the wave length of light reflected from an object when the object is said to be green and is recognized as green) is about 5^{-10} cm. This length was arrived at indirectly through readings and not by looking at green objects nor, least of all, by seeing a light wave. The question is: What does this length refer to; of what is it a property? It would be silly to say it is a property of the operation employed to arrive at it—that is not its meaning. It would be equally silly to say that "green," as a sense datum, has a certain length. Yet the length, 5^{-10} cm, has cognitive, communicative meaning. It is a property of an unobservable.

One can grant that both our decimal system and the metric units of length are conventional. This, however, does not make the length of a

[9] A. S. Eddington, *The Nature of the Physical World* (New York, The Macmillan Company, 1928), p. 252.

light wave conventional. We can grant, further, that the method of measuring length might vary from time to time. Still this does not mean that length is a property of an operation, or that the operation by which we determine the length is its meaning. Also, whether or not the length attributed to the light wave is the final one may be questioned. But in spite of all these objections we cannot get away from the logical implications that "length of," in this case, implies the existence of an unobservable whose length it is, and here we have a cognitive statement whose only referent is an unobservable.

After Philipp Frank spends much time praising operational definitions of concepts in physics[10] and defending the view that their sole meaning is operational meaning, he makes the following statement [italics mine] in connection with Bohr's computations to determine the size of atoms.[11]

The charge e of the electron is known by Millikan's experiment on the ionization of oil droplets; m is known from J. J. Thompson's experiments on the deflection of cathode rays in magnetic and electric fields; h is known from the photo-electric effect. From the known values of h, m, and e we obtain that r is approximately 10^{-8} cm. *This value agrees with the size of the atoms obtained by other methods,* e.g., Brownian motion, diffraction of x-rays by crystal lattices, etc.

Now if, according to operationalism, the meaning of a value is identical with the operational means of obtaining it, how could different means lead to the same value? Could it be that since these different methods of measurement lead to the same value they are *equivalent?* Do they have the same meaning? Operationalists must answer yes, but this *reductio ad absurdum* is clear to all. The only sensible way out of the difficulty into which Frank gets himself is to acknowledge openly that r is a property of atoms (unobservables), and regardless of how we obtain the property it still belongs to atoms. The property is quite intelligible. It can be thought, and, consequently, cognition in this case has unobservables as its object.

Frank goes to great length in trying to define "force" operationally. He says [italics mine]:[12]

---

[10] See Philipp Frank, "Foundations in Physics," *International Encyclopedia of Unified Science,* I, No. 7 (Chicago, University of Chicago Press, 1946).

[11] *Ibid.,* p. 44.   [12] *Ibid.,* p. 18.

What *really* happens *in* the stretched rubber is a state of equilibrium between several forces. The algebraic sum of the forces acting upon any particle of rubber is zero. To say that forces "exist" in this rubber would be as correct as to say that in the number zero the number five "exists" because five minus five is equal to zero.

Frank's statement is fairly clear. It follows from this that there is no such thing as pressure, or weight $(w=mg)$, unless something is moving. If, for example, the hand of the pressure gauge on a container is not moving, there *is* no pressure because the forces are in balance; they are equal to zero. It follows according to this operational definition that even if the hand registers 20 gm/cm^2, there is no pressure and hence 20 gm/cm^2 cannot be the measure of it. Similarly, according to Frank's thesis, if two weights are in balance, their sum also is zero, hence, we have the conclusion that there are not two weights, but no weights. If one insists that by definition a force is what it produces—some observable effect—then the word cannot apply to unobservables. But physicists do not make definitions for fun, and if a formal definition is inadequate or inapplicable, it usually drops out of scientific usage.

If we were to analyze Frank's definition carefully we would find that *no forces* are ever in a state of disequilibrium. No force can *act* without an equal and opposite force *acting* also. If the definition of "force," following Frank, depends on a state of disequilibrium, then a definition is impossible. Force cannot be defined operationally, and if a definition of it is applicable, it refers to unobservables.

But to return to Frank's example of the stretched rubber; suppose we cut it with a sharp razor, thus using very little energy. Then all will agree, including Frank, that it will have (exert) a force; say 3 dynes. What can be said about this? A new force came into existence! Maybe several new forces; forces that do far more work than the work necessary to cut the rubber. But if we cut an unstretched rubber, no force exists. If we can state in a lawful way the *conditions* under which "new forces come into existence," we will have to say in this case that the stretched rubber is one of the (necessary?) conditions. This means the stretched rubber is in a different state or in a different condition from the unstretched one. Does it actually have that condition and is it in that state *before* it is cut by the razor and *before* the new forces come into existence? Is the state of equilibrium a condition or state? If so, can one define operationally the differences between the stretched and unstretched rubbers when neither is acting on anything, when the sum of the forces is the same in each, zero? Such a definition is impossible.

These questions and answers explain precisely why any philosophy of science holding that unobservables are in every case fictitious is wholly inadequate. It cannot attribute continuous existence to anything but holds that the existence of everything (depends on?) is identical with what is directly observed. To try to get around the conclusion that existence depends on the directly observed by saying "directly observable" will not do. To substitute "observable" for "observed" is to substitute a possibility, a potentiality, for an actuality. There are no potentialities according to the positivist philosophy.

Operationalism and positivism have had their effects on psychology. Behaviorism, as developed by Watson and many others, was greatly stimulated if not suggested by the Russian physiologist Pavlov. In the main, Pavlov was interested in studying the overt responses of lower animals in relation to stimuli which are said to evoke the responses. He was concerned with both stimulus and response in so far as they were observable, and, if possible, measurable. "Mental" or "psychological" phenomena—the unobservable and nonmeasurable—were laid to one side.

Actually Pavlov was applying the objective method to a study of the responses of animals and to stimuli. Under Watson's influence this method became widely known as "behaviorism." Watson tried to turn a method into a metaphysics; he identified the subject matter of psychology with the method and the results of the method. He did not claim simply that the objective method is better than the introspective method for studying mind and psychological phenomena, such as thinking, wishing, and images. He denied the existence of such phenomena and held that the subject matter of psychology is confined to stimuli and responses, all of which are observable by any "normal" person. Thus Watsonian behaviorism is similar to Bridgman's operationalism in that both claim that the full meaning (all referents) of the concepts used in their respective disciplines is confined to observables: in psychology, to overt behavior; in physics, to procedures of measurement. Also, Watson's behaviorism is similar to positivism in that both hold the objects of cognition and the referents of all meaningful concepts to be observable.

More recently, operationalists, such as C. C. Pratt and B. F. Skinner, and behaviorists, such as C. L. Hull and E. C. Tolman, have given serious attention to methodology in science. After years of trying to interpret concepts in psychology in unadulterated behavioristic terms, Hull fell back on such terms as "habit," "drive," "excitatory potential," and "inhibitory potential." Tolman used the term "intervening variables," by which he meant certain unobserved (if not unobservable) things *inside* the organism which are necessary to fill the temporal gaps between stimulus and response and to account for the fact that often, from the standpoint of measurement and direct observation, the "same" stimulus was followed by an unanticipated (unusual) response. Tolman could have chosen to interpret responses as having a mere *statistical correlation* with stimuli. There was neither logical necessity nor compelling evidence for introducing intervening variables. The justification for his decision to do so is nothing other than the faith that psychology is a science and, therefore, its subject matter is subject to law and, consequently, when there are deviations and variations in the response upon the presence of an observable stimulus, then the observable stimulus is not the entire cause of the response. This, of course, implies that Tolman believes in causes as well as continuity.

But what justification is there for believing that the locus of the unobserved part of the cause (the intervening variable) is inside the organism? To believe in the inside of anything is to flirt with metaphysics, and to hold that the meaning of "insides" (the unobservable) is completely exhausted by observable outsides is to assign reality to surfaces alone—surfaces of nothing.

Tolman's ultimate hope may be to know intervening variables in the same behavioristic way that he knows molar, overt behavior, and, consequently, to say these variables (processes) are inside the organism is not to think of them as unobservable or as metaphysical entities. But as a psychologist he must deal with a living organism and his experiments must fall short of dissection. He may get at the inside by way of sensitive instruments, but in every case he must approach a knowledge of the precise nature of intervening variables by indirect inference—he must conjecture that what goes on inside the organism *causes* the instruments to behave as they do, but the readings on the instruments cannot be identical with these causes or intervening variables, lest the locus of them be changed from the organism to the instruments. However successful a psychologist may be in finding out what goes on inside by use of instruments, he is still dealing with unobservables whose existence is "proved" and whose nature is known by use of his instruments. Finally, the justification for believing that the locus of the intervening variables is the inside of the organism is identical with the justification we have for believing that unobservables cannot be exhausted by observables, and that there is continuity in the world of facts.

The terms "drive," and "inhibitory potential," used by C. L. Hull, indicate certain states of the organism. Hull believes, further, that the past experiences of an organism leave their effects in the nature of habits, inclinations, or dispositions. In other words what an organism has suffered somehow determines the response it is going to make to a given stimulus. Hull does not account for the response by what is present alone. He must bring in a past, something that cannot be experienced. He does not do so simply to save the causal principle nor to cover up our ignorance with a term. To be consistent he would have to believe that the organism has a nature even while it is not responding. Granting that the organism's nature cannot be known apart from observable responses, still its responses cannot be made intelligible apart from it. This is precisely what is meant by the temporal character of events and of processes; no one part of a process is intelligible apart from the others, even as a response cannot be understood apart from the past of the organism. The relationship between phases or parts of a process is always a cause-effect relationship, for one phase, temporally separated from the other, must be considered either a condition for, or a result of, the other.

Hull assigns to the organism a nature even when it is not responding and this nature can never be equated to responses, for if the organism were to die immediately so that none of the responses are made in fact, it would still have had that nature. What an organism is *now* cannot be identical with what it will do or may do later. The identification of the two, i.e., conceiving of all existents as fully actualized in a present, is not only to overlook the temporal character of process but also to deny

DO UNOBSERVABLES EXIST

that potentiality, possibility, dispositions, and prepotent response have any meaning.

W. W. Spence says,[13]

> The only meanings that these theoretical intervening constructs [Tolman and Hull] have *at the present time* is provided by equations which relate them to the known experimental variables—the environment measurements on the one hand and the behavior measures on the other. Such equations constitute the definitions of these terms.

It is very doubtful that either Hull or Tolman believes what Spence says. Certainly Spence's statement is confused. If the locus of intervening variables is inside the organism then the terms cannot refer to something outside it, namely, "environmental measurements" and "behavior measures." "Intervening variables" must refer to or mean something inside the organism. I believe that although "intervening variables," "states of the organism," and "excitatory potential," may have no clear meaning *apart from* measurements and observations of factors outside the organism, their referents are not to something outside. One end of a piece of chalk with a pencil mark on it can be referred to without mentioning the other end, but it cannot exist without the other end. So the inside of an organism presupposes an outside, and vice versa. But how foolish it would be to say one end of the chalk *means* the other end, even by definition. If Tolman and Hull want to define something, why not start with what can be observed? Something that does not exist needs no word to refer to it nor need we define words that cannot possibly refer to anything. Does Spence mean that these men are defining measurements? If so, why use queer metaphysical terms that suggest real variables? If Spence is correct, then "intervening variable" means, not something that intervenes, but *measurements of* variables.

When Spence says the meaning of intervening variables "is provided by equations which relate them to known experimental variables," what does "them" refer to? Not to the equation that does the relating. Not to the experimental variables, lest we be forced to be clear and say "the meaning of experimental variables is found in the equation

[13] "The Postulates and Methods of 'Behaviorism,'" *Psychological Review,* LV, No. 2 (March, 1948), 74–75.

which relates them to experimental variables (themselves)." Spence suggests, also, that these hypothetical terms may have some other meaning later. He does not say the only meaning they will ever have is found in the equation. This leads to the suggestion that sometimes we may find something inside the organism to which these terms refer. If so, would they be "found" by direct observation or inferred from instrument readings (external measurable variables)? If they are found by direct observation they would no longer be called intervening variables. If they are inferred by readings they would mean precisely what they now mean, for, after all, Tolman has a basis for believing in the existence of intervening variables, and this basis is found in the measurements and readings of instruments.

The basic question is: Can behaviorists get along without introducing terms that refer to unobservables? So far they have not been able to do so. Gustav Bergmann tells us that it is a matter of clarifying language.[14] Spence's difficulty is not wholly a matter of language but stems from his attempting an impossible task, for he, like others, is trying, both to reduce explanation to description and to find a basis for controlling the responses of organisms. Sheer description and the correlation of measurements will never provide a basis for control. Variables cannot be controlled by variables unless one is the cause or condition of the other. Explanation is found in the causal or conditional relationship between variables, and no stimulus is going to be followed by a response unless the response is the response *of the organism,* not of the stimulus.

The organism is the subject matter of psychology. What the organism is like can and must be inferred from what can be observed, if not measured. This is what all behaviorists should be saying instead of insisting that the basis of inference (evidence)—observables and measurements—is identical to what can be inferred from it (that for which it is evidence). They have confused description and explanation and have left the subject matter of psychology out of their science. That all inference in factual matters is *from* experience I do not question: that it is directly *to* experience without the intervention of causes (intervening variables) is false.

[14] See Bergmann, especially, "The Subject Matter of Psychology," *Philosophy of Science,* VII, No. 4 (October, 1940), 415–433.

Behaviorists, unlike Newton who said "The quantity of matter is the measure of the same," say *thinking,* not the quantity of it, *is* the measure of it, anxiety *is* the measure of it, a lie *is* the reading on the lie-detector. This makes the subject matter of the behaviorist the pointer readings of instruments when these instruments are in the neighborhood of living organisms. This neighborhood distinguishes psychology from physics and chemistry.

The denial of the existence of unobservables leads to a sort of reductionism which is suggested by Carnap's proposal that we adopt the language of physics or physicalism. If we are to use the language of physics in such nonphysical sciences as psychology, economics, and sociology, it follows, then, that we should use the same instruments for measurement. This is often done, and the psychologist frequently supports his claim that psychology is a scientific discipline by pointing to this fact. (Anxiety is measured by pressure gauges, tension gauges, and ammeters.) But what, finally, does this imply? It implies that psychology is reducible to physics and that a good psychologist is nothing but a poor physicist. Such reductionism is in opposition to the general theory of evolution which claims that there are qualitatively different kinds of forms and processes in the world. Since, according to the operational-positivistic view, the meaning of scientific terms is confined to operations and observed pointer readings, and since fundamentally the same instruments are used in measurements in various disciplines, it follows that the measurements cannot refer to different kinds of phenomena and that instruments or the means of measuring determine meanings; e.g., an "idea" is the measure of itself, and the electrical device for measuring it determines *what it is.*

On the contrary, I maintain that anything whatsoever that can be measured must be known to exist on grounds other than its measurability or actual measurement. We should not, therefore, rule out of court those things not subject to measurement by scientific instruments on that account alone.

The basic questions are these: Does nature have a structure of her own independent of men and sensations? If so, can it be known and referred to by statements? Is it intelligible, cognitive, and communicable? Can it be depended upon as men try to accomplish goals which are at present only envisaged but not yet witnessed by men? I believe so.

CHAPTER III

Understanding, Explanation and the Neutrality of Physical Objects

Understanding

THERE ARE TWO KINDS of understanding and two kinds of explanation. Understanding takes place when an object is comprehended in its immediacy, i.e., there is direct appreciation of what it is in itself.

Understanding takes place also when a thing is comprehended in its causal and historical relationship to other things, as one may know trees in the sense that he knows how to cultivate and nurture them.

The first kind of understanding requires direct insight into and direct recognition of an existing object. Bergson[1] calls this insight "intuition" and holds that it gives one a metaphysical understanding of things. Others, such as Bertrand Russell,[2] speak of it as *knowledge by acquaintance*. Although medievalists believed particulars could be known only through universal forms, they acknowledged that an experience of a particular object is genetically prior to, and a necessary prerequisite for, knowledge of its form or essence, and that the uni-

[1] See Henri Bergson, *An Introduction to Metaphysics,* trans. by T. E. Hulme (New York, G. P. Putnam's Sons, 1912).
[2] See *Our Knowledge of the External World* (rev. ed.; New York, George Allen and Unwin, Ltd., 1926), pp. 35 and 151.

versal is abstracted from what is given in the experience of the particular. A cognitive awareness of the sensed particular without a consideration of its relationship to other objects is a kind of understanding. Such understanding emphasizes the immediate qualitative aspect of the thing understood, and there is a sense in which the particular as particular can be known in its immediacy, causally unrelated to other objects. If expression and communication require that the meaning of the object, in so far as it is communicated, must involve mediate objects also, then this kind of knowledge is incommunicable. Consequently, the first kind of understanding may properly be called an intuitive understanding.

The second kind of understanding of an object is scientific, which requires a knowledge of how to predict, control, or produce the object said to be understood. Pure science implies this kind of understanding inasmuch as pure research makes use of experiments and laboratory techniques which lead to know-how and applied science, in which at least partial control over objects is attained.

The rapid growth of science, along with the tremendous impression its fruits have made on the minds of moderns, has led many philosophers to think of it as a way of life. They are inclined to believe that scientific understanding is the only kind of understanding. Pragmatists, positivists, and operationalists alike not only emphasize the value of scientific understanding, but claim that it is all-inclusive. Their philosophy is a protest against any other kind of understanding and against any metaphysics that claims to give us knowledge about the world of fact.

Their protest is legitimate in so far as it claims metaphysics is not a method for attaining knowledge and understanding of the relationship between objects in the world of fact. Metaphysics has not provided and cannot provide a method of predicting, controlling, or producing objects. It does not, therefore, give scientific understanding. Still a comprehension of the world in its immediacy, or an understanding of the nature of the objects produced by scientific method, falls within the scope of metaphysics. It would be absurd to assume that the means of producing an object *is* that object and that an understanding of the means is identical with an understanding of the end produced by it.

The only legitimate claim against metaphysics is that it is not a part of scientific method. This, however, does not degrade metaphysics nor deprive it of a necessary and worthy function. Its function is both to understand, in the nonscientific sense of the word, and, on the basis of that understanding, to serve as a ground for evaluation, choice, and freedom.

Producing and controlling are not ends in themselves. Men through applied science do not produce for the sake of producing. Producing is, rather, for the sake of the object produced, and what the object is like can be known only through an immediate understanding. Science can offer the method, but the method has nothing in it that can be used to evaluate the ends produced by it.

As a result, the attempt by pragmatists, operationalists, and positivists to assimilate all understanding to scientific methodology carries the antimetaphysical movement to the extreme and makes a just cause for those who cry out against "scientism." Science can offer methodological understanding only; the kind that makes possible the prediction and often the control of events, but such understanding is not a substitute for insight into the nature of objects known in their immediacy and distinguishable from other objects on qualitative, nonscientific grounds. Quality can never be assimilated to quantity and to scientific methodology.

Democritus said, "Sweet is sweet by convention and bitter is bitter by convention, but in reality there is nothing but atoms and the void." This is a clear exhibition of the confusion of methodology and metaphysics, of quantity and quality. Democritus believed colors, odors, and other experienced qualities do not belong to objects but are perturbations of the soul. Objects, according to him, consist of atoms whose final nature is expressible in pure geometric, quantitative terms. Aristotle justly criticized this view, saying Democritus, according to his own system, did not and could not state that for the sake of which change takes place, namely, ends qualitatively different from the means. The analysis of objects into atoms leads to an understanding of them *in so far as atoms are useful in controlling and producing objects having characters qualitatively different from atoms*. If one claims that such analysis gives the only available understanding of the nature of objects, he is asserting by implication that analysis leads to understanding the object analyzed, and that, consequently, it is impossible to comprehend or understand the nature of an object prior to an analysis of it. This view carried to its extreme leads to the corollary that objects are real and have ontological, objective status only in the sense that their ultimate, analytical parts are real. Whitehead uses the phrase "fallacy of misplaced concreteness" to denote the confusion of the nature of things with abstract concepts arrived at through analysis. I call it simply a confusion of method with metaphysics, of know-how with what is produced through know-how.

As will be shown in Chapters IV and V, the belief that the nature of objects or forms can be known through analysis is directly opposed to the theory of evolution. This belief stems from the rationalist's assumption that there is nothing new or different in the conclusion of an argument than was contained in the premises, and, similarly, that nature, contrary to the theory of evolution, is an unfolding of what is enfolded. Hence, new emergent forms, according to the argument, are unreal and possibly subjective. The theory of evolution, however, saves metaphysics from being assimilated to scientific methodology and claims the forms are not reducible to their pasts. The pasts of objects are known through science and belong to methodology. The "what" it is that has a past is known through direct inspection.

As suggested above, Descartes, the rationalist, held that qualities are subjective, in the soul. Here again is an example of one who confused the mathematical, logical, methodological understanding of objects with the metaphysical, intuitive understanding of them. British empiricists went to the other extreme and tried to reduce quantity to quality.

The theory of evolution, which originated in the nineteenth century and developed more extensively in the twentieth century under the form of emergent and creative evolution, laid the basis for a clarification of the distinction between and the relationship of quantity and quality, methodology and metaphysics, so that now there need be no confusion between the two, nor excuse for trying to reduce the immediate understanding of an object to the means of producing it. The theory of evolution enables us to grant the objective reality of qualitatively different forms as they emerge in time and to distinguish clearly between them and their histories, their pasts, the conditions for their emergence, as well as their analytical parts. Under the influence of the theory of evolution, qualities have been returned to the objective world.

Scientists now see that their main function is to find the histories of things and to state those histories in methodological terms so that prediction, production, and control of the form in question is made possible. Without violating a basic tenet of the theory of evolution, one cannot identify the form of an object with its history, its past, even as one cannot identify the novel or emergent form with the conditions for its existence. The necessity for distinguishing between the emergent and its past requires that a distinction be made between the two kinds of understanding: the historical, scientific, methodological understanding on the one hand and the metaphysical, intuitive understanding on the other.

I have maintained throughout this work that scientific understanding is concerned with means and methods only and is devoid of the evaluation of ends. Ends as such are not understood through science; only means can be understood scientifically. Ends are comprehended on nonscientific grounds, and a comprehension of them is a necessary prerequisite to evaluation and choice, which is nothing other than exercising human freedom in eliminating the actualization of many possible ends and determining the actualization of others, each of which could be achieved by the same scientific method. Freedom requires both giving assent to a limited number of evaluated ends and having the capacity, by aid of scientific understanding, to attain through behavior the ends assented to.

Explanation

Whereas the locus of understanding is the individual organism and need not involve more than one individual, explanation always involves at least two persons, the explainer and the person to whom the explanation is directed. One, however, can explain only what he understands and through explanation communicate what he understands. Corresponding to the two kinds of understanding—intuitive and scientific—there are two kinds of explanation.

The first kind of explanation, communicating to another what one understands by a direct insight into the nature of an object, is identical with giving a description of the object. Whether or not it is possible, through description, to communicate such intuitive understanding is debatable. Bergson believes any attempt to communicate knowledge of an object obtained through intuition fails completely. Description, he believes, is a way of going around an object; by it we fail to communicate the real structure of objects and only distort. Along with Bergson, other existentialists[3] believe objects as particulars are known directly, but any attempt to classify them is an attempt to make the temporal eternal. Reality, they believe, consists of particular, ineffable particulars. Whether or not a description of the particular communicates to another person the individual's insight into the nature of an object, all must agree that the individual can have an understanding of objects in their immediacy and that such understanding cannot be assimilated to scientific understanding.

In their revolt against explanation in terms of final causes (purposes) and against metaphysics in general, many philosophers and scientists say it is impossible to know *why* objects exist or *why* they come into existence. They conclude, therefore, that explanation in every case is impossible and that scientists can only describe what is in fact the case. Even a statement of the history of an object, including its "causes," some argue, is nothing but sheer description devoid of all explanation. Others, however, grant that a statement of *how* to produce objects is a kind of explanation and that the only meaning "why" can have must be assimilated to the "how." Thus, they would assimilate metaphysical explanation to scientific explanation. Scientific knowledge and understanding always involves mediate, distant phenomena which are concerned with causal relations, prediction, and control. If all that could be known about a present phenomenon had to be expressed in

---

[3] Michael Wyschogrod writes: "It has already been pointed out that the school of thought that posits a sharp disjunction between an existing and a nonexisting essence thereby involves itself in a difficult dialectic. If the disjunction holds, then what gives being or reality (in Kierkegaard's terminology 'factual being') to anything is its existence, the fact that it is. But nothing is just an existence—everything that exists is the existence of something. Yet the element that makes a thing be *something,* its essence, does not exist since it is the element that is the opposite of existence, namely essence. The result of this is that being or reality cannot be attributed to that element of something that makes it be what it is, but only to the fact that it is." *The Ontology of Existence* (New York, The Humanities Press, Inc., 1954), pp. 31, 32.

terms of scientific understanding, then nothing could be known about it in its immediacy. But this is not the case, and I contend that there is direct and immediate knowledge of objects immediately experienced, though this is not a scientific knowledge. As Bergson suggests, it might well be called a metaphysical understanding of things—an understanding that cannot be reduced or assimilated to the scientific dimension of thinking.

Actually from the standpoint of modern science and the theory of evolution, purposes, conscious aims, are confined to human beings. Taking final causes out of external objects does not mean they do not motivate men. An event takes place for a purpose, and there is a reason *why* it takes place, when an explicit awareness of that event, or a temporally prior symbolic representation of it, controls a person's behavior as he manipulates physical objects in order to actualize the event. The *why* as final cause has been taken out of physical objects. Nor do events in nature happen because of a direct control by God. Men alone have the freedom to change the natural order and they alone must assume responsibility commensurable with their freedom.

The second kind of explanation corresponds to scientific understanding. It is an attempt to communicate to another or others an individual's understanding of how an object is related to other objects historically and causally. It concerns the kind of understanding found in the know-how of science which is obtained through pure science and technology. In this sense of explanation, all laws of nature, theories, and basic principles explain (in so far as a person by means of them can communicate to others) that kind of understanding necessary for the prediction, control, or production of objects to which they pertain.

Scientific explanation (and understanding) is indeed confined to this second kind of explanation. Pragmatists have emphasized this fact in their claim that ideas, statements, laws, and theories are clear and intelligible only to the extent that they serve both as a basis for action and initiate in us the responses necessary for predicting and controlling those objects said to be understood and explained. This is a sensible view as long as it does not claim that the only kind of understanding is confined to means of producing or to behavior in so far as behavior enters into controlling the environment.

Pragmatists, in contrast to positivists, have shown that scientific understanding and explanation are necessarily related to behavior and to know-how. Positivists, in their revolt against metaphysics, were unable to relate scientific understanding to practice, behavior, know-how, but in a loose way confined them to Humean sensations, each isolated, atomic, and complete in itself. They failed to recognize that sensibilia, interpreted from the scientific standpoint, are stimuli releasing action necessary for the production and control of events but in themselves contain neither scientific understanding, know-how, nor explanation. Although sensibilia are required for releasing behavior, whose form has been determined by the symbolic process prior to the advent of these sensibilia, they do not and cannot prescribe the form of the act. Every scientific statement providing an understanding of an object involves human behavior necessary for predicting, controlling, or producing the object. Scientific explanation and understanding cannot be divorced from practice. Scientific understanding prescribes the technical form of the act, but assent to the act is determined by the selection of ends made on ethical grounds.

The Neutrality of Physical Objects

The theory of evolution stresses above all else that emergents (new forms, species, and mutations) cannot be reduced to their causes, their history. From the standpoint of physics and the doctrine of the conservation of mass energy, there are no quantitative differences in the world from time to time. What is new, then, is not a quantity or a quantitative difference, but a new quality, which makes a qualitative difference, a difference that cannot be expressed quantitatively nor in terms of other qualities. Each new form is unique in some essential, recognizable sense. Science is concerned with producing and controlling these forms, and it can do so by a knowledge of their pasts.

Scientific knowledge always involves scientific objects, which are confined to the physicochemical, that can be manipulated, directly or indirectly, by human hands. The purpose of the manipulation of physical objects is to produce ends or forms, whose qualities can never be known through a knowledge of their history, since, according to the theory of evolution, these forms are qualitatively different from anything that existed anywhere any time prior to their emergence.

The most significant implication of the theory of emergence for scientific method is in the claim that new forms emerge in time and, consequently, the form itself is not a stimulus or a cause for its emergence, or for the changes (the past of the new form) necessary for its emergence. In other words, the consequences of historical change do not control change. From the standpoint of the evolutionary theory of the emergence of new species, the species (forms) themselves are not that for the sake of which change takes place. No final causes are involved in evolutionary change. The theory of evolution advocates a complete despiritualization of nature and makes a definite break with Aristotle's thesis that the form or the end is that for the sake of which all intelligible, understandable change takes place.[4]

Since final causes do not motivate scientific objects, science can be concerned with efficient causes only. Efficient causes concern the history of objects or the conditions necessary for the production of the qualitative differences that distinguish one form from another. This confinement of scientific knowledge to the conditions for the emergence of qualitative differences is by no means a hindrance to science, for in effect it means that whereas prior to the despiritualization of nature (by evolutionary theory) science in theory could not control the order of events, the way is now clear for men, through science, to change and regulate nature in order to effect ends to which she is indifferent but to which men are not.

The despiritualization of the external world relegates purposive behavior to human beings alone. Whereas Aristotle believed entelechies (*telos,* ends) are in every living form and are causal agents determining biological organization, the medieval Christian theologians took ends and purposes out of the external world and placed them in the mind of God, and they defended the position that the natural order is a means only, created for the purpose of achieving God's purpose.

---

[4] "We have now discussed the other parts of animals, both generally and with reference to the peculiarities of each kind, explaining how each part exists on account of such a cause, and I mean by this the final cause.

"There are four causes underlying everything: first, the final cause, that for the sake of which a thing exists; secondly, the formal cause, the definition of its essence (and these two we may regard pretty much the same); thirdly, the material; and fourthly, the moving principle or efficient cause." Aristotle *On the Generation of Animals,* Book I, 715a (Oxford translation).

Under the influence of the theory of evolution and encouraged by the success of pure science in physics and astronomy, the modern scientists went one step further. They came to the conclusion that the natural order, though intelligible, is altogether neutral with regard to God's purpose and will lend itself indifferently to the accomplishment of alternative purposes of men.

Thus the steps from Aristotle to contemporary philosophy of science by way of medieval theology seem, first, to take purposes out of nature and place them in the mind of God, and, second, to take them out of God's mind and place them in man. It appears, then, that God is left out of the picture and that the theory of evolution necessarily denies the existence of God's will. This is not quite the case. The contemporary claim is that a scientific study of the external world offers no information whatsoever regarding how nature is to be used, or regarding the will of God. If men still claim to be able to know the will of God, they must know it on other than scientific grounds. The external world, however, will lend itself indifferently to accomplishing either the "will of God" or the "will of Satan." Neither God nor Satan has anything to do with the course of events in the external world. There are no miracles. Hence if the "will of God" has any meaning in connection with contemporary science, its meaning must be found through other channels than scientific research.

As a consequence, the many so-called acts of God have, one by one, been attributed to a natural order, which is altogether indifferent to purposes. Floods, famines, disease, fire, wars, and prosperity, since they are either predictable or under man's control, may no longer be attributed to the will of God. Nature is entirely free from purpose, and the responsibility for the ends actually achieved by using her as a means is on the shoulders of men alone. If men still believe they can learn the will of God, science will be of no avail to them in doing so.

Contrary to the belief of many, the despiritualization of nature does not imply a complete determinism in which man himself is caught up in a web of fate and inevitability in which every act is determined by extraneous forces over which he has no control. It implies, instead, a neutral world in which the course of events may be determined by men who, through the use of symbols, can select the ends to be accomplished by indifferent matter and indifferent laws of nature. Freedom depends on a despiritualized, external world and is not annihilated by it.

Neither freedom nor choice would be possible if Aristotle's view that all external phenomena are controlled by final causes were correct, or if the medieval view that events in nature are completely controlled by the will of God were correct. Doing away with final causes is the first prerequisite to a justification of the behavior of men as they set up control over nature. If God uses floods to accomplish His purpose, then any attempt by men to control them would be wrong. The same can be said for preventing disease, irrigating desert land, or for any planning whatsoever.

To say that the external world is neutral means two things, both of which are necessary for the freedom of man and for the application of science toward the achievement of ends selected on ethical grounds. (1) Not all relations between events are internal—many are external. If all relations were internal, the order of events would be fixed, and no amount of planning could change it. Events are indifferent to the spatiotemporal order in which they happen. The law of gravity is universal. Hence the stone will fall at any time at any place, regardless of what happens before or after it falls. Similarly, fuel is indifferent to the time or place it is consumed, even as an automobile has no concern for where it goes. (2) Not all relations in the external world are external—many are internal. If there were no internal relations, there would be no causal laws of nature, nor would there be physical objects having dependable characteristics and a dependable structure. The relationship between the electrons and the nuclei of atoms is internal, and atoms are dependable. Every causal law states internal relationships between the factors related. Laws and the basic structure of physical objects cannot be changed, regardless of what men do. Men are not free to change what they must depend on in exercising freedom.

To the extent that relations in the external world are internal, they are dependable and can be used effectively for various ends. And in so far as relations between objects in the world are external, there is room for exercising freedom in effecting alternative external relationships which result in the attainment of correspondingly alternative goals, ends, or purposes. Space and time are homogeneous. Consequently, they have no effect on any objects, and all spatiotemporal relations are external to a body. Thus whether oxygen is in juxtaposition to hydrogen is of no concern to either, but if in fact they are in juxtaposition, they will unite chemically and form a liquid in accordance with a law that no one can change. In controlling the process, man depends on both the fact that spatiotemporal relations are external and that the causal relations between hydrogen and oxygen are internal. Similarly, the floodgates will lend themselves to being opened at any time by the same means, but if they are opened at the "wrong" time the consequences may be disastrous..

Man's freedom consists in his ability to bring together different objects and processes in order to effect a new object or process through the manipulation of physical objects controlled by symbols. In Part II, Chapter XIII, it will be shown that man's freedom depends on three basic factors: (1) physical objects that can be manipulated, which presupposes their neutrality; (2) man's ability to manipulate objects; and (3) man's ability to control the act of manipulating objects by symbols for the consequence of the act.

A scientific understanding of objects refers finally to understanding how to produce them. Consequently, scientific understanding presupposes freedom, i.e., (1) the control of a man's behavior, as he manipulates physical objects, by symbols indicating the results of that behavior, (2) the consequences must be assented to and selected from alternative possible ones, all of which are equally attainable and, from the standpoint of descriptive science, equally rational.

Both freedom and scientific understanding, then, are correlative, and both are essential to the choice of ends made on ethical grounds.

Thanks to the theory of evolution and experimental science, scientific understanding is not a speculative matter. It involves, instead, human behavior controlled by symbols for ends produced by men through the manipulation of physical objects. Metaphysical understanding, which is largely intuitive, has been separated from know-how, and from scientific understanding. Both are necessary for freedom exercised by men in controlling the order of events, and neither is reducible to the other. The choice of ends must be a clear and separate act distinguishable from the scientific manipulation of objects necessary to effect the ends chosen.

The theory of evolution, the subject to which we now turn, is in effect a new theory of time, of history, of the past of phenomena, and it illuminates the meaning of scientific understanding and scientific explanation.

CHAPTER IV

The Theory of Evolution

Introduction

OFTEN NEW DISCOVERIES MADE in science alter the scientific method and change the attitudes of scientists toward their subject matter. Max Planck's discovery of the photon led to the quantum theory and, later, to the principle of indeterminacy as formulated by Heisenberg. The famous Michelson-Morley experiment of 1881, which tried but failed to detect the velocity of the earth with reference to absolute space (or the ether), was a major factor used by Einstein in the development of the special and general theories of relativity. Mainly as a result of a combination of these two discoveries Einstein developed the basic formula, $E = MC^2$, which states the equivalence of mass and energy. This formula is fundamental to a study of nuclear energy and the chain reaction of elements. The tremendous social, economic, and political implications of these discoveries are well known to all of us, for not only have they stimulated our hopes for a new social order in which men are relieved of burdensome muscular labor but they have led also to world-wide fears, and in many cases to cynical and futilistic attitudes.

Every major discovery has two significant effects: (1) It alters the methods and procedures of scientists; (2) It changes social, political, and economic attitudes and practices. The first of these effects belongs to pure science, the second to applied science and social behavior.

The theory of evolution is older than either the quantum theory or the theory of relativity. Yet many of its implications for scientific method have been overlooked. Clearly its impact on the theory of the nature of man and on the social sciences has been widespread, but as yet no one has examined carefully the implications of the theory of evolution for epistemology and metaphysics in particular and, in turn, its implications for scientific method. This is the aim of what follows.

The Tenets of the Theory of Evolution

1. The major tenet of the theory of evolution is that new forms of things come into existence from time to time. These new forms, though essentially unlike the conditions necessary for their emergence, nevertheless have a history or a past. The cause of an emergent is to be found in the past; and once it is found it is said to be the past of that emergent, that new form. But the past of an emergent can be approached and hypothetically posited only by way of the emergent, for, from the scientific and methodological standpoint, the past of an emergent can mean only the cause or the conditions necessary for the emergent to come into existence. Consequently, the scientific meaning of a past emanates from a present emergent form, and every past is a past of something, and "past" in itself has no meaning.

This reasoning may seem strange, but just prior to the theory of evolution, scientists were much under the influence of the mechanistic philosophy of Pierre Laplace, who held that a complete knowledge of the present (any present) would be a sufficient basis for predicting all things to come. According to mechanistic determinism, the entire future consists of an unfolding of what is enfolded, of making explicit what is implicit from the beginning of time, even as the theorems of geometry follow necessarily from pre-established axioms, and the conclusion of a syllogism from the premises. This doctrine holds that both the present and the future emanate from the past; consequently, their meaning is to be found in the past.

The mechanistic philosophy was a rebellion against idealism and against the belief that final causes or purposes, whether in the mind of God or in men, are factors determining the course of events and the ends attained. Those who believed final causes are effective in directing the course of events held that both the past and the present are significant only from the standpoint of goals or ends to be achieved in a future. Both mechanism and finalism try to understand events by getting at their causes, and for both, understanding and explanation consist in a knowledge of these supposed causes. Also, both—since they rigorously defend the view that a complete knowledge of past, present, and future phenomena is now possible in principle—must deny the emergence of genuinely new forms. The mechanists held all knowledge to be achievable through a thorough analysis of the present; the finalists through a complete awareness of ends.

But if at any given time complete knowledge of past, present, and future phenomena is possible even in principle, then it is obvious that additional experience of oncoming future events would not only be unnecessary to knowledge but superfluous and possibly a hindrance. For this reason both mechanism and finalism, with their entailed theory of complete determinism, rest, finally, on the epistemology of the rationalists who deny that the test of the truth value of statements about the world of events depends even in part on future predictable and observable characters of objects. Both mechanism and finalism break down at the same place and for the same reason. Neither, because of its rationalistic epistemology, can make use of future experience, to say nothing of the unique experiences of individuals, in acquiring knowledge. Furthermore, any epistemology able to make continued use of experience in acquiring knowledge must forsake the theory of a cut-and-dried universe with its accompanying epistemological doctrine of complete determinism. The theory of evolution claims that the doctrine of complete determinism is fallacious and, consequently, that complete predictability of events is impossible even in principle.

2. New forms of things, emergents, are unpredictable. The empirical school of philosophy seems to have established a major plank in the scientist's platform: all predictions of future events must be rooted in experience, and what can be predicted from a scientific basis must be like what has been experienced (the experimental basis for prediction). But since evolution means first of all that new forms, the like of which never existed before, come into existence from time to time, it follows that they are unpredictable. To hold with mechanism that these "new forms" are nothing but a rearrangement of primordial parts is to deny their objective existence and to hold that whatever novelty they have is "subjective," or psychological, or merely "new" to

us. Similarly, the finalist view that the forms acquired by the primordial parts (or matter, in the Aristotelian sense) must exist in some sense prior to their actualization is a denial of their genuine emergence. The mechanist believes that the causes of change are to be found in their completeness in the past, in efficient causes; the finalist hopes to find them in final causes, in forms, or goals, or ends that somehow effect all change and direct it toward the realization of these ends.

To hold that the causes of all phenomena can be known prior to their occurrence and that genuinely new forms emerge in time is a contradiction. Logically, we can justify predicting an effect on the basis of its cause only in the assimilating of the effect to its cause, even as the conclusion of a deductive argument is assimilated to its premises. Such a justification presupposes a rationalistic epistemology quite contrary to the empiricist's contention that experience offers the final test for the truth value of a prediction.

To say that the causes for emergents cannot be known prior to these emergents does not imply in the least that they have no causes. Rather, the reasons or causes for emergents cannot be sought nor, consequently, found prior to the emergents. For this reason pasts acquire meaning only with reference to present observables and the entire scientific meaning of a past is found in its explanatory function—a past explains a present. In this sense, pasts emanate from present phenomena, and, for this reason, *pasts become what they are by virtue of the present observables which they explain.* But since pasts emanate from present phenomena in the manner explained above, it is clear that those pasts could not have been a basis for predicting the original occurrence of the new forms, the emergents.

Although practically all scientists set up as an ideal the hope of predicting all future events in their field of study, the theory of evolution denies that this ideal, which belongs strictly to the rationalistic philosophy, is achievable in principle. It is of no use to say "but if we knew enough about the past and present then every future event would be predictable," for, according to evolution, a knowledge of the past can be approached only by way of those things in a present that call for explanation. To say, then, that a thorough knowledge of the present would enable us to predict all things to come is not only contradictory to the theory of evolution but it is also a denial of a major tenet of empiricism, namely, that experience is necessary to the attainment of knowledge, and future experience is no exception. Still, because of the influence of rationalism, which in turn held that processes in nature, like an Aristotelian syllogism, merely unfold what is enfolded, almost every scientist draws the conclusion that "sufficient knowledge of the present and past" will enable him to sit down with pencil and paper and chart the course of all things to come. The theory of evolution comes as a severe jolt to a mechanistic, idealistic, rationalistic epistemology based on the belief that "in the last analysis" there is nothing new under the sun.

Obviously the Mendelian law of inheritance is useful in predicting and, often, controlling the nature of the offspring of plants and animals. But there is no super-Mendelian law whereby the character of mutations can be predicted; in other words, there is no law by which we can predict new forms, emergents, and the theory of evolution implies that such a law is impossible in principle.

3. The scientific meaning of a statement about the past is identical with a statement of the conditions under which the emergent appears. Every statement about the past (or a past) involves a present object, and every history is a history of some known, present phenomenon. The first concern of every scientist is to account for certain existing things, and he always does this by presenting to himself ideationally, imaginatively, and hypothetically the (past) conditions which he believes were actually responsible for the emergence of the thing in question.

Although much emphasis has been placed, by positivists and pragmatists in particular, on the predictive, prognostic character of scientific statements, all predictions (about future events) presuppose a theory of the nature of the past—the nature of the history of present observables. If an astronomer predicts an eclipse of the sun, his prediction must be for some particular time: in 1916 he predicted the eclipse of March 27, 1919. In order to make such a prediction on a scientific basis the astronomer had to be aware of the history of astronomical events before 1916. He had to know, also, the relevant conditions at the time of his prediction—boundary conditions necessary for *all* predictions. Then he could make his predictions, and these predictions constitute a test of his theory of a past and of a history of present observables.

Every prediction at the experimental stage is a prediction designed to test a theory of the origin of some present, observable thing. Without a knowledge of the origin of things, applied science, the control of the order of events, would be impossible. As a corollary, a study of the history of events belongs to pure science and the pure scientist proceeds from the data, present observables, to a past, and he tests his theory of the past by predictions of future observables.

4. The theory of evolution gives us a new theory of history and, consequently, a new theory of the nature of time. As Bergson has shown, neither the idealistic theory that every event has a prevised place in a plan designed to accomplish a prevised end, nor the mechanistic theory that blind efficient causes are adequate to account for all change, takes time seriously. Neither recognizes the emergence of new forms. Both present us with a cut-and-dried order of events—a world in which nothing ever happens.

Although Aristotle is considered by many to be the first evolutionist, his theory is completely devoid of evolution from the Darwinian point of view. Aristotle held that the forms of things were "there" prior to their actualization in matter. Not only were the forms prior to their actualization, but they were necessary (as guides or controls) for changes in matter if matter acquired form. Matter for Aristotle had no character of its own but was defined as "pure potentiality"; it had no capacity except that of acquiring form. It had the capacity to be characterized by universals—eternal, changeless forms with no history, but recognizable in observable objects.

In all living things, according to Aristotle, *entelechies* are necessary as stimuli and, therefore, as causes, if matter, or living things, are to have forms. The monstrosities and freaks had no form and, therefore, no cause. And although, according to Aristotle, matter resists form, this resistance is passive and is not considered a cause of anything. This resistance is reflected in the monstrosity, the sport, and the freak, considered uncaused and without form. Had Aristotle been able to accept the sport as a *new form,* emerging without that form being prior to its emergence and the cause of it, he would have anticipated Darwinism and a new theory of history. Instead it was left to Darwin to argue that the forms have a history and that the sole function of the past from the standpoint of science is to account for the origin of the species.

It is just this theory of the nature of the past, conceivable only with reference to new forms, that offers a new theory of history. The past of anything is its history. Further evidence that Aristotle did not hold a theory of evolution in the Darwinian sense is found in his theory of the nature of time. Time is, according to him, a repetitious, monotonous affair, completely cyclical, bringing in its wake the ever repetitious occurrence of eternal forms, none of which had a history, all of which had an ontological status or "being" from the foundations of the world.

Augustine says it was not fate (blind causes) that determined the fall of the old Roman Empire but the will of God. For him all history was significant, intelligible, and explainable only with reference to God's plan. To understand history, then, one had to know God's purpose, and theology for Augustine was nothing other than a justification of the ways of God to men—a justification of the past and the present from the standpoint of God's plan of salvation. Since the plan was eternal and never changed, the order of events was likewise fixed, predestined, prescribed by God, an intelligent, efficient being. The theory that the Christian God is completely rational had widespread support throughout the Middle Ages. This strengthened the belief that every event has its preassigned place in an orderly world. Even miracles, though not completely intelligible to men, were considered orderly and rational from the standpoint of God's plan and purpose.

The Augustinian and Aristotelian theories of history are essentially alike. Both think of forms, ends (*telos, teleos*), as qualitative in character, recognizable or thinkable, but not measurable or quantitatively comparable and, therefore, not strictly rational or logical. According to Aristotle, a stone falls because of its nature, its form or end, and its end is expressed by saying it seeks the center of the earth. Similarly, the reason for establishing the Holy Roman Empire, according to Augustine, is the plan of salvation, an end, or God's purpose. The chief difference between these views is that for Aristotle ends are in nature whereas for Augustine they are in the mind of God. And although the Aristotelian prime mover was a stimulus for objects on earth, such as plants and animals, to acquire a perfect form, the forms aspired to exist for their own sake and not for the sake of the prime mover. Augustine believed that all change and the attainment of all forms whatsoever are for the sake of an end in the mind of God.

It was left to Hegel to develop a theory of history which is both idealistic and perfectly rational. His claim is that the same kind of compulsion or "force" that is found in reason, as it moves by its own nature from premise to conclusion in a compelling, dialectic manner, is found in history as it moves relentlessly from thesis-antithesis to synthesis. Hegel simply assimilated whatever temporal or historical dimension the universe has to logic or reason. History, then, is not only rational, it is a part of reason. Usually one thinks of the implications of the axioms of geometry as being timeless and, therefore, static; implicit, but not explicit. Hegel, however, attributed to the thesis (analogous to an axiom) not only its antithesis but also a dynamic, dialectic quality which could express itself only *in time*. The time it takes for the expression of what is contained implicitly in the thesis is history. It is in this sense that Hegel assimilated history to reason and thought of history as the temporal factor necessary for unfolding the implications of a great idea or a major premise.

5.   In contrast to Augustine, Aristotle, and Hegel, Darwin's theory of evolution interprets change as if it is neither purposive and stimulated by ends nor like the unfolding of the implications of a syllogism. The new forms emerge by chance (chance variations) and, by chance, answer or do not answer to an environment. There is no prevision of the form, and in that sense no reason why one form should emerge instead of another. Neither are the forms predictable, and in that sense nature is not like the unfolding of a syllogism.

Yet Darwin's theory is far from declaring that change has no cause or that the past of a new form is unintelligible. It implies that since we cannot predict the new forms, and since the form has a history or becomes what it is *in* time, we can look for its cause, its past, only after it emerges.

6.   Reasons for the emergence of new forms can be found only after their emergence, and never before. Reasons for the emergence of a new form are identical with the actual conditions necessary for its emergence, but these conditions are always qualitatively different from the new form to which they gave rise. One cannot assimilate the final stage in a process to any or all of the previous stages, even as one cannot, according to evolution, assimilate the effect to cause. The attempt to assimilate effect to cause is a vestige of rationalism by which men believed

that explanation of something consists in showing that it is not new; that it always existed in latent form and potentially, even as the conclusion of a syllogism is implicit in the premises.

Identity belongs to mathematics and to the measure of comparable objects but does not characterize the form and its history. The history or past of an object is, by definition, qualitatively different from the object itself. But since scientific explanation and understanding consist of knowing the conditions necessary for the emergence of a new form, and, finally, the production of instances similar to the new form, knowledge itself takes on new meaning. This is precisely what pragmatists have emphasized. Scientific knowledge is for the sake of action, and action is for the sake of controlling the order of events.

Although Darwin took for granted new and slight variations among the members of a species at any given time, his main purpose was to explain how these variations, in the struggle for existence in the environment of the members of the species, gradually gave rise to a completely new species. Since, however, in accordance with Darwin's belief that natural causes were continuous, neither spontaneous, catastrophic, nor abrupt (cf. Charles Lyell),[1] he could in fact never describe anything other than a cross-section of an unending, ever changing species. Only after the work of Gregor Mendel (*ca.* 1862) and, later, that of Bateson, De Vries, and finally Morgan and his pupils, was the science of genetics firmly established.

The basic tenet of genetics is that the cause of variations[2] among members of the species is to be found in the germ plasm of the ancestors. These causes are called genes, and many of the variations resulting from them are called mutations. Although geneticists agree with Darwin's thesis that through natural selection many mutant factors are lethal whereas others have "survival value" and are, thereby, selected, in the main their interest has been concentrated on the cause of the mutations and not on the conflict in the struggle for existence. The procedure of the geneticist is quite obvious: he arrives at the concept of "gene" only by way of his actual experience with the offspring of the parents—he constructs his theory of the nature of the history, the past,

---

[1] Charles Lyell, *Principles of Geology* (London, John Murray, 1830–33).

[2] See T. H. Morgan *et al, The Mechanism of Mendelian Heredity* (New York, Henry Holt and Company, Inc., 1915), Chapter I.

and the cause of the mutation only after first observing the mutation. The scientific evidence for the existence of genes consists of their effects, the observable mutations, offspring of parents, and the living observable individual forms.

Darwinism plus genetics has given us an entirely new theory of history or of the past, and this theory of evolution offers a new concept of time which was altogether lacking in the rationalistic-idealistic philosophy. According to the new theory, history or the past is related to the present as means to ends, as a necessary condition to effect, but no one can approach history directly. All history must be posited hypothetically as the best explanation for something present, as the most satisfactory account of the causes of forms, the like of which we want to predict and, possibly, control. There is no history per se. All history is a history of something.

7. But the most important implication of the new theory of history for metaphysics is that "the past," though unobservable even in principle, has meaning. Although all meanings necessarily involve observables which are experienced in a present, they are not confined to observables. Meanings, as referents of scientific statements, cannot be confined to a present, to say nothing of a knife-edge present. But purportedly the referents of scientific statements have an objective status, and if past (and future) can be referred to, but yet are not observable, it follows not only that there are unobservables but also that these unobservables, in some cases at least, are the referents of scientific statements.

The theory of evolution attributes a temporal character to objects and to whatever has existence. Neither rationalism nor idealism did as much. This durational, temporal character involves past, present, and future. The past, according to the theory of evolution, consists of the conditions giving rise to what is present, and the future consists of alternative possible observables, made possible because of what is present plus our knowledge of how the present came about. Here "past" and "future" mean what we can refer to in a scientific sense, or what we, at present, think they are.

John Stuart Mill, like Aristotle, defines matter as pure potentiality. But whereas Aristotle thought of matter as capable of supporting forms, Mill defines it as the possibility (cause?) of sensations. Neither could conceive of matter as anything other than what it, as matter, is not. Both reduced possibility and potentiality (matter) to something not matter, and could not understand it as something necessarily related to sensations, observables, and forms, but not identical with them.

Mill and Aristotle are not the only ones unable to grant definite referents to "possibility" and "potentiality" other than what is observable. The positivistic philosophy from Auguste Comte to the present consists in denying that scientific terms can refer to unobservables and in defending the position that the sole reference of meaningful terms is to observables. If they are correct, then the words "past" and "future" have no referents, nor could we speak significantly of anything but what is actual and immediate. Their failure is easily accounted for. First, they define the object of knowledge, and, consequently, the referents of all scientific statements, as observables. It follows from this definition that unobservables cannot be referred to or known. Their conclusion is that "cause," "condition," and "past" have no meaning, since they are not observables. From this conclusion they fallaciously draw another: unobservables have no objective status, no ontological status and, consequently, that metaphysics which purports to discuss unobservables is nonsense, since no metaphysical statement can have subject matter or referents.

It is one thing to say that all meaningful scientific statements must involve observables and another to say that their sole referents are observables. If some have drawn the conclusion that the major tenet of empiricism is that the referents of all meaningful statements are observables, the theory of evolution should show them that their conclusion is false. When we consider the origin of the solar system, of geological phenomena, and life itself, it is clear that the referents of our words are unobservable phenomena, and when we consider, further, that time is one-directional and, according to evolution, the past is irrepeatable, beyond recall, it follows not only that the objects of cognition, in many cases, are unobservables but also that observables, in so far as they are meaningful, have a temporal, durational character.

Although "past" has scientific meaning only in relation to that of which it is a past, a present observable, this does not imply that its meaning *is* a present observable. In accordance with the major tenet of empiricism, namely, that all scientific statements must be epistemically related to observables, the theory of evolution, with its emphasis on the temporal character of the natural order, implies that past and future must be epistemically related to present observable phenomena.

From this epistemological tenet the metaphysics of science must be derived. Both the theory of evolution and the scientific method of dealing with factual matters suggest a realistic metaphysics—the belief that unobservables exist, that there is a world-order independent of thought and perception, and that the structure of that world can be known, in part at least, but always through observables. The theory of evolution is a defense of the claim that unobservables have ontological status and can be the object of cognition. It holds also that these unobservables must be approached by way of present observables. Empiricism supports this claim.

What It Means to Believe in Evolution

The greatest obstacle preventing moderns from accepting the theory of evolution is by no means traditional theology, but rather a deeply ingrained rationalistic attitude repugnant to the belief that anything is genuinely new. This attitude, beginning with the Greeks, insists that understanding and explanation consist of assimilating the "effects" to their "causes," either in "seeing" the fully developed flower in the seed, or in "seeing" all change under the guise of eternity. It is difficult to understand that the statement "if we knew all that can be known about the present and the past, we could predict all things to come," is contradictory to the theory of evolution. But the reason for the contradiction is clear enough; the theory of evolution holds that (1) new forms emerge from time to time, the like of which have never existed in any form prior to their emergence, (2) the basis for prediction in science is observed phenomena, and we cannot in principle predict something the like of which has never been observed. The theory of evolution reverses the tendency to find the present in the past. It claims that we cannot know what the past is like except by reference to what it produces and to a present effect. This is why no historian can make a conclusive statement about the past. His statement must not only account for a present phenomenon, object, or institution, but it must continue to answer to future observables if it is true. New experience, new evidence, or the emergence of a new type of phenomenon may make his history out of date. There may be two senses in which there is or was "a history of Texas." First, what actually took place in the development of Texas, whatever that means, and, second, an actual account of how Texas came to be what it is today. The latter only can be the scientific meaning of its history. It can be approached only by way of (present) evidence (effects). All history written from a standpoint of evidence is nothing other than an attempt to explain the evidence.

To believe in evolution means to believe that a hypothesis in science explains or makes intelligible the evidence, but the evidence does not prove the hypothesis. The hypothesis, however, is not a summary of the evidence, nor is it a formal statement of the order of experience, whose function is to anticipate future experiences or events. The hypothesis is, rather, a statement of the cause of the evidence; a statement of how the evidence came into existence. In science all hypotheses and all theories based on evidence are of an explanatory nature, and to explain is to state what is believed to be the history, the past, or the cause of what is explained. Consequently, to believe in evolution means to accept the consequence that we do not support reasons (hypotheses) by the evidence, but rather that we rationalize the evidence.

A common argument against genuine novelty is that there must be a cause for everything, or, nothing comes from nothing (nihil ex nihilo). And since emergents are new in the sense that they did not exist anywhere any time prior to their emergence, they must come from nowhere. Obviously then, so the argument goes, they have no causes. The fallacy of this argument stems from the hidden assumption that effects must be in and like their causes. This is the old rationalistic argument over again, for it claims that there can be nothing new and that any "apparently new" form must be assimilated to its cause.

There is considerable argument against genuine novelty by those who believe that science can express the essential nature of objects and events in quantitative physicochemical terms alone. Since, therefore, the physical world is conservative, there being no increase or diminution of matter-energy, there can be nothing "really" new. Novelty, accordingly, is subjective—only an appearance. Colors, for example, can be expressed in terms of energy and light waves, and that is precisely what color is, so they argue. Similarly, sounds and tastes can be expressed fully by resorting to quantities and equations. "Living forms," likewise, are reducible to inorganic processes expressible in purely quantitative terms.

These arguments ignore a basic tenet in the theory of evolution, namely, emergents are qualitative and their nature cannot be expressed quantitatively. New forms are not *more* than their causes, as if there were *more* in the effect than in its cause; they are simply qualitatively different. There is not more of anything in the universe because of evolution; it is different from time to time. Bergson emphasized this point by showing that time cannot be spatialized; it cannot be quantified. We can recognize new forms and emergents, but we cannot compare them quantitatively with other forms. When scientists interpret the world from the standpoint of method, control, and production, they often express it quantitatively. When looked at from the standpoint of ends to be produced, it must be interpreted qualitatively. The question: What difference does change make in the world? has two answers. Quantitatively change makes no difference. Qualitatively it may, and every controlled process by the scientist, every application of pure science to practical problems, has the purpose of making a qualitative difference in the world of fact.

The inability of some to distinguish between emergents, new forms, and their causes is the inability to distinguish between ends and means, between metaphysics and methodology, between qualities and quantities. Identities belong to methodology whereas qualitative differences are found in ends. Anyone who interprets phenomena from the standpoint of method alone has the mechanist's attitude and will likely come to the conclusion that ends are "really" equal to the means. This is a confusion of methodology with metaphysics; a confusion of how to produce something with what is produced. This fallacious reasoning found its way into many of the sciences and led to such expressions as: "Green is really nothing but yellow and blue"; "Personality is nothing but heredity plus environment"; "A living organism is nothing but a certain combination of inorganic processes"; "The meaning of a statement is identical with the means of establishing its truth value." But the temporal, qualitative character of phenomena calls for a sharp distinction between methodology and metaphysics, means and ends, and requires that we never equate the two.

It is equally fallacious to interpret the world in terms of ends exclusively, in terms of observable forms or qualitative differences. This would acknowledge the existence of the sensed world only. In fact, it amounts to saying there is nothing in the world except what can be recognized or sensed, or, more narrowly, sensations alone. A philosophy that accepts either the quantitative, mechanistic, and methodological, or the qualitative, finalistic metaphysical interpretation of nature as complete has a superficial understanding of science. Science is not for its own sake any more than the method of producing something is for its own sake. Methodology is for the sake of ends, and ends cannot be produced and controlled without scientific method. If, however, we must place more intrinsic value on one than on the other, or if one is to be justified by the other, then the end justifies the means, not the means the end. This is tantamount to saying that the justification of "pure science" is found in its application, in technology, industry, or applied medicine. Method or knowledge does not exist for its own sake, and, consequently, neither does scientific knowledge. The purpose of knowledge for science is that it provides the means of producing observables and certain experiences, such as the experience of music, certain colors, or tastes, which are summarized by the hedonists as pleasures. Quite often these means are unobservable or at least not directly observable, yet known. This is the basis for the difference between the two ways of knowing: knowing by direct acquaintance (as one knows a toothache by having it) and knowing by being able to control, produce, or prevent.

We can never predict the precise nature of new forms, and consequently we must construct a past for each form *ad hoc*. This stubborn fact suggests that any particular present, with its set of actual events, is capable of producing alternative kinds of forms, but once a particular form is produced, it tends to reproduce itself; it tends to give to history and to time a repetitious, monotonous character. Consequently, the forms themselves are the only things that fix or stabilize possibilities or potentialities. But the possibilities and potentialities are not fixed in all available ways, but in a limited way or number of ways only. Yet, the possible must be approached by way of the actual, and what a past is like is known only through a present, for a past is precisely like the cause of the effect which it produces. A present becomes a past, and from the standpoint of its effects, a present becomes what it is only *after* its effects, which give it all the historical, causal meaning a present can have. And if the experience of the actual is necessary for our conception of the possible, then we cannot state in detail or in full what the potentialities of any present are. All that can be said about a given present situation is that it will *probably* produce a form which has been experienced previously, but what else it will produce, no one can say. The present, in so far as it will become a part of the content of history, must wait for a future in order to be so recorded. But the present as now experienced is not experienced as history, as the cause of a new form. It is experienced, rather, either in its immediacy or as effect, as something produced by its past. The present as history cannot be written till later.

There are recurrent patterns of events serving as a background against which the novel, the historical, takes place. Physicists state this background in terms of conservation theories (mass, energy), and it represents the persistency of forms and the tendency for the form to reproduce or perpetuate itself, but the nerve of time and evolution is the novel.

Although the ideal of many great historians, such as Spengler and Toynbee, seems to be to explain the large and basic ever recurrent patterns of history and, thereby, to predict what is to come, such a hope is contrary to the theory of evolution, with its entailed theory of history. History cannot be made into a deductive, rationalistic discipline. Those who try to make a predictive science out of history as history are trying to assimilate effects to their causes and are still burdened with the Laplacian doctrine that a thorough knowledge of the past or present (since quantitatively there is no difference) will enable us to predict all things to come. The inability to predict novel forms is not related to the fact that many phenomena can be predicted with only a degree of probability and that statistical laws only can be applied to them. There is not even a probability that a particular new form will emerge. Probability theory and prediction with a degree of probability rest on the experience of actual phenomena the like of which is predicted. For example, if there has never been a person who lived to be a thousand years old, one cannot state the degree of probability that a person in the future will live to be that old. Again, if the form of the new is inconceivable prior to its emergence, there can be no statement of the probability that it will emerge. All probability statements and all statistical laws are based on experience of the forms of things predicted, but in no case can this include the novel. All reasoning is *from* existence and the novel and not *toward* it. It is from the novel to history, not from history to the novel.

CHAPTER V

Evolution and the Scientific Method

Prediction and the Novel

THE MEANING OF EVOLUTION was not clear until after the development of the experimental method in modern science. According to the tenets of the experimental method, it is impossible on the basis of the data to predict with certainty what is to follow. Similarly, according to the theory of evolution one cannot predict the emergents or the new types of individuals that evolve from time to time. Generally speaking, our predictions regarding future events are uncertain, and in the case of evolution these uncertainties are due to the emergence of novel forms, the like of which have not been included in the data—the basis for prediction. If what happens in the future is in some essential respect unlike what we have experienced in the past, then indeed it is unpredictable with reference to prior experience. After an emergent is experienced, then the conditions under which it emerged may be sought, and if they are found it will be possible to predict when the form of the emergent will be repeated in other individuals.

The novel situations or events that give us exceptional experiences are the occasions for new interpretations of the past, new histories, and new theories. In fact, all scientific speculation is from the present to a past and to a future, and the present (or, better, a present) is characterized essentially by novelties or by what are called emergents.

EVOLUTION AND THE SCIENTIFIC METHOD

The novel is an event, whether we think of an event as an object or a relation. In the biological world a mutation is novel in that it does not follow from the Mendelian law. In human society, language and reflective thinking are novelties with respect to laws holding at the biological level. At the level of reflective thinking all creative ideas, all concepts leading to new inventions, and, indeed, all ideas leading to new practices and new habits, are novel. As Whitehead points out, in reflective thinking the mind enters into "the creative advance of nature," which is evolution. Evolution implies novelties that are a result of natural creativity, since indeed novelties have their causes and their ground in nature which is neither static nor repetitious but ever changing.

According to the theory of evolution the novelties constitute the basis from which time is abstracted. Measured time, however, depends on the repetitive phases of nature; but measured time is, as Bergson points out,[1] a sort of spatialization of time and does not give us the concept of time, which depends rather on irrepeatable events.[2] Hence, evolution implies the epigenesis of new forms or new kinds of things.[3]

Emergents have causes and they come about in an orderly fashion. Couple with this the fact that they are unpredictable and we come to the conclusion that it is possible to study the conditions under which emergents emerge (the past of an emergent) only *after* they have been experienced, and not *before*. This fact has implications for both the meaning of reason and rationality and also for the meaning of the past of an emergent. One of the functions of reason is to construct a past or an order from which the emergent can be predicted and thereby explained. Emergents, when first experienced, are nonrational simply because they do not follow from old accepted orders or, if you will, from old pasts.

The pasts posited by scientists account for what is present, namely,

---

[1] See Henri Bergson, *Time and Free Will: An Essay on the Immediate Data of Consciousness,* trans. by F. L. Pogson (London, The Macmillan Company, 1910), Chapter II.

[2] Consider the second law of thermodynamics and implications drawn from Carnot's cycle.

[3] See Arthur Lovejoy, "The Meaning of 'Emergence' and its Modes," *Proceedings of the Sixth International Congress of Philosophy* (New York, Longmans, Green and Co., Inc., 1926), pp. 20–33.

the novelties of today. The geological past is posited in order to explain fossils, mountains, deposits of gravel, and strata of the earth, which are here now. Should a new type of geological phenomenon happen under our very eyes, geologists would, no doubt, posit a past to account for it, and that past would never have been conceived apart from the phenomenon it was designed to explain. To test a statement intended to account for the data, one must predict future events. But events predicted by what accounts for the data (or by a hypothesis) never include the unexperienced emergents. Every hypothesis can be used to predict some event similar to one we have experienced. Such a prediction may have as its purpose the testing of a hypothesis, which will be of this general nature: if certain conditions are established, certain results (the predicted event) will follow. This amounts to testing one's belief as to what is in fact the history or past of an emergent. Once a belief is established, then the person may have a different purpose in making a prediction, in which case one would have accepted the hypothesis as a basis for predicting a future event without intending to test it.

History is constructed so that what it explains follows systematically and deductively, but such a history is based upon experience and what is to be explained. If history is used to predict future events, deductively, then one can predict only events similar to what has taken place in a past. All histories of civilization emanate from the presents of the historians who construct them. Contemporary historians may construct very different histories, each designed to account for the same present state of civilization. In that case we have something analogous to what is often found in the physical sciences when two or more scientists construct different hypotheses to account for the same data. These scientists may be testing their respective hypotheses simultaneously, and agreement among them is not reached on the basis of the data which were common to all of the hypotheses, but rather on the basis of whether or not what is predicted from these hypotheses comes to pass. If what hypothesis h predicts does not come to pass, then it is false. If what hypothesis h_1 predicts comes to pass in one or more instances, then it is confirmed in part at least, and under these circumstances the scientist may accept it without reservations and use it as a basis for deduction in questioning other statements.

EVOLUTION AND THE SCIENTIFIC METHOD

I have spoken of novelty and creativity without inquiring about the origin of new laws. Since laws are abstractions in the sense that they have no ontological status apart from phenomena, we may well conclude that new laws emerge from time to time. New laws imply new orders among phenomena, and new hypotheses are constructed, first, for the purpose of accounting for novelties and, second, in order to predict and control oncoming events. Had old laws been adequate to account for phenomena we would not need new ones, and it is because of emergents and experiences exceptional to old laws that new laws are required. Prior to the emergence of biological forms, the Mendelian law of inheritance was not operative. But the Mendelian law does not account for mutations, and once they emerge we have the problem of finding the conditions necessary for their emergence.

One of the implications of the theory of evolution for epistemology is that our experiences of mutations and other novelties constitute the basis for setting up new hypotheses. If the process of evolution continues, then novelties will confront us from time to time, and we will never have a theory or a law by which we can predict the entire future. Any doctrine, such as that proposed by Laplace, to the effect that "if we knew enough about the present we could predict the entire future" is implicitly a denial of evolution and novelty, or else it is sheer tautology.

The chemist H. N. Lewis illustrated the meaning of "emergent" by explaining that a thorough study of oxygen and hydrogen in separation from each other would not enable us to predict the result of putting them together. Water is qualitatively different from a gas, yet it is the result of the chemical union of gases. C. Lloyd Morgan has pointed out that emergents are not mechanical, mathematical resultants of their component parts.[4] And if C. A. Benjamin is correct in his belief that every law, when stated precisely, must be put in the form of a mathematical equation, then indeed emergents with their qualitative differences defy all prediction, for they cannot be stated quantitatively.

Arthur Lovejoy has described emergents in the following manner:[5]

[4] C. Lloyd Morgan, *Emergent Evolution* (New York, Henry Holt and Company, Inc., 1931), Chapter I.

[5] Arthur Lovejoy, *op. cit.,* pp. 26–27.

An "emergent evolution" may, then, be said to have taken place if, upon comparison of the present phase (called Ph. N), of earth-history (say that since the appearance of *homo sapiens*) with any prior phase (called Ph. A), there can be shown to be present in Ph. N any one or more of the five following features lacking in Ph. A. (1) Instances of some general type of change admittedly common to both phases (e.g., relative motion of particles), of which instances the manner or conditions of occurrence could not be described in terms of, nor predicted from, the laws which would have been sufficient for the description and (given the requisite determination of the variables) the prediction of all changes of that type occurring in Ph. A. Of this evolutionary emergence of laws one, though not the only conceivable, occasion would be the production, in accordance with one set of laws, of new local integrations of matter, the motions of which, and therefore of their component particles, would thereupon conform to vector, i.e., directional, laws emergent in the sense defined. This first mode differs from the others in that it implies no quantitative variability of the prime or irreducible existents (other than relations) in the system under consideration. (2) New qualities and, especially, classes of qualities (e.g., the so-called secondary qualities) attachable as adjectives to entities already present, though without those accidents, in Ph. A. (3) Particular entities *not* possessing all the essential attributes characteristic of those found in Ph. A., and having distinctive types of attributes (not merely configurational) of their own. (4) Some type or types of event or process irreducibly different in kind from any occurring in Ph. A. (5) A greater quantity, or number of instances, not explicable by transfer from outside the system, of any one or more types of prime entity common to both phases.

Metaphysical Implications of Evolution

When one asks, Is the world spiritual or material? he is asking a metaphysical question. Probably in the back of his mind is the assumption that ultimately everything is reducible to one kind of thing and that everything is "really" what it can be reduced to. Still farther in the back of his mind is the assumption that there is nothing new under the sun and that what existed at the beginning of time is all there will ever be "really." In this sense many tend to reduce reality to the stable unchanging factors in the universe or to what might be called causes.

The "effects" of causes are, of course, temporal and therefore unreal. We must get back of the changing, phenomenal world, so the argument goes, and discover the unchanging, real world.

Lovejoy writes:[6]

> There is an old and persistent tendency in the human mind to conceive of the causal relation as rationally explanatory, and therefore, to assimilate it, vaguely or explicitly, to the logical relations of inclusion, implication, or equivalence. That "there cannot be more in the effect than there is in the cause" is one of the propositions that men have been readiest to accept as axiomatic; a cause, it has been supposed, does not "account for" its effect, unless the effect is a thing which the eye of reason could somehow discern in the cause, upon a sufficiently thorough analysis. This antipathy to the notion of an absolute epigenesis has left its mark deep and wide upon the history of thought; it appears, indeed, at the very outset of Western speculation in the struggles of the physiologers with the supposed difficulty of admitting qualitative change.

This rather universal practice of "reducing" things to other things is an indirect defense of our customs and habits.[7]

Novelty calls for a reconstruction of one's environment and of one's relationship to that environment. In general it appears to be easier to assimilate an effect to its cause and thereby deny novelty than to accept the novel at its face value and make the necessary readjustments. Yet many experimentalists do not hesitate to argue that there is "really" nothing new under the sun and that all that is or ever will be existed from the foundations of the world, if not explicitly then implicitly. Such an argument amounts to a denial of the theory of evolution.

Without the innovation of novelties there would be no excuse for defending institutionalized ways of thinking and acting, for habit would carry us through every eventuality. To push the argument a step further, without change there would be no consciousness of our practices and we would not, therefore, state the nature of our institutions, for we could live by habit alone and all thinking would be altogether superficial. To accept the novel as irreducibly real may amount to giving it a central place in experimental logic and in the laboratory method

---

[6] *Ibid.,* p. 20.

[7] See A. J. Ayer, *The Foundations of Empirical Knowledge* (New York, The Macmillan Company, 1940), p. 197.

of solving problems. In fact novelty furnishes the basis for the experimental method and provides the external conditions necessary for creative thinking. Also, the significance of "past" and "future" hinges on present novelties. And as Mead says, ". . . reality exists in a present."[8] Our historical constructions are designed to account for a present, or a part of it, and to put our conduct on an intellectual basis. But to justify our conduct from an intellectual standpoint is to explain that it will lead to a certain prevised future consequence, which involves anticipating a certain future.

Contrary to the purely deductive manner of explaining the present with its emergents (which amounts to reducing the emergent to its conditions/causes for emergence), the doctrine of emergent evolution accepts the emergent at its face value, "with natural piety," and contends that only after emergents have been experienced can pasts be constructed to account for them. This is not only consistent with experimental logic but is identical with what a scientist does when he solves a factual problem. The scientist does not reduce the novel, the mutation, the exceptional, to its causes, but tries to find the conditions under which he can control the new form. He does this by first constructing imaginatively a past from which the factor in question may or could follow. This past is posited hypothetically and must be tested for its validity. For example, when Becquerel noticed an outline of a metal key on an unexposed photographic plate in his desk, he experienced something exceptional to the ordinary, which gave rise to the problem of finding the conditions under which such a thing could happen. This problem was left to the Curies who solved it by their discovery of polonium and radium.

The discovery of polonium and other radioactive elements amounts to a discovery of the cause of certain experienceable effects. A scientific statement of the past of an event is identical with an explanation of it. The scientific meaning of these pasts or histories is confined to: (1) their explanatory dimension with reference to exceptional events, and (2) their predictive potency, which may lead to a control of the kind of effects these pasts were designed to explain. A scientific understanding of a present object gives the ability to act successfully with reference

---

[8] G. H. Mead, *The Philosophy of the Present* (LaSalle [Ill.], Open Court Publishing Company, 1932), p. 1.

to a similar future object of which only the symbol is present. The symbol of that object is based on the past of a present, and both a past and a future are significant only with reference to a present whose past and future they are.

Both the theory of evolution and the laboratory method support what I call "experimental reasoning," which is a form neither of deductive reasoning nor of inductive reasoning. In experimental reasoning, one studies processes and stages within processes from a qualitative stand-point. For example, if one wants to know how to produce more corn per acre, he must start with certain given factors and arrange them spatially and temporally in such a way as to get the desired effect. Or if one wants to preserve food, it may be done by keeping it cool. But how can one start with certain given factors and produce a refrigerator? These problems are not solved by induction or by deduction alone, but involve experimental reasoning also, which requires that human con-duct and the manipulation of objects enter into the process of solving the problem.

Data, Emergents, and Pasts

The data of any problem give rise to a conflict in attitudes, and the data are identical with the novel phase of the present that is experi-enced. There is a conflict in attitudes whenever old attitudes do not an-swer to the novel phase of the present, or when the present calls out contrary attitudes or tendencies to act in a manner contrary to a rela-tively well-established habit. In 1798, Count Rumford (Benjamin Thompson) found that in boring cannons the heat produced was not proportional to the amount of shavings. This fact was contrary to the caloric theory of heat, which states that heat is a material substance con-sisting of very fine, diffusible particles. For if heat is a substance, then there is a limit to the amount any object, such as cannon, can contain. Count Rumford found, however, that through dulling the bit, an un-limited amount of heat appeared to come from the cannon. This ex-perience gave rise to conflicting attitudes, for since the old attitude did not answer to the new experience, some new attitude had to be formu-lated. Finally the new attitude was expressed in what is called the "kinetic theory of heat." To account for why atoms within a cannon acquire greater kinetic energy during the process of boring, a second theory emerged, namely, the theory of the mechanical equivalent of heat. This amounts to saying that the greater the amount of work applied to boring a cannon, the greater the rise in temperature of the cannon.

Problems arise only because certain factors in the present have not been accounted for. To give an account *of* them is simply to state what must be accounted *for,* and it can be accounted for or explained only by finding an order of events which includes the data. Explaining the tremendous increase in temperature of the cannon consists of finding those conditions leading up to or producing the event in question. In science the problem emanates from exceptional experiences or from emergents, and an emergent is explained when we have both stated its history and verified that history by experiments which involve waiting for the occurrence of the events which are predicted on the basis of that history.

These histories have the status of hypotheses. They account for the data from which they emanate, but in modern science the data are not collected for the purpose of accounting for a past or for supporting a preconceived theory. Neither do they serve the purpose of defending old attitudes. To understand the functional relationship between the novel and the pasts we spread behind us is to recognize that the pasts constitute an *interpretation of* the data. An interpretation of the data leads to a theory that accounts for them. The pasts not only have the function of accounting for the data but also serve as instruments by which future events can be predicted. When a theory is stated and its relationship to the original data is forgotten, its sole value is in its predictive potency. At first thought one might be inclined to say that the only reason for constructing hypotheses, laws, and theories is to predict and, thereby, possibly control or adjust ourselves to oncoming events. But on second thought, we realize that the very basis for the construction of hypotheses is the data that come to us in the form of exceptional experiences, and that what we can predict on the basis of these hypotheses must be similar to the events taken cognizance of in these exceptional experiences. This is why both the pasts we spread behind us and the futures we predict emanate from the present.

The past of a lower animal is there in the form of its biological structure and in the form of habits or patterns of behavior, whether they were acquired during the lifetime of the organism or inherited from its ancestors. The sole import of its past is to be found in what is here now, and it is expressed in the functional relationship between the animal and its environment. As a rule that relationship is expressed in terms of acquired and inherited patterns of behavior.

It is not necessary to assume that lower animals are cognizant of their pasts. Nor do they take cognizance of the future by ways of symbols. Rather they "live in" a present, and the spatiotemporal extent of their present is delimited by the spatiotemporal distances between the organism and the physical objects to which the organism is responding, whether or not the response is by way of distant stimuli, such as are received by the senses of smell and sight. If a dog responds to the odor of a distant carcass, then that present of the dog is confined to the time and space required in reaching and consuming it. The dog has no symbol for the carcass. His responses are conditioned by things present in the form of sensations which serve as stimuli for an act which can terminate only in a future. The present, then, involves a future from an analytic point of view, but to the dog the act takes place as a whole, undivided and unanalyzed.

Now if, as opposed to lower animals, men are able to represent an act by use of symbols and, therefore, carry on an act vicariously, and if, in addition, they are able to analyze an act into its various parts, then the spatiotemporal dimensions of the act may be greatly extended. But to express an act vicariously requires the use of symbols, for only by symbols can we preserve or represent an act to ourselves—carry on overt behavior covertly. In fact it is only through the use of symbols that we can set up calendars and thereby keep a past intact and anticipate a future. In a sense our statements about the relationship between symbols and the past and future are circular, for a symbol must stand for something that can enter into one's conduct only later or in a future and, therefore, a symbol stands for something away from us. If a symbol stands for something, m, serving as a condition for the existence of some other thing, e, then it refers to the past of e, and e is future with reference to m. Whatever is a past, then, is always a past *of* something, for it is always the condition for the existence of that thing. Apart from that of which a past is a condition, it has no scientific meaning. The pasts we construct are thought of as conditions for the emergents whose pasts they are.

For men to stimulate themselves through symbols does not mean that their actual response is to something absent, as if men can act on objects not here now. Rather, it means that the symbol determines the actual response to one among a practically unlimited number of possible objects to which one could respond. This is the same as saying that through the use of symbols men are able to *select* the immediate stimuli to which they respond, and the selection is always made with reference to that for which the symbol stands, which is not here now, immediately present, but away from us in a future.

The temporal dimension of the present of a man behaving under the influence of symbols is not delimited by the spatiotemporal distance between him and the physical object to which are attached present sense data such as odors, colors, and sounds as it is with lower animals; but it is delimited by the spatiotemporal distance between him and that for which his symbols stand *in so far as* the referents of these symbols actually enter into the present behavior of the man. It would be foolish to believe that since one can predict some event that will take place fifty thousand years from now his present is increased to that extent. But if one begins to build a house for a purpose, then his behavior is controlled by the symbol for the finished house, and to that extent his present behavior will culminate when the house is completed and to that extent his present is enlarged.

In general, the spatiotemporal extent of a present is determined by the referents of the symbols that control one's behavior, in the sense that these symbols determine the immediate stimuli to which one responds, as well as the kind of response made to them. Scientific meanings must be incorporated in behavior, and the past and future have scientific meaning only in so far as the referents of symbols standing for things away from us can be incorporated in behavior. It is easy enough to understand what it means to act with a purpose and, therefore, to incorporate the future distant object within the act, for this means that the on-going act can be completed only if the distant object becomes an integral part of it. But what is the meaning of pasts and a past?

To the degree that one's behavior is integrated and therefore intelligent, the past that conditioned his behavior is organized. To that extent also a person or a group of persons may speak significantly of his or its past. Intelligent behavior, whether of an individual or a group of individuals in co-operation, presupposes an organized past. But the past of one person may differ from that of another, as the past of one people from that of another. Certainly every generation posits a new past, and each does so on the basis of problems, and the nerve of these problems is found in situations to which old habits, old attitudes, old institutions, and old pasts will not answer. The geologists of each generation present us with different pasts. The discovery of new kinds of fossils, different strata of the earth's surface, the presence of deposits of radioactive elements may lead to the construction of a new past that will explain them. In the case of the inanimate world, the past is said to leave its "imprint" upon the present. But the belief that the imprint of the past is present can be defended only by first assuming that the order of events in a particular field is the same today as yesterday, or that the laws of nature do not change. Once this assumption is granted we are justified in learning through experience just what these laws are and were. Once we learn what these laws are, we can construct a past that will explain the present, and only what is present can be said to be the imprint of the past. This is tantamount to saying, what is present is present, and if what is present is thought to be an imprint of what preceded it, it is only because through experience we have learned the order of events and the laws of nature.

To give an example, the lead that exists alongside uranium deposits may be said to be an imprint or a result of a past only because we have learned through experience that uranium decomposes into lead. And the age of the earth can be estimated from these deposits because we have learned through experience the half-lives of all the elements in the uranium series.

To think that an analysis of the present reveals the past or that the past is "preserved" in the present is contrary to scientific method. The past is there only as hypothesis, even as the laws of nature by which these pasts are inferred are there as hypotheses. And unless one can distinguish between means and ends or between an event and the conditions for it, "past" has no meaning. One who says the past leaves its "imprint" means probably that the present emerged from knowable conditions and that there is an integral relationship between means and ends or, in general, between the present and its past. A past is posited as the necessary condition for that of which it is a past. Whatever is not a necessary condition for the emergence of an event is not a part of its past. Every past must make a difference in a present, and it is only by virtue of these present "differences" in the form of emergents that pasts can be conceived and accepted as explanations of these differences.

The past of a lower animal manifests itself in the animal's biological form and its behavior patterns, whether inherited or acquired. Actually, however, the statement that a dog had such and such a past is significant only if it is testable in some manner; i.e., only if we can apply the hypothesis and if upon applying it the anticipated consequences occur. Again, to say that the horse had such and such an ancestry may mean in a scientific sense simply that certain skeletons, including that of a present-day horse, can be arranged in a certain way, and since that arrangement is possible, and since the present-day horse-skeleton is at one end of the series, the rest of the skeletons belong to the ancestors of the horse. Whatever is meant must have some bearing on present and future events. It is easy to see how much the theory of biological evolution enters into medical practice and thereby affects behavior in treating patients. What else the theory means is a moot question, but in any case, theory must get into practice before it has scientific meaning.

Lower animals are not cognizant of their pasts; but the pasts we attribute to them either have or do not have survival value when an animal is confronted with a novel situation. H. J. Muller believes mutations happen by chance—with no foreknowledge of the novel situations that they may encounter—and whether or not mutations can cope with the environment has nothing to do with their origin.[9] Today, certain houseflies are immune to DDT. According to Muller's thesis it would be unwise to assume either that nature had prevised the advent of DDT, or that the subjection of certain flies to it was instrumental in the emergence of offspring immune to it. What are problems to human beings are not problems in the same sense to lower animals, and their "solution" of these "problems" is not effected through reflective think-

[9] H. J. Huller, *Out of the Night* (New York, Vanguard Press, Inc., 1935).

ing, but by accidental confluence of mutations with a peculiar environment that will answer to them in such a way that the life process can continue. There is no causal relationship between the presence of DDT and the emergence of flies immune to it.

In general there is no purpose in the emergence of mutations, for it is not the case that for every mutation there are corresponding aspects in the environment leading to survival. Nor can the mutant form, by taking thought or otherwise, reconstruct the environment and guarantee its survival. Rather, the environment of the mutation, so we are told, "selects" (or "rejects") the mutation; but the mutation does not select the environment. This amounts to saying that lower animals are not able to symbolize the overt act of adjustment to the environment. Hence, they cannot analyze the act and reconstruct it in accordance with the demands of an environment. Nor can they reconstruct the environment in conformity with the requests or the peculiarities of the mutant form. According to the generally accepted view of biologists, changes take place in biological forms by mutations effected by genes, just how nobody knows,[10] but at least these changes are believed to be causally quite unrelated to simultaneous changes in the geological, geographic, climatic world. Alongside the changes taking place in biological forms are those environmental changes which perchance answer to the needs of the mutation.

The symbol-user can carry the act of adjustment over into consciousness and effect a confluence of form and environment that, for the time at least, spells the survival of the form. Men are essentially different from other animals in that they are symbol-users and, consequently, fabricators. In general, to symbolize is to distinguish and, therefore, analyze. Analysis is necessary for reconstructing the analytical parts. Symbolization enters into the act of analysis as well as the act of synthesis by directing the act, which amounts to controlling it with reference to an end, only the symbol of which is here now. The symbolic process, then, is a necessary condition for freedom and constitutes the psychological basis for it. In its most general meaning an act is a bond or a union between the form and its environment, and it may be committed with reference to an end that has survival value.

[10] See Erwin Schrödinger, *What Is Life?* (London, Cambridge University Press, 1946), especially Chapters II, III, and IV.

Before this can be done, however, the form and its environment, along with the act, must be thought of as integral parts of a process. "Environment," "form," and "act" are, then, abstractions from a process which in fact always involves all of them, and no one of them can exist apart from the other two. The process with its integrated parts is internalized in reflective thinking. Since in fact it takes far less time to think a process of adjustment than to carry it out overtly, it is possible to entertain alternative possible integrations of form and environment through action or alternative processes.

To internalize an overt process of adjustment is to be conscious of the spatiotemporal order of the stages of the process in so far as these stages will not be carried out automatically through habit but must be initiated and controlled by use of symbols standing for them. If the problem is to hang a picture, the sole function of thought may be to find a hammer and a nail; the rest of the act will be carried out by habit. In internalizing the problematic stages of the act, one always thinks in terms of means-end relationships; the solution of a problem always involves conjuring a means to an end. Devising means-end relationships is identical to positing a certain past or a certain history for an event that will occur later. The means are quite often in question in a problematic situation, but they are in question only in relation to the end whose attainment is conditioned by the factors immediately present; and only what is present can be the springboard for connecting means and ends, pasts and futures. To speak of a past that cannot somehow get into the future by way of a present act is as meaningless scientifically as to speak of means independently of ends. Just as means and ends are abstractions in the sense that each is insignificant apart from the other, so past, present, and future are abstractions when considered each by itself. One is able to posit a past for a certain present anomaly, but the test of the validity of that past can come only in a future.

To scientifically minded students of the humanities or of human social phenomena, present anomalies give rise to problems in society, and these anomalies condition the selection of facts, for only the facts that are relevant to our problems have any significance. If the stock market crash of 1929 is to be explained, economic activities of the previous decade take on new meaning; and in 1930 what economists said took place from 1920 to 1928 is quite different from what in 1928 they said took place during those years. The statement in 1930 of what took place from 1920 to 1928 is a statement of a history of a crash. Prior to 1929 no such statement was made. It is always after a peculiar event takes place that men look for its history—never before. But even the history of an economic depression must be put into such form that it makes a prediction as well as a difference in economic behavior.

Since histories, if they are scientific accounts, must be subject to test through prediction, none of them are known to be true on a basis of "an analysis of the data." Even if the data are acquired from the tomb of Tutankhamen, all of it is here now, present. The "past" is gone and our knowledge of it is only by way of what can be inferred from present processes, not from an analysis of the data. Actually the isolated data "refer" to a past in the same way in which the word "yesterday" does. Data considered apart from natural processes of which they are parts will signify nothing beyond themselves. Hydrogen signifies water only in so far as it has been experienced in relation to water. It is a common error to assume that an analysis of the data reveals a synthesis. To understand data requires a synthetic act of mind. But that the data selected are related in the external world in accordance with the relation tentatively prescribed by mind is a matter to be tested by experience. The posited relationships between data are always spatiotemporal relationships. At first the relationships between the data are unknown. We press a button and see a track in the cloud chamber. What is the relationship between the two?

Contemporary and Noncontemporary Events and Their Causal Relationships

We are often told that if two events are simultaneous they are not causally related; however, many contemporary processes enter into relationship with each other and result in a process that includes them as analytical parts. When any two or more contemporary processes enter into a common process, they are causally related, and this relationship sustains a common process. Hydrogen and oxygen atoms are processes apart from each other, but they may enter into and sustain another process called "water." I call this kind of relationship a "sustaining causal relationship," in order to distinguish between it and the nonsustaining or, better, the "creative" causal relationship, such as is found when novelties emerge out of conditions in which they were not to be found as analytical parts.

If we consider the world as consisting of all present events we recognize offhand that a certain event, *e,* is integrally or causally related to some events contemporary with it, whereas it is causally unrelated to many others. The falling stone is causally related to the earth which is its contemporary, the pressure of a gas is contemporary with the walls of the container, and the life process of an organism is contemporary with its environment. To hold the position that an event, *e,* is causally related to some events contemporary with it, but causally unrelated to others, is identical to maintaining that the relationship between some contemporary events is internal whereas other relationships are external. But the import of the thesis that there are sustaining causal relationships is that no event is complete in itself apart from an environment. Rather, all events must be treated as processes, and this requires that we consider their analytical parts as abstractions in that they do not in fact exist apart from each other.

My primary interest in distinguishing between sustaining causal relations and creative causal relations is to discuss the latter type in connection with a scientific theory of history or, better, a natural theory of evolution. Not all that is past with reference to the present is the past of a certain present event. And yet whatever is past is past with reference to some present event. The history, or the past, of an economic depression may be quite unrelated to the history of an eclipse. The past of The University of Texas is different from the past of the rise of communism in Russia. It is said that the Hegelian philosophy contains the basis for both German fascism and Marxism, and if so the pasts of these political systems intersect in at least one point. Similarly, if men and apes have common ancestors, their pasts intersect. But their pasts are not identical. The differences between men and apes can be accounted for on the basis of their pasts, and a statement of these dissimilar pasts explains how the differences in the two kinds of animals arose. Parenthetically, we may say that prior to the intersection of the pasts of any two or more intersecting events, their pasts were identical.

It is easy to see that intersection, resulting from a process, proceeds from the present and goes backward, and not vice versa. As a rule we are used to thinking that the evolutionary process proceeds forward from the trunk of the trees and branches out into the limbs. In that case, histories or pasts of different animals would not intersect, but rather their pasts would be dissected. But also, according to this older explanation of evolution, the process of evolution would yield nothing but what was there, enfolded from the beginning of time, and an analysis of the present would give us the nature of the past inasmuch as past and present would be alike in content.

Every present event has a past and its past is identical with the conditions necessary for its emergence. Pasts are always causally related to presents, and any influence concerning the nature of the past of an event is by way of that event. To say that two events, e and e_1, have different pasts is to say that the events constituting the past of e are internally related to e, whereas they are externally related to e_1, and vice versa. But, of course, the pasts of two events may intersect, and therefore all that is past with reference to the intersection is a part of the past of both the intersecting events. For example, the past of the wooden table and the wooden chair may intersect in the tree. In practical language this means that one may begin with a tree and produce either a table or a chair, but the past of a table (considering it as an event emerging out of a process) must be different at certain points from the past of a chair, lest these pasts not yield different kinds of events. Every different kind of past must result in a different kind of present event. The only reason for wanting to know pasts is to be able to predict and possibly produce and thereby control future events. The pasts of present events become "interesting" to scientists and they desire to know them only if these present events can somehow affect human conduct.

For an account of an event, e, to be scientific, it must relate that event to others in a causal, dynamic way, demonstrating that the event, e, is the end product of a series which constitutes the history of e. In that case, also, e is considered an end, whereas its history is considered the means. History is a means to an end, and scientists are concerned with means-end relationships. Pasts are significant only in relation to a present world which is there as a necessary condition for behavior that will terminate in a future. History is authenticated in habits that have been established in us by reflective thinking and answer satisfactorily to oncoming events similar to the original anomaly. Thus any proposed histories are verified only in conduct, and the test of the objectivity of a historical account comes finally neither in emotional satisfaction nor in reason, but in satisfactory behavior prompted by that account.

CHAPTER VI

Functional Laws and the Problem of Control

What Scientists Know

SCIENTISTS THROUGHOUT HISTORY have been motivated by the conviction that at least a part of nature is intelligible and knowable. To the ancient Greeks this meant it is possible to grasp the universal form of a particular object and to portray the laws of nature as "picturizations" or models of change, even as the motion of celestial bodies may be depicted in terms of circles and epicycles. Aristotle assumed that men could *recognize* the universal form in the particular, and that the form not only gives reality to particulars but also makes them intelligible. Skepticism arose among the ancients, not over the problem of whether the external object exists or not but over the problem of *what* it is that exists. That it *is,* presumably was given in experience. Nor did the ancients doubt that the forms in objects were the same in kind as the forms in the mind. But is the form now in the mind the same as the form in this (present) particular object? If not, then, according to the ancients, the particular is not known, and skepticism arose at that point.

The early modern rationalists, such as Galileo, Descartes, and Leibnitz, tried to state the knowable aspects of objects in terms of numbers and the measurable alone and held that nonmeasurable entities, which include sensations, are subjective. They assumed that the forms of physical objects, as well as the laws that express changes in them, are identical with the forms of reason as expressed by mathematical symbols with the aid of rules of logic. In this way they hoped to resolve the problem of skepticism, for they stated the nature of the object of knowledge and set up the method of testing statements for their truth value. These rationalists thought they had reconciled their metaphysics with their epistemology when they had described the nature of the world in such a way that it could be known by their mathematico-logical method.

According to Descartes a statement is true, and therefore there is knowledge of its referents, if it is so clear that it cannot be doubted or if it follows logically from such statements. But the rationalistic method of eliminating skepticism and ensuring certainty was put in question indirectly, if not directly, by the then newly established scientific laboratories and the experimental method. Despite the fact that rationalists belittled the place of sense experiences by calling them secondary qualities and by placing them in the soul, if laboratories and experiments were to be of scientific value then these experiences had to be considered indispensable to a knowledge of the external world. If one grants that sense experiences are indispensable to a knowledge of the world of fact, then the following problem arises: How can one arrive at a knowledge of the external world by way of sense experiences? Or, how is it possible to begin with subjective experiences (subjective as defined by rationalists) and end with knowledge of the objective world? Or, again, granting the validity of logic and rational analysis, how can the nature of the "cause" (the external world) be inferred from the "effects" (sense experience)?

Since the time of Hume, then, skepticism has arisen because of the difficulty, if not the impossibility, of arriving with certainty at the goal toward which cognition is directed. It is not sensations that we want to know but rather the structure of a world that is there independent of our sensations. To say the least, we want to know how to control the conditions for sensations, and such knowledge requires an understanding of these conditions. Scientific understanding consists of more than the ability to classify objects and to state their properties. It requires that one know the laws of nature, the causes of existence of phenomena, so that both prediction and control will be possible.

FUNCTIONAL LAWS AND THE PROBLEM OF CONTROL

Hume was neither a thoroughgoing rationalist nor a thoroughgoing empiricist. Hence, he remained a skeptic. He could have resolved his skepticism by claiming that the object of knowledge and cognition is sense experience itself, and that, therefore, there is no epistemological problem of arriving at a knowledge of the causes of experience; i.e., by assuming that "cause" is a meaningless term in the sense that it cannot refer to what can be known, namely, sense experience. The recent positivists have "solved" the problem of skepticism in just this way, but Hume, out of respect for the rationalist thesis that the aim of cognition is a knowledge of the laws of nature, of causes, unobservables but thinkables, remained a skeptic.

Some experiences are illusory. "Illusion" does not imply that a person is not *having* the experiences he thinks he is having but, rather, that what he judges to be the cause of such an experience is found not to be the cause, or that the events do not come to pass in a lawful, anticipated order. The illusory experience signifies something in the external world, whereas in fact there is nothing answering to what is signified. In short, the referent of the sign (the interpreted experience) is subjective, not objective. Every statement about illusions implies a distinction between the knower and the known, or between the knowing process and the object of knowledge. But if there is a distinction between the knower and the object of knowledge and if sense experience, which may be illusory, is indispensable to a knowledge of the factual world, we have the problem of justifying a belief in the truth or falsity of statements referring to the world of fact, not sensations.

Since there is a distinction between the "illusory" and the "valid" experience or, more correctly, between valid and invalid interpretations of experience (used as signs), and, consequently, between the subjective and the objective, one must test the interpretations based on experience to find out whether they are valid.

Besides the assumption that the external world is knowable, experiments expose another assumption, namely, that it is only through a study of nature that any hypothesis proposed by man can be tested for its validity. This in turn implies a distinction between order and confusion, and scientists (by their assumption that nature is intelligible) are quite willing to attribute disorder and confusion, if any, to the human mind and, on the other hand, to defend the thesis that the external world is lawful, intelligible, knowable. For an event to be lawful it must be predictable. The laboratory method reminds us that our evidence for the order and the dependability of the external world is to be found in experience. Yet sense experiences, being relative to man, do not constitute the object of cognition. It is not man that is dependable and orderly. Rather it is nature and the laws of nature. These laws, these orders, cannot be changed, regardless of what men do, and they are included among the ends toward which cognition is directed.

Consequently, although sense experiences are not the objects of cognition, we can defend the thesis that they are nevertheless an indispensable part of the basis for arriving at the goal of cognition (namely, an orderly world existing independent of man and his experiences) only by positing a *causal relationship* between the world to be known and the means by which we know it, between the external world and sensations. Our evidence for order among events in the external world is confined to sense experience, and, as a corollary, evidence for causal relations between phenomena in the external world will be found in the persistency with which a certain order in certain sense experiences is repeated.

Neither sensations individually nor their order strictly imply the existence of atoms, electrons, or molecules, which presumably are their causes. Yet if objects are intelligible in a scientific sense, men will be able to manipulate and control them through a knowledge of the objects and their laws. Even if one were to control merely the order of perceptions and sensations, physical objects would have to be manipulated, and their laws would have to be known. The fact that men desire not just to know but to control nature, coupled with the hope that through scientific knowledge they can do so, leads to the conviction that the means of control, unsensed physical objects, exist, and that the changes they undergo are lawful. Man's freedom could not exist if, as Berkeley held, individual sensations are merely signs of sensations to follow, or of those that preceded. That would leave man only an anticipator and spectator of uncontrollable experiences. Man is free only because he can manipulate objects and control the spatiotemporal order of events. A knowledge of laws is, therefore, indispensable to freedom.

There are three general types of laws, descriptive, functional, and hereditary. A descriptive law is a statement of the order of perceptible changes that take place in a single object or a statement of the spatio-temporal order of events related. A mere description of what happens after planting a seed of cotton might be considered a law of nature. It is natural for the seed to sprout and grow into a plant that blooms, produces more seed, dies. Similarly one can describe roughly what happens when a stone is dropped. All description must be stated in qualitative terms or in terms of objects that can be sensed. Thus, description is confined to the phenomenal order or to the world of appearance. Berkeley held there is no such thing as a material object. He maintained that a sensation serves as a sign for other sensations to follow, and that the "laws of nature" are nothing but statements of the order of sensations. If Berkeley were correct it would be impossible to control the order of sensations through a knowledge of laws. Since sensations can be *had* but not manipulated, they cannot serve as a basis for control. Although certain sensations may be much desired and others abhorred, a scientific knowledge of them consists not in having (or suffering) them but in understanding the conditions under which they can be produced or avoided.

A scientific understanding of any phenomenon, therefore, has come to mean a knowledge of factors necessary not only to predict it but to control it, if not in fact, at least in principle. For this reason positivists have insisted that if statements are meaningful it must be possible to test them in principle if not in fact. Also, for this reason, pragmatists claim that knowing is for the sake of practice and control. Positivism and pragmatism both defend the view that functional laws furnish the prototype, the ideal, for all laws of phenomena.

Every functional law states a quantitative relationship between the referents of the terms in the law. Each term in a functional law refers to all members of a class of factors, and these factors differ from each other quantitatively only. The general nature of functional laws is given by the following formula: $X = f(y)$, where y may refer to any member of the class, y, such as v, u, or w. But every functional *factual* law (in contrast with purely formal, i.e., mathematical or logical laws) must contain qualitative concepts also; for example, velocity, acceleration, conductivity, resistance, stress, strain, friction, or vibration. When precisely given, a functional factual law states the numerical identities existing in qualitatively different things, although each of these may be

different in degree from other members of the class to which it belongs. The numerical identities can be stated only if we can find that
constant which, when multiplied by one of the variables of the equation
stating the functional law, will give the numerical value of the other
variable: In the case of pressures of gases with a fixed volume, we may
say (within certain limits) that the pressure is a function of the absolute temperature: $P = f(t)$, or $P = (k)t$, where k is a constant which
when multiplied by t will give us the numerical value of the pressure.
If a certain variable is a function of more than one other variable, then,
in order to express the relationship in the form of a law, it must be
discovered whether the numerical values of these other variables are to
be added to each other, multiplied together, or whether one or more
is to be subtracted from or divided by the others. For example, gravitational force always involves at least two bodies and varies with the
quantity of the masses involved. But it also varies with the distance between the masses, and the problem is to state precisely (by use of an
equation) just what the relationship is. The force of gravitation is a
function of the quantity of the masses involved and also a function of
the distance between the masses. Finally it is determined precisely that
the force varies inversely as the square of the distance between the
masses and directly in proportion to the product of the masses, and we
write:

$$F = k[(M_1 \times M_2)/D^2]$$

where k is the constant of proportionality or the constant of variation.

To take another example, we find that the amount of heat that will
flow through a rod depends on several factors, each of which may vary.
The actual law for heat transfer is:

$$H = k[At\ (T_2 - T_1)/L]$$

where H is the amount of heat (measured in calories or British thermal
units), A is the cross-sectional area of the rod, L is the length of the
rod, t is the time of flow, T_2 is the temperature of the hot end of the rod,
and T_1 the temperature of the cold end. The constant of proportionality, k, will depend on the units used and will vary if the units are
varied.

If, between members of classes designated by the terms x and y used to express a law, there is a functional relationship such that for the value of any particular member of *x* there is a member in class *y* having a corresponding value, then *y* is a function of *x,* and *x* may be said to be the independent variable. Then *y* would be said to be the dependent variable; i.e., $y=f(x)$. Quite often it is a matter of choice which of two functionally related variables will be called *dependent* and which *independent*. For example, the (gravitational) action of body *x* on body *y* is simultaneous with *y*'s equal and oppositely directed reaction. Strictly speaking, *x* and *y* act on each other simultaneously, and the word "react" suggests a temporal lag where in fact there is none. Similarly, according to Boyle's law, under constant volume the pressure and temperature of a gas vary simultaneously. But we may say the pressure of a gas is a function of its temperature or that its temperature is a function of its pressure. Thus we may say that action is a function of reaction, or reaction is a function of action, especially since they take place simultaneously.

Functional Laws and the Problem of Control

Bertrand Russell points out that the expression of laws in terms of equations does away with the metaphysical basis for the concept of causation in science. Yet the concept is not abandoned, but rather it has been transferred from metaphysics to methodology.

In actual practice the independent variable is that factor in the equation of a functional law that can be manipulated and used to control other factors. The actual selection of the independent variable will depend, then, on circumstances at hand, materials available, and the end desired. The pressure of a gas can be controlled indirectly by controlling the temperature and the volume directly. In that case the pressure would be a function of temperature and volume. It may be practical and desirable, however, to control the volume by controlling the temperature and the pressure.

Similarly, the pitch of sound produced by vibrating strings varies with the length, mass, and tension of the string *(L, M, F)*. That is, the number of vibrations per unit time is dependent on these factors; e.g.:

$$N=f(F, L, M)$$

We can see that "vibrations" cannot exist apart from something vibrating even as pressure and temperature cannot exist apart from bodies. The length, the mass per unit length, and the tension of strings can be controlled without consideration of vibrations, but the number of vibrations per second cannot be controlled without consideration of tension, length, and mass, which may be independent variables.

To say that functional laws do not state causal relationships but are used, nevertheless, for purposes of control may amount to saying that there is a distinction between scientific formulas and what is called the "know-how" of science. We will notice that no functional law tells us how to initiate processes which, once begun, take place automatically and according to law. In fact it may be impossible to state in the form of a law how one can apply laws. Furthermore, it may be impossible to state in the form of laws, or "scientifically," the conditions under which the laws "operate." Chemists, biologists, and all scientists using hereditary laws seem to be much more aware of the problem of the relationship between "know-how" and laws or formulas than scientists in other fields. For example, chemists recognize that the results or "yields" of chemical processes can be balanced with the elements entering into the processes. And contrary to the method of expressing laws by use of mathematical equations, the chemist indicates in his formula the temporal direction of the process: He writes:

$$2H_2 + O_2 \longrightarrow 2H_2O$$

And although the chemical formula indicates the temporal direction of change and thereby shows us that the balance indicated by the formula is a balance of conditions (or molecules) separated temporally, the formula does not state the conditions under which the process will take place. At ordinary room temperature hydrogen and oxygen will not enter into a chemical reaction, but we can introduce a *catalyst*, e.g., small pieces of platinum, which will initiate the process. Apparently, in many cases, once the process is initiated the catalyst has had its effect, and could it be withdrawn the process would continue without it until a relatively stable balance was reached. Once such a balance is reached it is possible to begin other processes by bringing other catalysts to bear on the chemicals under consideration, or by bringing this chemical together with another chemical and another catalyst. But the manner of bringing chemicals together and the nature of catalysts are never included in chemical formulas. The "know-how" of science is not, and possibly cannot be, given in the form of strict scientific laws. But we find, rather, large volumes, in physics particularly,[1] telling us how to set up experiments that will demonstrate laws of nature.

Laws Are Neutral with Respect to Ends

Since there is a distinction between pure and applied science, or between research for basic or fundamental knowledge and its application to practical problems, it follows that scientific laws must be stated in a way that leaves them neutral to the ends for which they will be used. Also a statement of the particular circumstances under which a law may be applied and the particular purposes for which it will be used must be left out of the statement of a law. If a statement of how and when laws are to be used were included within them, then they would not be universal nor would they constitute basic knowledge. Were this the case value judgments would be confined to pure research, for the ends to be accomplished through the use of science would be prescribed by the means.

Science is used and laws are applied only when men want to change the status quo, or only when men want to effect ends that would not be effected at that time if processes were left to themselves. To apply a law, one must start with the world as it is and effect desired ends only through controlling that part of the given world which is causally related to the end sought. The temperature of the air in a room can be raised by producing an electric current in a "resistance wire," and one can control the temperature by application of natural laws, among which would be: heat produced $= kI^2Rt$. But this law will not tell one where to get the means of control nor how to make connections necessary for the production of an electric heater. Only the conditions for the electrical process can be set up, and one cannot, through taking thought or through his behavior, make laws of nature or give to natural processes their pattern. Once the conditions for them are present, all processes in nature take place automatically. Changes and, in some cases, the rate of change can be directed toward certain ends, but men

[1] Witness R. M. Sutton, *Demonstration Experiments in Physics* (New York, McGraw-Hill Book Company, Inc., 1938).

cannot determine either that there be change or that some kind of process go on continually. Since there are change and automatic processes independent of men, we can depend on nature. And because there are processes continuously, irrespective of the application of laws, time is always an independent variable.

Since time is one-directional or irreversible, it follows that the conditions for the application of a particular law may vary from time to time; and since laws are universal, one cannot include within them a statement of how to apply them. Furthermore, since time is not cyclical, at least a great deal of the future is indeterminate. This does not mean that future happenings have no causes, but rather that out of a great number of possible processes only a few can be initiated, and the future will depend on the nature of the few. Through choice many of the possible future ends are eliminated and some are actualized. Choice, evaluation, and thinking are at least catalysts necessary for the convergence of certain external processes with their consequences.

The conditions for a process may be considered a part of the cause of the process. Any natural process, such as the flow of electricity, water, heat, the uniting of atoms, or the explosion of gases, depends on conditions, and it is the function of science to discover these conditions in order to control processes. When a current of electricity is flowing, the amount of flow is controlled by controlling the conditions. The same can be said of all controllable processes. A relatively stable and dependable world is necessary for the control of any process, and causal relations must be stated in terms of conditions. That is why one can never deduce causal relations from functional laws, which are in the form of equations and give us numerical identities. Wherever men control events, they assume that there is a cause-and-effect relationship between the objects manipulated and the results produced. This assumption is necessary to the method of scientists. If in any particular case one must discover through experiments what follows from given conditions, and if laws state only the identities holding at any two or more moments during change, then the order of the sequence is not given in law but is presupposed by the law. Yet it is only to sequential relations that the principle of causation applies—the result of any change or process is determined by the change or process, but it does not refer to the numerical identities between any two states in the process. The numerical identities hold whether there is change or not, but causes are present only where there are also qualitative differences in change. There cannot be simply numerical identities between two stages in change. There are qualitative differences also and change is recognizable only because of them. The often-quoted statement that an effect can never be greater than its cause is entirely beside the point. Causes and their effects may have numerical identities, but as cause and effect they must be qualitatively different, and qualities are nonadditive. To find the cause of a is to find the necessary and sufficient conditions that will yield a. The belief that it is possible in principle to find these conditions rests on the assumption that there are alternative possible processes and conditions, some of which will be actualized only if others are not. In order to find causes, men must be free to and capable of controlling nature at least to an extent, and there must be both internal and external relations between the analytical parts of nature.

Formulating and Testing Functional Laws

One of the necessary factors in both formulating and testing functional laws is sense experience. It is possible to use experiments or to employ the laboratory method for formulating and testing laws only if certain things can be controlled. To perform experiments one must work within a closed or isolated system. A laboratory scientist begins with a system in which as a rule there are a number of variables. His problem concerns that whose history or conditions for existing he is not at first able to state. Yet the scientist assumes that the thing in question has conditions for existing, and his problem is to find what factors in the system are functionally related to the item under consideration. If item x occurs, it must have a history or it must have conditions under which it occurs, and not all things past constitute *its* past or the conditions necessary for it. The problem of the scientist is to find its past.

After experimenting with various kinds of conductors the scientist may feel ready to formulate a law, for he thinks that he has discovered all factors functionally related to electrical resistance. He may tell us that resistance is a function of the kind of conductor used (Cu, Co, Ni, Au, Hg), the temperature of the conductor, the geometric shape of the cross-sectional area, the size of the cross-sectional area, and the length of the conductor. He puts this information in the form of a functional equation which is used as long as it serves him adequately. If, however, he finds exceptions to the law of resistance, he is justified in looking for factors in the environment not included in the law but which are thought to be functionally related.

A scientist is justified in formulating and accepting a functional law when he is able to control the dependent variables, through its application.

A statement of factors in the environment which are unalterable is excluded from the law, even though these factors are necessary for the application of the law. If, for example, all strings for instruments were of the same mass per unit length, then mass would have been left out of the formula. As the factor of gravitation is ever present, it probably has something to do with the application of most physical laws, but it is also usually excluded from the statement of them. Then there are variable factors, one of which (but no particular one) is necessary. For example, every falling body must have shape, but no particular shape; every organ pipe must have structure, but no particular structure. These are left out of the law.

John Dewey writes: "Since the time of Mill, the view that scientific laws are formulations of uniform and unconditional sequences of events has been generally adopted."[2] This statement is not quite in accord with the facts. Offhand Dewey's statement appears to apply to functional laws, but on closer analysis we find that a functional law states only that there is a numerical equivalence among the variables at any given time. The temporal order of a sequence of events may be presupposed, even as control and causal (internal) relations between factors stated in the law are presupposed, but they are never stated formally. Werkmeister writes:[3]

The existential "pattern" was replaced by a generic "rule"; and where static pictures of fictitious circles had failed to account for the "irregularities" of

[2] *Logic: The Theory of Inquiry* (New York, Henry Holt and Company, Inc., 1938), p. 442.
[3] W. H. Werkmeister, *A Philosophy of Science* (New York, Harper & Brothers, 1940), p. 43.

planetary motions, the dynamic and functional equations explained perfectly the processes of nature. And henceforth, functional equations were regarded as the prototype of all "laws of nature."

What Werkmeister says is certainly true of many laws, especially all laws that can be put in the form of equations, but the functional equation by itself does not state causal relations, nor does it state the order of sequences. Yet in application these causal relationships and unconditioned sequences of events may be tacitly assumed.

Functional Laws, Cause, and Conditions

John Stuart Mill's canons of induction are concerned with finding causes or conditions for events. Through an application of these canons we may conclude that a is the condition (or contains the condition) for b if a is always followed by b and if in the absence of a, b does not occur. In that case a is or contains at least a part of the cause of b. Here it must be assumed that a and b are separated temporally, and that b occurs after a. And although it makes sense to look for orderly sequences of events, laws and the formulation of laws should not be confused with the problem of causation. Functional laws can describe the state of affairs in a given situation within certain limits, but their referents will be confined to contemporary factors and not to a sequence of events. From Hooke's law it follows that if under a force of one dyne the length of a spring is increased by one centimeter, then under a force of two dynes it will be increased two centimeters (within the elastic limits). But the law states simply that stress is proportional to strain, and as far as the law is concerned, stress and strain are necessarily simultaneous. Mill's canons lead to some such conclusion as this: If a weight is placed on a spring balance (dynamometer), then the spring will become longer. Here the temporal order of events is stated, but this is not included in Hooke's law.

The law of the reflection of light informs us that the angle of incidence is equal to the angle of reflection. Here again nothing is said about how to produce the incident ray or the reflected ray, and nothing is said of cause-and-effect relationship. The scientist may say that the angle of the reflected ray, r, is a function of the angle of the incident ray, i; that is, $r = f(i)$. Although the scientist knows that the incident ray is temporally prior to the reflected ray, he does not include this fact in the law. Nor does the law tell us how to produce or control rays of light.

Consider the formula for calculating the amount of heat "generated" in a wire by an electric current, heat $= kI^2Rt$, where k is the constant of variation, I is the amperage, R is the resistance, and t is the time. Heat is the function of time, but time cannot be considered a cause of heat. Heat is caused by the flow of a current through a conductor having resistance. And yet the current-flow and the production of heat are simultaneous, even as current and resistance are simultaneous, and no causal relations can be inferred, nor can we conclude from the law that I and R exist prior to the heat "produced."

CHAPTER VII

Hereditary Laws, Necessity and Indeterminacy

Hereditary Laws

HEREDITARY LAWS apply to phenomena that are separated in time, and they include statements of both the conditions for the occurrence of factors and those factors. These laws, if written in the form of equations, do not express numerical identities, but express results or yields; and if causal relations can be inferred from laws, it is only from the hereditary laws. Instead of assuming isolated atomic parts of nature and beginning with them in constructing a theory of how hereditary change is possible, we should assume that there are processes of which the "parts" are finally abstractions, since they cannot exist by themselves.

Processes always involve change of spatial relationships of the parts (or factors) entering into the process, and this change is relative to the parts themselves. When iron and sulphur enter into a chemical process there are changes in the spatial position of the atoms relative to each other, and iron sulphide is the result: $Fe + S \rightarrow FeS$. If the change of spatial relationship among the parts entering into change yields *qualitative* differences, then the parts have established new internal relations which they did not have in separation, and the result is a different kind of unity and a different kind of process from the process sustained in the analytical parts existing prior to the new process. An atom of iron, Fe, has a certain kind of organization, and so does an atom of sulphur, S. But in iron sulphide there is a different kind of organization.

If bodies change positions without undergoing qualitative differences as a result, change has occurred but no process. Laws expressing such change are not hereditary laws. The results of nonhereditary change can be expressed adequately in quantitative terms, but results of hereditary change cannot. The burning of magnesium may at first be expressed thus:

$$Mg + O_2 \rightarrow MgO$$

But the equation must be balanced so as to maintain numerical identities, and we write:

$$2Mg + O_2 = 2MgO$$

Yet there is a qualitative difference (as well as numerical identities) between magnesium and oxygen in separation and magnesium oxide.

The reader will notice that new processes result from the confluence of two or more other processes. We do not have the problem that would confront us if we were to assume unrelated, static parts. The chemist is not concerned with why Fe and S will unite. Also, he is not concerned with the "forces" involved or the "affinities" that exist just before the new unification takes place or while it is taking place. Explanation and law can never get "inside" the process to that extent, and probably Henri Bergson is correct in maintaining that science cannot get inside of or state the durational character of process.[1] Be that as it may, scientific laws are suitable for human practice and control, and whether or not one can discover the metaphysical structure of nature through them is of little concern to the practitioner.

Both unintegrated and integrated factors are necessary for processes. Unintegrated factors endure throughout the process, but their internal

---

[1] A. N. Whitehead has developed the "epochal theory of time," according to which time is not infinitely divisible actually but only intellectually. Time "happens" in chunks or in indivisible units having a durational character in contrast to being a compilation of durationless instants. An instant, then, is an abstraction which does not characterize real time. On this point, see Whitehead, *Process and Reality* (New York, The Macmillan Company, 1930), especially Chapter II. Also, see Henri Bergson, *Time and Free Will* . . . trans. by F. L. Pogson (London, The Macmillan Company, 1910).

relationship with other factors in the process remains unchanged. (This is true even if there are no internal relationships.) A catalyst is included among the conditions for a process, and its internal relations with other factors remain unchanged. Also, any process presupposes an environment that is relatively stable, since its environment remains unchanged with respect to internal relations between it and the process whose environment it is.

Integrated factors enter into dynamic relationship with one another. Their internal relationship respecting one another is different in the results or in the new process. It is because of this change in internal relationship that we are warranted in speaking of yields, or results, or of qualitative differences. Without these qualitative differences we could not speak of the "cause" or condition of x in contrast with x. If potassium chlorate is carefully heated to the melting point no free oxygen is present. If, however, a small amount of manganese dioxide is dropped in this compound, a chemical change will take place. The result will be potassium chloride and oxygen:

$$2KClO_3 \rightarrow 2KCl + 3O_2$$

Here the unintegrated factors are the catalyst, manganese dioxide, and the environmental factors, such as the container holding the parts together spatially, and possibly gravity which keeps the parts from scattering. These unchanged enduring conditions are not causes but conditions only.

The results of the process, $2KCl + 3O_2$, are temporally later than $2KClO_3$. For this reason they are called the results of the integrating factors. (Here we may conceive of "integration" as both positive and negative. When the results constitute more processes than were there in the beginning, it is called negative integration. Otherwise it is positive integration.)

When a hereditary law is exemplified, something in the yield has been inherited from the integrating factors, but there is also something new. In cases of chemical processes, what is inherited can be expressed quantitatively. For example, the mass is constant, and the number of atoms is the same before the integration and after. In this sense, and speaking loosely, the "cause" leaves its imprint on the "effect." By virtue of the qualitative differences between condition and yield, we are justified in speaking of time as having a direction. Certain chemical processes suggest that time is not only cyclical but reversible; for example, $H_2O + CO_2 \rightleftharpoons H_2CO_3$. But the chemical synthetic process and analytic process will not take place under the same conditions. The strokes of a pendulum "mark time" or measure time, but time conceived of in relation to processes is based on qualitative differences without which time could not have direction and without which we would not speak of conditions in contrast to things conditioned. Accordingly, we would not have the concept of inheritance.

In the above remarks hereditary laws have been considered largely from the standpoint of chemical changes. But "inheritance" and "law" are also applicable to other phenomena and especially to biological phenomena. In the case of biological inheritance the form and not the content is inherited. Every gene in the germ cells of the parents tends to express itself by superimposing certain definite characteristics on the offspring. In strict inheritance the offspring inherits not only certain physiological likenesses of the parents but also certain factors which reside in the germ cells of the offspring and which, in turn, tend to stamp these original likenesses on *its* offspring. But where there are mutations and the emergence of new characteristics, strict biological inheritance has broken down and there are, then, qualitative differences similar in a general way to the qualitative differences in chemical processes.

In biological inheritance there are chemical processes within the change that results in the inheritance of the form. In other words, there are chemical processes within biological processes. According to geneticists the genes are responsible for the organization of the chemical processes that take place in the organism. Erwin Schrödinger holds that there is a sort of "code script"[2] in every cell of every living organism, and in a given organism this code script is the same in all of its cells. It is responsible for the organization of the cells into a unity. When two germ cells unite, thus initiating a process resulting in a new individual, the code script, the genes, inherited by the cells of the new individual is a result of the combination of the two code scripts from the parents.

[2] Erwin Schrödinger, *What Is Life?* (London, Cambridge University Press, 1946), pp. 20 ff.

Contrary to the genes, which tend to superimpose a certain organization on chemical processes, the chemical processes do not tend to superimpose their character on anything beyond the chemicals present. But if a dog eats a rabbit, the code script in the cells of the dog superimpose themselves on the cells of the rabbit, for the rabbit is dead and the organization is gone. Since the chemical processes are continually under the influence of the genes or the code script in an individual organism, and since these chemical processes are necessary for the organization that takes place, they constitute the chemical conditions for the biological organism. There are also physical or environmental conditions necessary for the biological organism. These conditions in their qualitative form are stable during biological development and change but, unlike the enduring factors in chemical processes, they cannot be expressed quantitatively. Thus, it is only the biological form and not quantity of material entering into it that remains unchanged.

Biological Inheritance and Causal Relations

As Russell and others have shown, if two events, *a* and *b,* are separated temporally, it is difficult to imagine how they could be dynamically or causally related. But those who deny the existence of causal relationships will have difficulty in making sense of hereditary laws, and especially of biological hereditary laws. According to the biological laws of inheritance, not only is the form of the organism inherited, but so is the organizing "agent," the genes, the code script. The geneticist cannot explain the meaning of "gene," say, by confining his remarks to what is here-now in the gene. He cannot explain its meaning by referring to physical changes and chemical processes alone, although these changes and processes may be a necessary condition for the existence of genes.

To put it in Whitehead's terms, it takes time for genes to be what they are, and it takes considerable time. It is supposed that genes cannot exist apart from a living cell, and it is pretty well agreed that the genes have their spatiotemporal loci in the chromosomes. But the concept "gene" did not emerge from our study of the chemical processes that take place in the chromosomes. Geneticists would never have had the concept of genes had they not first had the problem of accounting for resemblances and differences among organisms related by descent. W. E. Castle defines genetics "as the science which deals with the *coming into being* of organisms."[3] As pointed out above, neither the chemical elements nor the physical bodies are inherited by the descendants of an organism. Rather it is the form, or the organization of physical and chemical processes. Hence, when through analysis of the living organism geneticists come to the cell, the chromosome, and finally by hypothesis to the gene, they are looking for something responsible for the offspring being like (or unlike) the parent form. The genes determine the biological structure of the descendants.

Some believe that all "evolution" is but a matter of complexity and organization of prior existing parts. Even so, physical and chemical processes are organized in a definite, relatively stable way in a living organism, and the genes are responsible for this organization. This means that the biological structure of a descendant is determined by something existing prior to it, namely, the genes or determiners. Geneticists support this idea in their claim that the mechanism for determining the particular form of a biological organism is to be found in its parents.

To deny that there are causal relations between the genes in the germ cells of the parents and the biological structure of the descendants is to deny that genetics is a rational, scientific study. It is plain enough that H. J. Muller and others, through changing the internal structure of chromosomes in drosophila by subjecting them to x rays, were able to effect mutations. These men not only proved that the cause for mutations may be located in the chromosomes of the germ cells of the parents, but also that they are natural factors partly under the control of the scientist. There are necessary relationships holding between parents and descendants. But how can this be?

As I have indicated, a gene or a determiner is not a chemical process or a process such as may be carried on inside of an atom, although atomic and chemical processes presumably are necessary for the existence of genes. No atom tends to superimpose its organization, its form, on anything outside of itself. Nor does a chemical pattern, such as is found after uniting Fe and S, tend to superimpose its form on other

---

[3] H. H. Newman (ed.), *Evolution, Genetics, and Eugenics* (2d ed.; Chicago, University of Chicago Press, 1925), p. 295.

atoms. In *What Is Life,* Erwin Schrödinger presents an excellent statement of how new genes emerge in the germ cells of plants and animals. He shows how quantum chemistry is related to the evolution of new species. Schrödinger leaves the impression that he has accounted for the fact that genes organize the many cells into a living unity, but in fact he has explained only how the internal structure of the chromosomes is changed by quanta of energy that affect the chromosomes by chance. He takes for granted that cells tend to reproduce themselves, but leaves untouched the problem of the organization of the many cells in a single individual.

Hereditary laws definitely imply causal relations. As suggested in Chapter VI, one of the reasons for rejecting the principle of causation is that early modern scientists began using functional equations. Under the influence of Hume, who assumed that sense experience alone is the basis for valid beliefs and that sense experiences are atomic—each complete in itself and confined unto itself—all types of causes were put in question. Apparently Hume emphasized that causes must precede effects absolutely. This belief, together with the opinion that nature can be analyzed into atomic parts each complete in itself, precludes the belief that there are processes in nature.

Processes not only involve interaction between the parts entering into process but, since they are orderly or lawful, they involve organization which is identical with the pattern for the process. But pattern and organization imply duration. Bergson and Whitehead[4] have emphasized that whatever requires time to be what it is cannot exist at an instant of mathematical time. If an event necessarily has a durational character or a temporal spread, then indeed it has past, present, and future in it. If we consider the duration of an event measurable and therefore mathematically divisible into parts such as before and after (though not actually divisible), we must conclude nevertheless that the termination of the event is in some sense present at its beginning. Again, any event "covers" or overlaps other events even as the life

[4] See A. N. Whitehead, *The Concept of Nature* (Cambridge, The University Press, 1920), Chapter III. Henri Bergson, *Creative Evolution,* trans. by Arthur Mitchell (New York, Henry Holt and Company, Inc., 1911). *Durée et Simultanéite, a propos de la Théorie d'Einstein* (Paris, F. Alcan, 1923).

span of an individual extends over particular experiences of the individual. If, then, *d* extends over *d'*, in the following manner

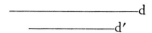

we are able to conceive of *d* as having a "before" and an "after" relative to *d'*. But if we consider that "part" of *d* coincident with *d'* we must conclude that the "parts" before *d'*, simultaneous with *d'*, and after *d'* are in some sense simultaneous with each other and contemporaneous with *d'*. In other words, the pattern or the organization of an event is contemporaneous with every analytical part of the event.

The cells of the bodies of metazoa when considered apart from the body are no longer cells. And if by abstraction we arrive at the concept of the form or organization of a metazoan apart from the matter organized, it follows that we can consider the matter apart from the form. The matter so considered would not be matter on a biological level, but on a physical or chemical level. There is something in the gene that exists both prior to and simultaneous with the organization in the descendant. Its presence is felt throughout the process of development of the embryo and continues to give organization to the physical and chemical processes that take place in the descendant.

The gene is a determiner or a cause, yet its effects exist simultaneously with it. It cannot exist apart from a living form, and yet it gives organization to the form. For this reason we are justified in this particular case in saying that the cause does not precede the effect absolutely.

Through the influence of biology, Whitehead, G. H. Mead, Bergson, and others have arrived at their respective doctrines of organism. Whitehead maintains that every event has a unity about it comparable to the unity found in a living organism. The exponents of doctrines of organism do not assume that we can begin with a world in which the analytical parts exist independently of each other. Hume has shown us that if elements are isolated in the beginning, then they can never be related dynamically or causally. But instead of starting with Hume's atomic parts of nature as apparently the positivists do, I suggest that we begin with processes in which the parts are integrally related. Processes have a temporal spread. A process implies an integration and organization among the parts. "Parts" are abstractions relative to that of which they are parts. There is no problem of getting the parts together. As Whitehead points out,[5] it is a matter of preventing ourselves from thinking of abstractions as constituting concrete reality.

The doctrine of organism shifts the loci of causes. Causes are not "between" parts separated temporally. A cause endures during the process and is present in every analytical stage of the process. The cause leaves its imprint, and, for that reason, is present in some sense in the terminus of a process as well as in the beginning. A cause must be thought of as that which lends organization to the parts which without its influence would not have been organized as they are.

An idea may be considered a determiner or a conditioner of a consciously controlled act. It is present at the beginning of an act and at every stage in the act. Also, the result of the act, or the complete act, inherits something from the idea. An idea cannot be reduced to the act which it organizes, and yet the act in some sense is a condition for the idea, since an idea is the beginning of an intelligent act as well as that which gives the logical structure to it. Here we should not conclude that causes in every process are ideas. Ideas are of a different order than genes in the biological organism. Yet it should be made clear that the doctrine of organism makes room for the principle of causation which is inconsistent with a doctrine of atomism. Through working out the implications of the hereditary laws we are led to the concept of organism and, in turn, to a respectable principle of causation, and finally to the view that only if ideas serve as causes of behavior, can men act purposively and freely.

Laws and Necessity

The logical basis for scientific theories is closely related to the principle of causation. Theories furnish a rational justification for relationships between events. They state that certain events are related of necessity. This means that they are causally related. And the results of any two or more events causally related can be stated in the form of a law. The kinetic theory of gases and liquids gives reasons for the ex-

[5] *Science and the Modern World* (New York, The Macmillan Company, 1925), pp. 75 ff.

periences we have with regard to gases and liquids. Boyle's law does not furnish reasons for phenomena, but the kinetic theory of gases makes these phenomena and our experiences of them rational and, therefore, necessary. A statement of the lawful order of events may help us predict phenomena, but it will not enable us to control them. The Mendelian law of inheritance does not of itself give us the genetic theory necessary for control, though it enables us to predict. And in making this distinction between laws, which may be confined to phenomena and our experiences of them, and theories, the basis for control is established. One does not control events by predicting them or by sense experience. One does not control color by colors or sounds by sounds. One can control colors by manipulating things not colored, namely, atoms, molecules, material things. But these entities are posited as the foundation or causes of experienced phenomena.

Of course, it is utterly impossible to prove that the conditions for experienced phenomena exist by arguing that experiences of phenomena are their "effects." Philipp Frank[6] may be correct in his belief that the principle of causation is conventional and posited arbitrarily. In that respect it may be like other assumptions such as "phenomena are intelligible," or "there are dependable uniformities in nature," or "experience is an adequate basis for prediction." Certainly the principle of causation or any other principle, such as the principle of least action, the exclusion principle, the principle of indeterminacy, refers to methodological devices which cannot be "experienced" in the ordinary sense of the word. The chief question with regard to the principle of causation is this: Does it refer also to events existing independent of mind; does it refer to something other than the experienceable?

I am of the opinion that the particular forms of the principle of causation or even of the principle of indeterminacy are conventional. But that there must be some such conventions as a basis for science is not conventional. One must posit an external world existing independent of sense experience and cognition as a basis for practice and control. One does not simply have the sensation of "standing on the ground." One also believes there is a necessary basis for that sensation. Otherwise our predictions and our control of the order of sensations would

[6] *Between Physics and Philosophy* (Cambridge, Harvard University Press, 1941), Chapter I.

have no logical justification. It is no more possible to prove the principle of indeterminacy on the basis of experience than it is to prove the causal principle.

Apparently men often confuse the meaning of the causal principle with the meaning of prediction. If two events, e and e_1, are causally related we ought to be able to predict one of them, the effect, on the basis of the presence of the other, the cause. But just because we can predict a future event on the basis of a present one does not mean that they are causally related, for one can predict when the sun will come up on the basis of the pointer readings on a clock. If two events are necessarily and causally related, then one of them would not have taken place without the other. To identify causation with prediction is to put the locus of its significance in epistemology, whereas actually it belongs to the external world. The question is not: Can we predict event e on the basis of the presence of e_1? but rather, Can we in principle if not in fact control the occurrence of e through controlling e_1?

Sense experiences give us evidence of something not sensed. When sense experiences indicate to us a certain kind of past, we think of that past and the present sense experiences as being causally related. For example, the present Code of Hammurabi indicates to us not only a certain geographic-geological past, but also a past that includes certain peoples with their way of living. The only scientific way in which such pasts are indicated to us is through sense experiences. Yet the sense experiences are present, and the past to which they refer is gone. But that the present has such and such a past can be supported only on the assumption that there are natural processes which include both a present and its past. Within these natural processes (phenomena having durational character) we assume that the phases of the process are integrally related and that the earlier phases constitute the condition for the later ones. This is the meaning of "causation" as used traditionally.

Since causes cannot be sensed, but rather since we always sense discrete, discontinuous events, "cause" and "causation" are metaphysical terms. What "cause" refers to are the dynamic relationships that cannot be had in sense experience, which is necessarily discrete and necessarily divides the integrally related durational phenomena so that they can be sensed at all. Sensations are a means of knowing the external world, but in having sensations we do not *become* those external processes, and hence we cannot feel or sense causes.

It is reasonable to ask: What evidence do we have against the theory that there are causes? What evidence do we have for such a theory?

Laplace and others of his time formulated the orthodox definition of "cause." According to Laplace, the caused is predictable and the predictable is caused. But inasmuch as physicists are unable to predict both the position and the momentum of an electron in its orbit, Heisenberg and others have accepted the principle of indeterminacy, for they assume, with orthodox physicists, that if an event is unpredictable it is also indeterminate (by which many mean uncaused).

Apparently the positivists assume that the *experiential evidence* for causation has broken down. Probably all positivists will agree that there is no evidence for causes or for causation. But probably they will agree also that if the solution of every problem were unique (or completely determinate, as was assumed by classical physicists), we would have concrete evidence for causes and for causation. This assumption is false. Let us examine the thesis that the belief in causes can be tested by sense experience.

Let us assume with the positivists that "cause" is a metaphysical term referring to something that cannot be sensed. Now suppose every phenomenon were completely predictable or that the solution of every problem were unique. Would this assumption imply that there are causes in nature and that metaphysics makes sense? Obviously not, for the theory of causation is a metaphysical principle and sense experiences do not have "cause" written on them any more than they have "genes" or "electron" or "point" or "space" written on them. Furthermore, we must remember that "indeterminism" is a metaphysical concept also, and one dares say that among the positivists "indeterminism" refers to something not dependent on sense experience; i.e., it is a doctrine about certain relationships or the lack of them between phenomena. Suppose Heisenberg did not think of indeterminism as a metaphysical principle, but simply identified indeterminism with unpredictability. In that case he would not pass judgment on whether or not there are dynamic relations in the external world. This interpretation of Heisenberg's view is suggested especially when he speaks of the influence of instruments and light waves on electrons. Max Planck writes:[7]

The Principle of Indeterminacy is in reality an alternative hypothesis which takes the place of the strictly causal method in quantum physics. But Heisenberg himself would be one of the first to protest against the idea of interpreting his Principle of Indeterminacy as tantamount to a denial of the principle of causation.

If one assumes that by sense experience we can disprove that there are causal connections, then we should be able to prove the negation of the causal principle. Now the contradiction of the causal principle is this: (1) There is (perfect) chaos so that any event out of an infinite possible number of events is as likely to follow a given event, e, as is any other event; e.g., the probability of any event, e_2, following any other event, e_1, is 0. (2) All relations are external; e.g., a statement of law, even by approximation, is impossible. A. J. Ayer argues that if every event were causally connected to every other, science would be impossible.[8] He is correct. But it is equally true that if no event were causally connected with any other, science would be impossible. What Ayer is suggesting is that a belief in causation is a hindrance to science. But the contradiction of the monistic statement, "all events are causally related to each other," is "some events are not causally related to some others." Neither of these statements, however, contradicts the statement, "Some events are causally related to some others." And unless Ayer can show that sense experiences imply perfect chaos, he cannot show that they imply no causal relationships in nature.

Probably the positivists will suggest that we stick to sense experience and not go beyond what it strictly implies; i.e., do not speculate or make bad metaphysics. Here we must recall once more that if one function of science is to read out of nature what men have erroneously read into her, then there must be a world that exists independent of mind, and this world is there as a condition for both "good" and "bad" metaphysics. If this is true, the structure of that world cannot be stated

---

[7] *Where Is Science Going?* trans. by James Murphy (New York, W. W. Norton and Co., Inc., 1932), p. 32.

[8] See *Language, Truth, and Logic* (London, V. Gollancz, Ltd., 1936), p. 243.

in terms of something dependent on men or on minds for its existence; namely, in terms of sense experiences. But sense experiences never logically imply theories or laws. Rather sense experiences are accounted for by theories and laws. The external world that we posit as an explanation of our sense experiences is a world of continuous events or processes, the locus of causes is within these processes, the supposed general nature of these processes is found in our theory of space and time, and space and time are not sensed.

Indeterminacy and the Quantum Statistical Method

Traditionally, scientists assumed and clearly stated that the reason for their inability to obtain absolute accuracy in measurements and, therefore, absolute certainty in predictions, was to be found in either our unwieldy, cumbrous instruments of measurement or in personal factors such as the temporal element involved in observing instruments as well as the carelessness with which we sometimes measure. *The locus of the inaccuracy in measurement and prediction was said to be in us and in our instruments, not in the things measured.* Again, in orthodox physics the reason for not obtaining absolute conformity between the results of measurement and the "nature" of things measured was thought to have its basis in methodological procedure, not in the objects measured. Until recently scientists hoped to overcome to a greater and greater extent this lack of conformity so that they could at least approach complete conformity asymptotically. They hoped to do this by an ever increasing refinement of instruments on the one hand and by an ever increasing carefulness in using these instruments on the other. When this ideal of orthodox scientists had been achieved, they thought, methodology, epistemology, and metaphysics would at last be united into a perfect scientific method and would fit together like three peas in a pod.

Due to recent discoveries in light and energy phenomena, the former hope of classical science has had a tremendous shock, to say the least. A summary of its consequences was expressed by Heisenberg (1925) in what is called the *uncertainty principle* or the *principle of indeterminacy.*

In 1900, Max Planck discovered that energy-emitting "black bodies"

(any element, such as radium, which decomposes into some other element—hence, any radioactive element) emits energy in "handfuls," as
it were, or in amounts always divisible by a constant, h, known as
Planck's constant and equal to 6.55×10^{-27} erg sec. This means, in
contrast to a basic principle in classical physics, that energy is emitted in
"packets" or in *quanta* which finally constitute the least possible amount
of energy that can be emitted from a body, or transferred from one body
to another. It is as if one were buying marbles all the same size, each
weighing one ounce. In that case the weight of any amount of marbles
one could buy would always be divisible by one ounce without remainder. Also, one ounce would be the greatest common divisor in
every case. One could never buy 3.5 ounces (or marbles) or 4.25
ounces, or any other fractional amount. So with Planck's constant—it
tells us that energy is not infinitely divisible actually; that in the physical world the amount of energy transferred from one body to another
is always divisible by a certain constant. This means that the classical
theory that energy is infinitely divisible and therefore that the transfer
of energy is perfectly "smooth," even as a line is continuous or as any
number is the sum of an infinite number of fractions, is untenable.
For example, if an electron jumps from an outer orbit (or higher
energy level) to an inner orbit (or lower energy level) it will give up
an amount of energy divisible by Planck's constant, h. Of course, every
electron moving in its orbit around the nucleus has kinetic energy as
determined by the equation, $KE = mv^2/2$, where m is its mass and v is
its linear velocity.[9] But the practical problem arises: Can one, by experimenting, predict at once both the position (with respect to the nucleus, using an x, y, z, co-ordinate system) and the velocity (or momentum) of an electron? The answer is no, and this is the reason: The
position of an electron must be detected by means of light; i.e., by
allowing light of either short or long wave length to impinge upon
the electron and be reflected back upon a recording instrument (not
necessarily the *observer*). But when light impinges upon an electron it

---

[9] Slight corrections have been made by Sommerfeld. These corrections are in
accordance with Einstein's contention that the mass of a body increases with
velocity. By making these corrections, the advance of the perihelion of Mercury
can be accounted for, and, when applied to atoms, this leads to the now widely
accepted belief that the orbits of electrons are elliptical, not circular.

will change the velocity of the electron. This will either increase its velocity, and thus its kinetic energy, to the extent that it will move into a higher energy level (or outer orbit), or it will decrease its velocity with the possible effect of making it move into an inner orbit. In either case, the velocity, and possibly the energy level or position, is changed.

A longer light wave might be used, in which case the velocity of the electron would not be changed so much, since the kinetic energy of the longer wave is less than that of the shorter.[10] But the longer the light wave the less the accuracy with which one can determine the position, since there is a greater distortion. Conversely, the shorter the light wave the greater the change in momentum of the electron. This is a dilemma for classical physics and is resolved by the Heisenberg uncertainty principle at the expense of one of the basic hopes of classical physicists: the hope that through a continuous refinement of instruments absolute determination or prediction of the present and future states of the physical world is possible. But since absolute prediction is impossible, what must be said about causation? We will return to this question later, but now let us consider more carefully the physical limitations of absolute prediction.

Heisenberg says essentially this: *There is something in the nature of our method of knowing* (through observation by way of more or less refined scientific instruments) *which forever precludes an exact knowledge of what we seek to know.* This much we do know: The degree of certainty (or probability) with which we can know the actual state of the physical world (or electrons) can never be absolute (or one). The possible error in finding the position and velocity of an electron (or any other thing) is expressed by $\Delta x \cdot \Delta v \geqq h/m$, where Δx is the possible error in determining position and Δv is the possible error in determining velocity, h is Planck's constant, and m is the mass of the particle. If m is large, then the margin of error is correspondingly small, and vice versa. This implies that the margin of error increases in proportion to the attempt to get exact, detailed knowledge of the world.

This predicament is analogous to the egocentric predicament in

---

[10] Since $e=hv$, where h is the universal constant and v is the frequency, it follows that e changes as the frequency changes, since the velocity of light is constant.

epistemology according to which the knower affects the object of knowledge, thus forever preventing the mind from getting hold of the structure of nature as it is, independent of mind. Heisenberg says that scientific instruments are a part of the environment which can never be eliminated in the knowing process, and that their relation to the object of knowledge is not external but internal.

Now the exact extent of the "effect" of the instruments, light waves, etc., on phenomena measured cannot be known. When it comes to that problem we find ourselves lost in an undefined area, the very nature of which prevents exactitude. It follows, then, and of necessity, that prediction with absolute certainty is impossible from a practical standpoint and that the only epistemological basis for a belief in causes is put in question. The only evidence for causal relations is that there are recurrent patterns of events which recur when we are able to predict and thereby test the relationship (causal) between events.

But the question of causes raises its head once more and in a new form. When Heisenberg says that instruments affect the things measured, is he not relying on a causal principle? Is not this the same as saying there is a causal relation between instruments and what they are applied to? Planck thinks so. The hope that continuous refinement of instruments would finally prove that there are such things as causes in the objective world (since the proof was to consist in complete predictability—admittedly an indirect proof) has been shattered to the point where many are willing to forsake it. The proof that causes have an ontological, objective status cannot consist in complete predictability. If one still believes in causes, the evidence and proof must be other than that advocated by orthodox physicists.

Up to this point, taking for granted Heisenberg's experimental basis for his belief that causation in the traditional sense is forever beyond proof, there is still no evidence or logical proof that causes do not exist in the external world. A proof that causes do not exist must be identical with the proof that there is "perfect chaos" in the world. The *evidence* for causes and causal connections is order or law. A statement of probability is not the same as a statement of chaos, nor is the statement of chance. Both such statements entail epistemology as well as metaphysics, for they involve the knower as well as the known. Evidence for a world incompatible with law and order must consist of experiences happening in a perfectly chaotic manner. But perfect chaos is unthinkable! And here we run into the suggestion that the nature of mind precludes a knowledge of chaos, and that, conversely, mind apart from sense experience is wholly responsible for the concept of causation; e.g., Kant's suggestion that causation is a mental category known a priori, but superimposed on the experienceable world. This does not satisfy most scientists, and this is not what is meant by causation today, nor is it what was meant in the past. Nevertheless, on the basis of recent developments in physics, Max Planck says:[11]

> It is true that the law of causality cannot be demonstrated any more than it can logically be refuted; it is neither correct nor incorrect; it is a *heuristic principle;* it points the way, and in my opinion it is the most valuable pointer that we possess in order to find a path through the confusion of events, and in order to know in what direction scientific investigation must proceed so that it shall reach useful results.

No doubt many readers are still unconvinced that new experiments with light phenomena and with electrons have justifiably put in question the old belief in causation. But let us consider another most interesting phenomenon which has bearing on our problem and, I think, lends weight to the argument of those who deny that we can have a knowledge of causes.

Since light consists of elemental, indivisible parts called photons, it follows that a definite number of these photons are emitted from a light source. Fractional amounts of photons are never emitted. This is the same as saying that the amount of light emitted from a source is always divisible by Planck's constant, h, without remainder. Suppose, now, that a ray of light is incident upon a plane-surfaced piece of glass and that two-thirds of the light is reflected and one-third is transmitted to the other side (see Figure 1).

If, then, 3×10^{27} photons strike the surface of the glass, 2×10^{27} of them will be reflected, while 10^{27} of them will be transmitted. But what will we say if $3 \times 10^{27} + 1$ photons are emitted from the source and strike the glass? One thing certainly: the "extra" photon will either be transmitted or reflected, not both. Of course, the classical physicist

[11] *The Philosophy of Physics* (New York, W. W. Norton and Co., Inc., 1936), pp. 82–83.

would like to do one of two things. He would like to divide the photon into three parts and "allow" one part to be transmitted and the other two parts to be reflected; but quantum theory forbids. Next, he would like to say that there is a special or particular reason (or cause) for each individual photon's future behavior, and *if we knew more about these particular circumstances we could predict the future of the "extra" photon*. But this begs the point in question. We can "know

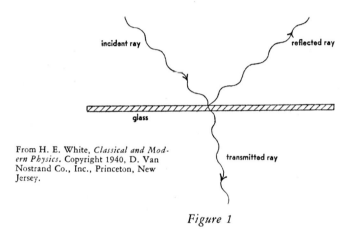

From H. E. White, *Classical and Modern Physics*. Copyright 1940, D. Van Nostrand Co., Inc., Princeton, New Jersey.

Figure 1

enough" only by using instruments, and our instruments are such that they refuse to serve us beyond a certain point. Furthermore, one cannot make a law or a science by studying a particular instance. Laws have to do with more than one photon, or any other one thing. Consequently, one could never predict the behavior of a particular photon. In short, we can predict the behavior of things only in so far as their behavior *is not peculiar*. Moreover, so far as control would permit, all photons were emitted under exactly the "same" circumstances. This is in accordance with the request of classical physics, which maintains that law and order are possible because of duplicable conditions. Now if we think of the "extra" photon as not necessarily the first or last to be emitted, but as any one of the group chosen at random, it becomes increasingly clear that its future is unpredictable. Our conclusion must be that the future of any particular photon is unpredictable and, therefore, in classical parlance, uncaused. But if the future of any particular photon is uncaused, it follows that the future of the group as a whole is uncaused despite our prediction to a high degree of probability.

Then, one might answer, the probability is 2/3 that the extra photon will be reflected. But obviously this degree of probability does not refer to a particular photon. To make our probability statement explicit we would have to say that past experience shows that approximately two out of every three of a very large number of photons were reflected by the glass. It is almost a *non sequitur* to say: "Therefore the probability that a particular photon will be reflected is 2/3." This "inference" is very confusing. Does probability refer to expectancy or to external events? If it refers to expectancy, can we be *certain* that it is true? If it refers to a particular event, how can it mean anything at all? For either the future of the event is determined or it is not. If it is determined, the number 2/3 cannot be applied to it, but rather we must apply the number 1. If the future of a photon is not determined, numbers do not apply with any significance, which is to say, the number 1 is as good as any other number such as .666 . . . , and vice versa.

The problem of causation will not be settled one way or the other for a while. Yet we can conclude from the previous considerations that today it is practically impossible to prove by predictions that there are causes in nature. It is for these reasons that a belief in causation must remain a conviction, but a conviction necessary to complete the logical basis for science. This conviction can never be proved by experiments; yet we have much evidence for it. So far, we have little and incomplete evidence against this conviction. The example cited above in which the future of a particular photon is indeterminate from the standpoint of prediction is the best evidence against the causal principle.

The quantum statistical method is in a sense the reverse of the sampling statistical method. Instead of studying individual cases and arriving at conclusions about the group as a whole, the quantum statistical method studies groups as wholes and deduces therefrom facts about the individual members of the group. Millikan's famous oil-drop experiment is a clear example of this method. (See any recent physics textbook.) In this experiment, Millikan successfully calculated the amount of electric charge on a single electron (4.802×10^{-10} esu.). Yet he did not reach this figure by studying isolated electrons. He always dealt with a great number of them and found in each case that the amount of charge was divisible without remainder by this number, 4.802×10^{-10}. The experiment is roughly this. A single oil drop (observable under the microscope) is allowed to fall between two uncharged plates. Its terminal velocity under gravity is calculated—it will reach a finite terminal velocity because of air friction. After the oil drop is charged by means of radium or x rays, the plates are charged by means of a battery. If the bottom plate and the oil drop have like charges, there will be a repelling force between the two and the velocity of the oil drop due to gravity will be retarded. It may either be balanced in mid-air or have its direction of motion changed so that it will start moving upward (see Figure 2).

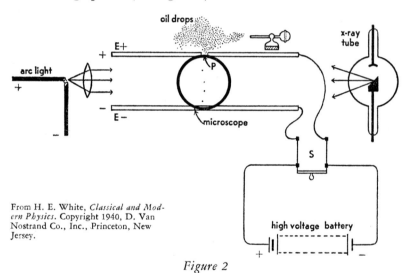

From H. E. White, *Classical and Modern Physics.* Copyright 1940, D. Van Nostrand Co., Inc., Princeton, New Jersey.

Figure 2

Through a careful study of the changes in velocity of the oil drop and a correlation of these changes with its mass, the charge on the plates, and the distance between the plates and the oil drop, it was possible to determine the amount of charge on a single electron. Suppose, for example, the force of repulsion between the charge on the plate and the charge on the oil drop is divisible without remainder by 4.802×10^{-10} dynes and that this number of dynes is the greatest common divisor in every case. Then, although the number of dynes repulsion (or attraction) might be 2 or 3 or any other whole number times 4.802×10^{-10}, it is obvious that the charge on the unit of electricity (the electron) is 4.802×10^{-10} esu. Thus Millikan came to a knowledge of the amount of charge on a single electron by studying electrons in groups and not individually.

This method of studying groups and determining thereby the nature of individual members of the group is new in science. It is a new way of thinking and reaching conclusions about individuals. The probability aspect of such a study has a different locus than does the sampling statistical method. When one uses the sampling method, a full knowledge of an individual case or sample is assumed, but knowledge about the group as a whole of which the sample is a specimen is not certain but probable. For example, if the first ten beans extracted from a bag are white, it is "probable" that the rest are white. The quantum method is just the reverse. When a single group is studied we know only that the group has a certain general characteristic, such as a certain mass or a certain electrical charge. If through using the quantum statistical method we want to know about some particular feature of an individual member of the things studied, we must study at least two groups before we can begin to have an inkling of the extent to which the feature under consideration attaches to a single member of the group. Furthermore, the feature studied must differ quantitatively in the two (or more) groups studied. For example, if we want to know the weight of a single marble and if we use the quantum method—always weighing more (probably thousands) than one marble at a time—then we must weigh at least two groups of marbles before having the slightest suggestion of the weight of a single marble. If the first group weighs 90 gm and the next group weighs 120 gm, we know very little about an individual marble. Yet, assuming that every marble weighs the same as every other, we know that no marble weighs more than 30 gm. If we continue weighing groups of marbles and find the following weights, 90 gm, 120 gm, 240 gm, 30 gm, 60 gm, 750 gm, 3,000 gm, 75 gm, 45 gm, we know that no marble weighs more than 15 gm, since 15 gm is the greatest common divisor. We continue still further to see if 15 remains the greatest common divisor. If so, then our conclusion is that each marble weighs 15 gm, and we use this conclusion until it breaks down in practice.

Once a conclusion about the individual members is reached, this knowledge is used deductively to infer knowledge about the relationship of the individual member of the group to other members of the group; e.g., through knowledge of the amount of electric charge or of the mass of a single electron, one constructs imaginatively the whole atom and also calculates the nature of different elements. At this junction let us take note of some fundamental differences between the sampling statistical method and the quantum statistical method. (1) The sampling method studies individuals as individuals and proceeds to pass judgment on members of the group not studied, whereas the quantum method studies the group as a whole and proceeds to pass judgment on individual members within the group studied. (2) The sampling method considers many characteristics of individuals which may not be evaluated quantitatively, such as the fertility of seeds, the color of beans, death, and many other qualitative features of individuals, whereas the quantum method deals only with measurable characters, such as weight, mass, electric charge, or velocities. Although the sampling method may be applied to measurable characters, the quantum method may not be applied to qualities that cannot be measured. (3) The quantum method leads to definiteness with regard to scalar qualities, such as mass or electric charge, but gives probabilities with regard to vectoral quantities. The sampling method gives only probabilities.

The point of contention between those who want to generalize on the quantum method and those who still believe events and objects are predictable with certainty is this: Are phenomena by their very nature indeterminate and unpredictable, or does the indeterminateness (uncertainty) and unpredictableness lie within the observer and his instruments? Those who would place the unpredictableness in nature make, of course, a metaphysical principle of it. They call it the principle of indeterminacy. Those who place the unpredictableness in the observer and his instruments believe that it is merely a methodological obstacle to be overcome and that it cannot be made into a metaphysical principle. Even if the refinement of our instruments of measurement and of careful observation cannot be accomplished in full, i.e., even if complete predictability is unattainable, this does not mean that the principle of causation is to be given up.

The principle of causation means two things, which should be separated. The first and most important part of its meaning is this: no event happens without a sufficient cause. This means that some relations between certain events are internal and not external. The second and less important part of the meaning of the causal principle is: whatever is predictable with certainty is caused, and whatever is caused is predictable with certainty. Laplace is responsible for this interpretation of causations, and the positivists, along with all who would deny the validity of the principle of causation, seem to accept the second part of its meaning as the whole of its meaning. The ability to predict a certain event, e_2, on the basis of e_1 is evidence that there is a causal relation between the two, but this is not the primary meaning of the causal relation. Fundamentally, for events to be causally related means there are internal relations between them, and this implies an order.

Suppose we ask the indeterminists why they believe the causal principle is untenable. They will answer somewhat as follows. "An event, e_2, cannot be predicted with certainty from e_1, but e_3 may follow with equal probability." Does this deny the causal principle; i.e., that there is no internal relation between e_1, and e_2 or e_3? Certainly not. It may mean that we cannot predict e_2 or e_3 with certainty, but that we are, nevertheless, certain of their probability. The contradiction of the causal principle is this: (1) There is perfect chaos so that any event out of an infinite number of events is as likely to follow e_1 as any other: the probability of e_2 following e_1 is $\frac{1}{\infty}=0$. (2) All relations are external: a statement of law, even by approximation, is impossible.

When we stop to think of how the indeterminists have tried to refute the causal principle, we see their folly more clearly. Briefly, they say: "Inasmuch as our measuring instruments *affect* the things measured, there is no cause." We would grant that complete predictability might be but an ideal and attainable only by indirect inference and not by direct experience. But this does not mean that all relations between events are external. Admittedly our instruments, the observer, and things observed are all in nature and, therefore, probability is in nature. But the ideal of science has been and still is this: to separate those things which belong to nature independent of man from those things which exist only in relation to man or have been superimposed upon nature by man. *The limits of observation cannot be attributed to the things observed.* The causal principle can save us from confusing the nature of observation with things observed, and the application of it today will have the same results as it had in early modern science; namely, it will help maintain the distinction between a world existing independent of man (his intellect and his emotions), and a world constructed out of imagination. Traditionally, the belief in the existence of a lawful, predictable, external order of events was a great boon to science and encouraged men to find the causes or conditions necessary for controlling nature. We do not have to go far to find many misinterpretations in modern physics.[12] Arthur Compton, in *The Freedom of Man,* concludes from the uncertainty principle that man is free! A. S. Eddington, in *The Nature of the Physical World,* strikes a similar note when, on the basis of the principle of indeterminacy, he concludes: " . . . we may note that science thereby withdraws its moral opposition to free-will."[13]

It is not far from such unwarranted nonsequential misinterpretations to a medieval world filled with all sorts of capricious spirits: however, our fast developing control over the order of natural events is concrete evidence that we are not living in a chaotic world. Our rapidly increasing power to predict with greater precision than ever before is evidence that our inability to predict absolutely is not the basis for the belief in an undetermined order of events. All this confusion can be clarified if we make the proper distinction between causation as a metaphysical principle and prediction as a hallmark of the presence of causation. But the absence of the hallmark does not contradict the presence of causes.

One inexcusable mistake is made by those who would disprove the causal principle by the fact that prediction with absolute precision is at present methodologically impossible: they, like Hume, try nevertheless to *account for* this inability to predict. They try to give an *intelligible account* of how the instruments, the light wave and its length affect things measured.

---

[12] See Philipp Frank, *Interpretations and Misinterpretations in Modern Physics,* trans. by Olaf Helmer and Milton B. Singer (Paris, Hermann & Cie, 1938).

[13] (New York, The Macmillan Company, 1928), p. 295.

CHAPTER VIII

Pure and Applied Science

Concepts and Definitions

"PURE SCIENCE" and "applied science" are correlative concepts. Together they encompass the scientific method. In accordance with the general thesis that knowledge is for the sake of achieving ends freely selected on ethical grounds, I define "pure science" as that part of the scientific method concerned only with acquiring neutral knowledge. Neutral knowledge does not entail the particular ends for which it may serve as means, yet in principle it must be applicable to alternative possible ends. Nature, excluding men, has no purpose, nor do any of her parts. She is neutral, having no concern for ends or for values. Scientists in the field of pure research try to formulate statements that are true, irrespective of human purposes. For example, the statement, "stress is proportional to strain," is neutral with reference to ends and gives us neutral knowledge. Hooke's law, even as a hammer, may be applied to various ends indifferently.

Applied science is the appropriation by man of neutral knowledge and material objects for the achievement of desired ends. It has no meaning apart from ends or goals or purposes. A purposive act is one guided and controlled by a symbol standing for the results of that act, or, in any case, by a symbol for what is believed to be the results of that act. Hence the application of knowledge requires that the applier anticipate certain results which are ordinarily called ends; and they are ends relative to the means used to accomplish them. When considered by itself the scientific means consists of neutral objects and neutral knowledge acquired through pure research. All neutral knowledge may become means which, of course, logically entail ends.

There is a distinction between *nondesired* ends and *desired* ends, even as there is a difference between wanting to know what the results will be, say, of mixing red and blue pigments, and desiring those results. But to desire these ends is a different matter. A good scientist doing pure research is unbiased, which means that he is indifferent to the results of his experiments. Whatever the end, a pure research scientist accepts it with natural piety and does not mix his desires with the results of experimentation.

Where knowledge is being applied, a certain end is desired. In trying to effect an end by use of scientific principles or laws, it is assumed that that end would not have occurred *at that place at that time* without the intervention of purposive behavior, without acting with a plan. This implies that there are alternative possible future events and that when scientific knowledge is combined with purposeful behavior it is possible to determine specifically the nature of the events that will take place.

If there were only one possible spatiotemporal order of events, we would not use the word "possible" and, of course, there would be no practical value in desiring ends, to say nothing of science. Even for an end outside of time to be desired, such as a heaven after death, there must be alternative possibilities. There is no sense in desiring an inevitable event if its spatiotemporal locus is fixed. Pure science is neutral with respect to desired ends, but the application of science requires that an end or that particular ends be selected, and knowledge attained in pure science is neutral simply because it lends itself indifferently to the accomplishment of alternative possible ends. Although science does not force certain ends upon us, our choice of ends that will be actualized by using neutral knowledge as a part of the means, may be conditioned by pure science; for choosing or not choosing to do a certain thing is always conditioned by whether or not we think we can in fact do it.

Valuation and Science

The selection of ends by use of intelligence is an act of evaluating. There are different kinds of acts of valuation, but in general an act of valuation involves (1) a comparison of at least one thing, *a,* with at least one other thing, *b,* (2) drawing a conclusion, on the basis of (1), either to the effect that *a* has a certain means-end relationship to *b* or to the effect that *a* has a certain good-better relationship to *b* (or both). For example, through comparison we may conclude that the following are true: (1) quinine is a specific for malaria fever; (2) jewels are better than metals for watch bearings; and (3) friendship is better than enmity. Here we have three different kinds of value judgments. (1) specifies merely a means-end relationship, whereas (2) and (3) specify relationships of betterness.[1] Again, (1) and (2) are value judgments concerning means to ends and therefore they are concerned only with the *extrinsic value* of the things considered. (3), however, is a judgment resulting from a comparison of ends and is concerned only with the *intrinsic value* of the things considered. All value judgments presuppose objects, each of which has at least one value, although the object in question may have that value only in relation to some other object.

Any particular end having intrinsic value in one context may have extrinsic value in another context. One may hunt food in order to eat. In that case hunting has extrinsic value with reference to eating, which in that context has intrinsic value. Eating may, in turn, be a means to another end, and with reference to that other end it has extrinsic value. But in every value judgment involving a means-end relationship there is a distinction between the means and the end, and, consequently, between that, in the items compared, which has intrinsic value and that which has extrinsic value. If there is something, *e,* that has intrinsic

[1] Evaluations are never with respect to the absolute good, but always involve a comparison of one value with another. When applied to an evaluation of means to ends, this indicates that there may be alternative means, but no necessary means. This is in accordance with the view developed by A. P. Brogan in "The Implications of Meliorism Concerning the Relation between Value and Existence," *Sixth International Congress of Philosophy* (New York, Longmans, Green & Co., Inc., 1927).

value only, then in every judgment involving *e* in a means-end relationship, *e* must be an end. Similarly, if there is something, *m,* that has extrinsic value only, then in any judgment involving *m* in a means-end relationship, *m* must always be a means.

There are also nonvalue judgments; for example, " 'all men are mortal' is true" is a nonvalue judgment, or " 'the table is thirty inches high' is true." These judgments concern neither the extrinsic nor the intrinsic values of things. They treat only either of what was or will be a status quo or a part of it, or of what is the status quo or a part of it. If one reasons deductively and from nonvalue judgments exclusively, there will be no value judgments. This applies to formal logic and to all other formal disciplines. Also, there are many cases of inductive reasoning where value judgments are lacking; but value judgments are required for experimental reasoning or for experimental logic. All reasoning about experiments and about the relationship between sense experiences requires value judgments about means-end relationships. We can make value judgments in the formal sciences only in cases where choice is involved, and such choice will as a rule concern the axioms, and will take on some such form as this: axiom *a* is more desirable than axiom *b,* because *a* is a better means for proving certain theorems. Once the axioms are accepted, the theorems follow of necessity.

Pure scientists dealing with factual material confine their judgments to two types: first, nonvalue judgments, and, second, value judgments, which concern extrinsic values only. Examples of the first are: "It is raining." "There will be an earthquake in Asia next month." "This fossil is six million years old." The second, value judgments, includes: (1) all judgments confined to means-end relationship and not involving the concept of betterness (for example, "grease will prevent the wheel from squeaking"), and (2) all judgments including both a means-end relationship and the concept of betterness, excluding considerations of desired ends (for example, "for airplane propellers aluminum is better than wood"). Under (2) we must make a very careful distinction: (2) includes all judgments of this general form; for a given end, *e, a* is better than *b* as a means. This does not imply that *e* is desired. We might go so far as to say that *if e* is desired, then *a* is better than *b* as a means. But to desire *e* is a different matter, and to judge that *e* is better than *e'* is a judgment concerning the intrinsic value of *e* and *e'*. Intrinsic value judgments are not made by men acting in the capacity of pure scientists. They are made on ethical grounds.

One may argue that there are no pure scientists. At times, at least, a research scientist must be "disinterested" in the particular outcome of his experiments. Since the establishment of scientific laboratories, scientists have boasted of their unbiased attitude toward the outcome of experiments, even as they have boasted of the neutrality of fundamental or basic knowledge. Usually, the wishes of the scientist are not allowed to enter into the conclusions drawn from data and from experiments. James B. Conant,[2] in stating how chain reactions in U^{235} were discovered, said that some scientists had hoped such control would be impossible. Nevertheless, these hopes did not affect the fact that it *is* possible. These scientists were able, for a time at least, to separate wishes from the stubborn facts, and in doing so they were unbiased. If the words "unbiased scientist," "disinterested scientist," "stubborn facts," have any referents, then so does the expression "pure scientist." This does not mean that a pure scientist cannot become a practical person and look at his findings from the standpoint of their application to desired ends. Nor does it mean that it is possible for a person to live the life of a pure scientist—i.e., to maintain continuously the attitude of a pure scientist. But there are stages in the scientific method, just as there are stages in every act of reflective thinking of nonscientists, and pure science is a stage in the scientific method preceding its application.

The pragmatists have emphasized that in reflective thinking, whenever and wherever it takes place, the thinker must be careful to exclude his emotions, his wishes, his aspirations from the act of collecting the data and from interpreting them. And although it may be the case that reflective thinking is meaningless apart from a problematic situation (apart from a desire to maintain certain on-going processes, or to stop them, or to institute new processes), the thinker, nevertheless, must separate temporarily the fact that he desires certain ends from the process of collecting and interpreting the data. There

[2] In an address delivered at The University of Texas in the spring of 1948.

are phases in the process of reflective thinking that must be free from bias or from desired ends. Yet this separation is not an absolute one, nor is there an absolute separation between pure and applied science.

Value Judgments in Pure Science

There is no such thing as knowledge for its own sake, nor is there such a thing as rational conduct not preceded by reflective thinking. E. A. Burtt, Dewey, G. H. Mead, Peirce, and others have explained carefully the steps in the scientific method and have emphasized the belief that reflective thinking by individuals in situations outside the laboratory should nevertheless be patterned after the laboratory type of thinking. These men have expounded the thesis that the "laboratory type of mind" can be and should be the standard for laymen also. In short, these men have stressed the view that rational conduct presupposes a plan or a conception of the relationship of behavior to the results of that behavior. The test of the plan is in its application, and the results of its application must be accepted without reference to one's liking. If our thinking is to be effective then our ideas must answer to the structure of the world, which has a stubbornness about its structure that cannot be changed by prejudice and fanciful thinking. In successful rational behavior our plans must answer finally to the unconditional laws of nature.

If the experimental type of reasoning advocated by the pragmatists has its prototype in the scientific method, it lies in the fact that pure and applied sciences are stages in the method, and pure science must be devoid of desired ends, whereas applied science presupposes them.

Reflective thinking was first carried on in problematic situations not in laboratories, and the emergence of laboratories meant that the solution of a problem was to be given a more general form, or, in other words, the problem itself was formulated in a general way so that the solution of it would be applicable to situations at different times and places, and not just to a particular situation. Galileo, for example, had no interest in the way a particular object as a particular fell. Second, the emergence of laboratories represented socially organized reflective thinking, and in pure research the scientist performs only a part of social behavior necessary for achieving socially desired ends. Pure research, then, represents a sort of division of intelligent social behavior. In ordinary life, when we use nontechnical language, we depend partly on the peculiarity of circumstances to give meaning to symbols.[3] In pure science, however, exactness and precision are demanded so that ideas may be communicable from one person to another, possibly separated by generations, irrespective of the peculiarities of the environments of these persons. Precision is directly proportional to universality. But universality is inversely proportional to the specification of particulars. For this reason and to the extent that knowledge is fundamental, it is neutral with respect to particular ends or, in general, with respect to its application to desired ends.

The emergence of scientific laboratories in the seventeenth century was an indication that society recognized the importance of science for human welfare. This social consciousness is clearly detectable in the fact that there are many state and nationally supported scientific laboratories. By virtue of these laboratories a part of the method of achieving socially desired goals has become institutionalized. Pure research must be looked on not only as a social enterprise but also as an investment for posterity. It has been made into an institution.

To clarify the scientific method—to give a general statement of it— is to state its form in its universally social dimensions. Pure research leads to fundamental knowledge. Fundamental knowledge is neutral knowledge. Because of the social dimension of neutral knowledge some have mistaken it for absolute truth unrelated to social human perspectives. A general statement or a law based on the experience of an individual or individuals can never get away from experiences of some individual, and knowledge, expressed in terms of the intellectual tools of that culture to which the scientist belongs, cannot transcend *all* culture. The problem of the scientist is to express his findings so that they will apply to more than the problems of his immediate generation and culture. His problem is to express knowledge in a universal language that is nevertheless applicable to problems in particular cul-

[3] See Bronislaw Malinowski, "The Problems of Meaning in Primitive Languages," Supplement I, Ogden and Richards, *The Meaning of Meaning* (New York, Harcourt, Brace and Company, Inc., 1930).

tures. If a scientist who succeeds in giving to knowledge this universal form understands what he has done, then he understands also the meaning of the social dimension of knowledge.

Basic knowledge is neutral not only because it *does not* but also because it *cannot* specify the particular ends to which it may be applied. Statements having possible reference to more than one particular spatio-temporal event, and yet not specifying any one of these particular referents, have a universal form. The application of scientific knowledge involves a particularization of neutral knowledge, for it is possible to apply knowledge to particular situations and to *particular* problems only. And desiring specific ends is a necessary factor in determining when and where neutral knowledge is to be applied. Ethical evaluation is a consideration of alternative ends (each of which is made possible by materials at hand and by scientific knowledge) with the intent to subscribe to some, but not all, of them. Choice amounts to permitting a symbol for one of the ends considered to control the act which, if successful, leads to the attainment of the end symbolized.

Since basic or neutral knowledge is characterized by universality it follows that while one is acting in the capacity of a pure scientist, he cannot evaluate the ends to which neutral knowledge may be applied. Furthermore, a pure scientist may evaluate means with reference to ends only if a particular end, i.e., an end having a particular spatio-temporal locus, is not specified. For example, a pure scientist may judge that $2H_2$ plus O_2 will yield $2H_2O$, but this information has a universal form and refers indifferently to various particular instances, and then only after one has interpreted this formula by assigning to it particular referents.

Applied Science and Value Judgments

In so far as society supports pure research, it delegates to pure scientists the task of furnishing a part of the conditions necessary for solving problems in society and for attaining goals selected on ethical grounds. Pure science is an investment by society in something to be used, we know not how, when, or where. Pure research could not have become institutionalized, nor, consequently, could scientists have constituted a community of persons held together by a common bond, were it not for the fact that the group of scientists includes far more than the immediate society of any individual member of the group. Not only has the scientific community become world-wide, but it has taken on a historical, temporal dimension so extensive that many individuals consider science a *cause* to which they are willing to devote their life efforts. In this sense the welfare of society and society itself can become objects of devotion, as Auguste Comte has so clearly indicated in his suggestion that we substitute Society for God.

The community of scientists has both its virtues and its drawbacks. Some of the outstanding desirable consequences resulting from the fact that there is a world-wide community of scientists are: (1) the results of pure research must be expressed in a universal language understood at least by the scientists; (2) the community of scientists is continuous in the sense that the death of individual scientists does not mean the end of the institution; (3) accordingly, by (1) and (2), scientists are obliged to express scientific knowledge in universal form not confined to a community of scientists existing at any one time; (4) since scientific information must have a universal form, it cannot specify the particular ends for which it may be used.

The main drawback resulting from the fact that pure scientists constitute a community is that often they tend to think of pure research as an end in itself, and of most, if not all, ends to which pure science is relative as being confined to scientific institutions. As a consequence, some scientists pass value judgments concerning ends which purportedly have intrinsic values, although these ends are really confined to pure research and have extrinsic value only. Often one or another scientist thinks and acts as though the scientific community is complete in itself and exists for its own sake. Such a philosophy of science is analogous to the erroneous belief that knowledge exists for its own sake.

There are good reasons in the history of science why scientists are inclined to retreat into their institution and look there for intrinsic values. In theory the Greeks separated knowledge from practice. This separation, as Dewey points out, probably took place because the Greeks had slaves for menial tasks, which made room for an exploiting aristocratic class to which sophists and men of science belonged. For the Greeks, science was for its own sake, not for the sake of practices carried on by slaves. It is not a long way from the Greek attitude to the belief held by early modern scientists, Galileo, Descartes, and others, to the effect that an intellectual joy resulting from a knowledge of the mathematical splendor of nature is the basic reward of scientific investigation.

The retreat into the laboratories by early modern scientists was stimulated and made almost complete by the entrenched clergy of the day. Probably the secrecy[4] that shrouded many of the experiments carried on in early academies of science was due to a conflict between science and what may be called "vested interests." The vested interests at that time had no notion of the technological consequences of science, but they feared the possible impact of science on theological dogmas upon which the unity of the church depended. It is clear that a retreat into the laboratory was a defensive measure necessary for guaranteeing immunity for the scientists. This was an immunity from inquisitors, authorized or unauthorized, who purportedly were protecting basic social institutions and eternal values.

Early academies of science had charters from their respective governments, which meant simply that the State furnished protection for members of these academies, but they furnished no financial support. Neither the members of these scientific institutions nor the men who protected them saw with any degree of clarity the necessary relationship between pure research and practice. Both scientists and clergymen settled for what is known as a division of learning. Yet, it was clear to the scientists that they were purchasing immunity at a price. The price they paid is implicit in what is known generally as a division of knowledge into two compartments: natural knowledge and divine knowledge.

Vested interests guaranteed immunity to scientists provided they would not meddle in affairs having anything to do with the social and religious attitudes of the people. Of course, neither the vested interests nor the scientists of that day were interested in the technological import of science, so the covenant concerned primarily the "values" of

[4] Martha Ornstein, *The Role of Scientific Academies in the Seventeenth Century* (New York, Columbia University Press, 1913); also Dorothy Stimson, *Scientists and Amateurs: A History of the Royal Society* (New York, Henry Schuman, Inc., Publishers, 1948).

the Church, and the argument was over matters of fact. The Church had erroneously assumed that questions of value were questions about facts and that value statements were statements of facts. It erroneously assumed also that the chief end of man as well as the method of attaining it had been prescribed by God. Little did the clergy realize that through science men would not only find new means of attaining ends but that also the concept of man would change, which in turn gave rise to new and alternative goals which not only increases man's freedom but makes ethical decision more significant. For these reasons the first research laboratories of modern science were cut off from the world, and a relationship between pure science and applied science was not suspected, by the laymen at least. And few if any at that time suspected that science would change our social goals or our values. Practically everyone was thinking in terms of absolute, fixed values based on facts which presumably had been revealed previously to representatives of the Church.

Here, in the early history of pure research, there is no integration of pure and applied science. At that time many thought of pure science as the pursuit of knowledge for its own sake, and the Greek theory of knowledge still prevailed. The main difference was in the technique of arriving at knowledge and in the subject matter. But science was apart from a world with its everyday problems. This explains why statements of the discoveries of early scientists were neutral with respect to ends outside the scientific community. The men of practice, and, in particular, men interested in economic affairs, finally broke the internal circularity of pure science and began to apply neutral knowledge toward the accomplishment of particular ends set up by individual laymen.

The leaders of the industrial revolution were responsible for making science an integral part of a practical world. Originally the revolution had its philosophic justification in a laissez faire economic policy, which implies in effect that the ends for which science was to be used as a means were not prescribed by society acting as a unit, but rather by individual members of society using their own individual judgment. The laissez faire doctrine maintained that the good, the welfare, and the values of the community and of the nation consisted in the good, the welfare, and the values of the individuals, each motivated by self-interest. The question under discussion that led finally to the explicit formulation of the laissez faire policy was not concerned with whether science should be used for practical ends, but rather, who should prescribe the ends; the individual or society through government? As things went, the Church was left out, and economics was neither under the control of the government nor of the Church. But planning goes with the prescription of ends. The laissez faire policy, therefore, gave individuals not only the right to set up ends at their own discretion, within very broad social limits, but also the right to plan for the welfare of the nation. Our industrialized technological world is a result, but not the only result.

Today we have in acute form the problem of whose function it is to prescribe the ends for which pure research is to be applied. This, of course, entails both the problem of who should do the planning for scientific research and who should select the goals that may be attained through its application. This problem has nothing to do with who has the power to control our technology, which necessarily involves science, both pure and applied, but rather with the question of who can do it so as to assure us that civilized society will survive. Today we are confronted with the serious question of whether it is possible to continue the laissez faire policy with regard to planning and the prescription of ends. This is a problem concerning applied science and values. One thing is clear: pure research cannot prescribe the goals for which it may be applied. Nuclear energy does not say how it is to be used or that it is to be used at all. It follows, then, that before science is applied, goals must be chosen, and the choice is made on ethical grounds, for a consideration of values as ends to be achieved lies completely outside the scope of pure research.

Probably it was the atomic bomb that brought the pure-research scientists out of their laboratories and persuaded them to learn what many social scientists had known for a long time; that pure research must become an integrated part of a legalized national and international political program. This implies that pure science, applied science, and social values must be taken into account, perhaps by our political representatives, in securing the welfare of nations and of a civilized society. Pure science must be looked at in relation to its application and finally in relation to social values. Science is used as a means

APPLIED SCIENCE AND VALUE JUDGMENTS

of getting away from undesired practices and ways of living only in so far as it furnishes us desired ways of living having desired consequences or values. The futures we try to instate through science as a means are not simply duplications of pasts. Nor do we want to perpetuate the entire status quo. And although experiences of certain past and present conditions are a part of the data necessary for setting up future goals, these goals are not identical with past or present conditions. As explained previously, a comparison of alternative (perhaps future) changes in our social and economic institutions, with respect to betterness, involves value judgments. And confronting present-day societies in free nations is the problem of establishing a commission whose function will be to co-ordinate and direct in broad outline pure research and its application toward social and economic improvement. The members of such a commission must have a theory of value and they must be able to decide on some of the basic human individual and social values.

Probably no one knows beyond question precisely which basic human values are desirable—what values the members of society are willing to defend and work for, regardless of the cost. And it is quite possible that there is a conflict in society over our commonly accepted basic values. Are the pacifist Christians willing to live by their principles at any cost? Are scientists ready to defend the practice of freedom of thought and communication under all circumstances, and are they ready to hold that such freedom is essential for the survival of a civilized people? Do we put peace above freedom? Are economists willing to defend a laissez faire policy even at the expense of democracy? Do we put religious freedom above political freedom? There are many other problems involving values and value judgments that have not been settled with any degree of clarity, but in democratic societies men are pretty well agreed that certain values have priority over others. A major problem consists in preserving several values if possible, although it may appear offhand that some must be given up to save others. For example, at present our political representatives put national security above the privilege of free and open discussion about nuclear energy, and apparently they believe censorship of scientific information is necessary to national security. This is the first time in history during peacetime that scientists in a free nation have been denied the privilege of communicating openly with scientists of any other nation about basic scientific principles, or about the "secrets" of nature. In fact at present, scientists are not permitted to communicate certain scientific information to certain other citizens within their own country. This suppression of scientific information infringes on the freedom of scientists and, therefore, makes a world-wide community of scientists impossible.

The ideal would be to have both freedom of communication among all scientists *and* national security. But national security is now believed to be of higher value than freedom of communication, and, presumably, it is thought to be a necessary condition for the latter. Where must freedom of communication be checked in order to guarantee national security? There are good scientists who argue that national security is not increased one bit by suppressing basic scientific information.[5]

Values and the Interrelationship of Institutions

There are many problems connected with science and social values today, but the following discussion will be confined to major issues only. The major institutions that must reconcile themselves with each other in the modern world are the religious, economic, political, and scientific. In fact, in industrialized countries all these institutions exist together more or less integrated and more or less in conflict, at least at certain points. The manner in which these institutions are co-ordinated in any particular country is known as that country's "culture." The conflict between institutionalized values, such as those found in religion, in economics, in politics, and in science, lends support to the view that we do not have an adequate philosophy of civilization or of culture by which these conflicts can be resolved. If there are conflicts between religious values and economic values, or between religious values and scientific values, and if we do not have a philosophy whereby these conflicts can be resolved, then the conflict will result in the final domination of some value or values in one institution over those in another. If, for example, there is a conflict between property rights

[5] See especially Norbert Wiener, *The Human Use of Human Beings* (New York, Houghton Mifflin Company, 1950), Chapter VIII.

and civil liberties, the conflict may be resolved at the expense of property rights, unless it is resolved by a social philosophy, with its ensuring governmental stipulations and regulations.

Religious institutions, and the "values" which they aspire to achieve and purportedly defend, are believed by some to be diametrically opposed to science and technology. C. E. Ayres has spent considerable time propounding and defending the thesis that technology is the nerve of Western civilization and that:[6] "It is the technological continuum which is the locus of truth and value." Ayres is saying that "values" whose locus is in institutions such as the Church are not values at all, but are, rather, stagnant, static, ceremonial patterns of behavior, many of which are a hindrance to the technological continuum, and that at their very best they "permit" technology and science, but in no case do they stimulate or cause the continuum. To put it in more systematic form, Ayres says that institutionalized values, such as those presumably found in religious institutions (to say the least), are not even a part of the conditions necessary for technology. Again, he says, institutionalized "values" are not in the least degree an integral part of technology. I think Ayres is mistaken. For better or for worse, technology in Western culture has developed *within* a culture of which the Hebrew-Christian tradition is a vital, integral part. The Hebrew-Christian tradition, accompanied by its justification, theology, and its control over civil institutions, furnished, in Western civilization, the cultural matrix within which the following emerged and grew: the experimental laboratories or pure research, the capitalistic system, technology or the application of pure science for the attainment of certain desired ends, and democracy. Historically we find even among primitive societies that some sort of economic system and some sort of political organization are always accompanied by a philosophy of culture, which in most cases we might better call religion.

A philosophy of culture is always a justification for the mores and folkways which include at least political and economic practices. And for better or for worse, we will find not only the exponents of democracy and of science, but also the entrepreneurial geniuses, defending their institutions by humanitarian principles borrowed from religion.

[6] "Economic Value and Scientific Synthesis," *American Journal of Economics and Sociology,* I, No. 4 (July, 1942), 348.

The sense of decency and humanity we now have did not come from the technological continuum nor from our economic system. America's criticism of modern communism as an economic system amounts to an attempt to show that communism with its entailed values is inconsistent with our basic, ethical, humanitarian principles as expressed in religion and democracy. Capitalists are more inclined to attack communism, not on the grounds that it is contrary to free enterprise, fair competition, and other capitalistic values, but on the grounds that it is inconsistent with our ethical, religious, humanitarian, and democratic principles. Even if we grant that present-day communism in Russia is more efficient in feeding the people than the economic practices of the czarist regime, we say, nevertheless, that, for our part, we would rather have more freedom and less food. And in passing such a value judgment we fall back on principles beyond the scope of economics. Were not financiers eager to have business corporations considered as *persons* in order to benefit at court from the protection our civil laws offer persons?

The concept of peace and the dream of world unity came to us through religious channels. And although the atomic scientists are exclaiming humanitarian principles and world unity, we must not assume that they discovered these principles in the laboratory while working on problems of atomic energy. What they are advocating are the teachings of great religious leaders who lived centuries ago. And although Ayres says the locus of truth is in the technological continuum, it is easy enough to see that the concepts, truth and honesty, and an ethical code were present before the emergence of, and are conditions for, modern science. Furthermore, there is no conflict between the humanitarian principles expressed in the great religious and the social ethical standards propounded by many of our present-day physical and social scientists. That there are undesirable political, economic, and social conditions, was not learned through pure scientific research or through our analysis of the "technological continuum." We learned through experience and prior to the introduction of democracy, pure science, and our present economic systems, that certain intrinsic values are found in human relationships. A code of ethics was and still is the instrument by which we try to guarantee that these values will not be sacrificed in a technological, mechanized world.

Americans still rest their case for the defense of our economic system and of our political system on ethical principles which are designed to secure those conditions in human, social relationships found to be valuable.

Thorstein Veblen points out that financiers will as a rule give *good* reasons for what they do instead of the *real* reasons. From this fact, however, it is clear that the final justification of an economic system is to be found in a philosophy of culture having ethical principles at its base. It is not the case that modern science or even modern economic systems have no need for ethics. We will find, rather, that a philosophy of civilization grounded on basic ethical principles both constitutes a justification for the institutionalized values of democracy, science, and economics and furnishes the matrix for the emergence and development of these institutions. This means that a human society with an ethical system which prescribes how men shall behave with respect to each other is a necessary condition for the emergence of the scientific method and a technological world.

This, however, is not to say that early ethical codes were not concerned with economic matters or with ways of effecting ends, such as those effected in fishing, hunting, and herding. But it is to say that the basic values, not to be sacrificed for other values, are found in human social relationships not identifiable with any particular act, or any particular kind of act involving the acquisition or the consumption of economic goods, even though these relationships may be experienced in technological behavior or in some other kind of behavior. Although man is an animal, he is not a lower animal, and the basic values in any civilization are higher than those found at the economic level, in the sense that they are more worthwhile, more satisfactory, more to be desired, and more desirable.

Science and technology are means for achieving ends and for securing values outside of science and technology. The degree of the efficiency of technological practices is not the final test of their worth—they must not interfere with but must, rather, ensure ethical values.

How Institutional Practices Condition Our Choice of Ends

There is a direct causal relationship between pure science and our choice of ends. Pure science does not and cannot determine for us the particular end or ends for which science is used as a means. Nevertheless, pure science conditions our choice of ends, for in an industrialized scientific world the man of practice always asks whether or not his goals are achievable before he undertakes them. The test of the achievability of ends is left to science. What is not achievable in principle is of no value to the practical man. Modern science has left many old values unchanged and has laid the basis for the introduction of many new ones, but it has not given us "scientific" values in place of others. The effect of science on our theory of what is valuable is this: Only what is achievable (in principle at least) can be of value, and often through scientific knowledge we learn what is and what is not achievable. Many of the old religious "values" must be rejected. Yet many are maintained. Now to say that only the achievable is valuable is not to identify the valuable with the achievable. Many things achievable through science as a means are of no value or have negative value. For this reason we say that science does not determine for us what is valuable, for science cannot tell us what is satisfactory or desirable. It can only tell us in many instances whether or not what we do in fact desire is attainable and, therefore, what may possibly be of value.

The pure scientist does not and cannot discover intrinsic values. If he could, this would be the same as prescribing the ends for which his knowledge is to be used as a means. As a pure scientist one must confine his judgments and discoveries to means. One who applies neutral knowledge is, for the time at least, a technician, but its application is always preceded by the selection of an end. And one who selects an end is, for the time at least, a judger of intrinsic values. In many cases in ordinary life a man is a pure scientist, a technician, and a judge of intrinsic values, with reference to a particular problem. This is more frequently the case with relatively isolated persons, such as pioneers. Or, we may say generally, the greater the demands of self-sufficiency, the greater the necessity for an individual to be a pure scientist, a technician, and an evaluator of ends, all in one.

Ethical value judgments emerge only in problematic situations. Also, only then are intrinsic values considered. And although the business of considering alternative ends may in many cases precede a knowledge of how to attain them, the final ethical decision of giving assent to any one of them is conditioned by whether we believe we can attain them in fact. Understanding the nature and meaning of problems is a guide to the formulation of neutral knowledge. Because of an understanding of the general nature of problems we can acquire knowledge that is neutral with respect to particular problems. For this reason there is a distinction between the stages in the solution of problems or, in general, between the pure scientist, the technician, and the evaluator of ends. The requirement for this social division of function is not that all problems must be social in nature. Rather the division is based on two facts, namely: men can state the general characteristics of problems, and men are able to act in different capacities. Again, we are able to state the nature of problems socially, and because we are a society, different persons can perform different parts of a social act. Naturally the question arises: Who is to be the pure scientist, who the technician, and who the appraiser of ends?

Until quite recently in the history of civilization the ends of society and, consequently, the less inclusive ends of individuals, were prescribed by religious "fathers." This meant that anything going under the name of government was controlled finally by the "fathers." Probably Aristotle was one of the first to conceive of politics and the study of government as a science. And no doubt the Stoics developed a theory of law and of government by a careful consideration of facts and a careful use of logic. But, for the most part, all political leaders, kings, monarchs, and dynasties, justified their political status on religious grounds. Modern science emerged within the Hebraic-Christian matrix, and, consequently, it is not difficult to understand why religious leaders thought (and still think) that their main function was to prescribe goals for the people and to preserve religious values.

There is no denying the fact that religious values have had considerable effect on the way in which science has been applied. The technology of the Western world has been conditioned by religious institutions. For the most part financiers have been members of religious institutions and have justified their practices before the bar of religion, but it was not a simple one-way affair. Yet it is clear that religious institutions continue to lose prestige as trustworthy appraisers of values for these reasons. First, the basic values according to theologians were purportedly achievable only in a world to come. Second, judgments concerning values achievable on earth were made without consideration of the scientific means of achieving them. This implies that in many cases members of religious institutions prescribed a nonscientific method (a mystical, "supernatural" method) of achieving ends. Third, many theologians looked upon pure research and the scientific method of solving problems as if they were identical with a materialistic metaphysics and as if, consequently, scientists were trying to deny the reality of many values (such as those found in moral, ethical behavior and in human social relationships) highly cherished by theologians and institutionalized by religion. Fourth, many spokesmen for religious institutions failed to recognize the relativity of values and for that reason became dogmatic and did not consider ends in relation to means. This led to a distortion of the relationship between behavior and its consequences, and often led to an overemphasis of the value of the form of an act, irrespective of its consequences for that particular place and time. According to this early theological view, all value judgments concerning both means and ends (or behavior and consequences) could presumably be made prior to a problematic situation which, in older terminology, is merely a temptation. The prescription for the "temptation" is given in advance. Fifth, quite often theologians have spoken as if "materialistic success" is a hindrance to the spiritual welfare of a people.

Poverty seems to have been a great market for religion. Men should be fed, but not well fed. Those in dire economic circumstances fall an easy prey to religious institutions. The practice of religious institutions in these matters tends to drive a wedge between economic values and religious values, or between the "material" and the "spiritual." Finally, many theologians failed to recognize either the functions or the limitations of theology. These theologians confused the kind of "truth" they claimed to know (which may be simply an ethical system and a set of values they are willing to advocate) with the truth of factual statements. We find that scientists are able to test many factual statements accepted as true and basic by theologians but found to be false by scientists—questions concerning the geocentric universe, the age of the earth, the theory of evolution, and the distinction and relationship between "races." For these reasons there was and is conflict between science and religion, at certain points at least.

Science has not failed. But many laymen believe that science has failed, and quite recently we find that many physical scientists have a deep sense of failure. The layman's attitude is the result of confusion over the nature and function of science. As a rule the "scientifically minded" layman substitutes science for religion and therefore expects science to discover a new set of values for mankind. One who substitutes science for religion looks on science as having, first, an iconoclastic function, which is, of course, negative. Science has had that function only in relation to factual statements and not in relation to what men find valuable and satisfactory. Second, the layman often thinks of science as having the positive function of discovering intrinsic values, whereas in fact science has no such function.

As I have explained previously, the scientist acting in the capacity of a scientist is not concerned with judgments about intrinsic values. The knowledge scientists can offer us about bacteria can be used either to get rid of disease or to spread it. It is not up to the scientist to tell us that bacteria should or should not be used as a war-weapon. Given an end, the scientist can help us, but he cannot give us an end. The layman's belief that science has failed is due to his misconception of the function of science and to his uncritical acceptance of the statement that truth will make us free, coupled with the belief that science gives us truth with a capital T, and that such truth embraces all values. But to argue that science is all-inclusive will lead finally to the conclusion that intrinsic values are unreal, since in fact science cannot deal with them directly.

The deep sense of failure that has developed quite recently within the community of physical scientists is due to both a confusion and a disappointment. As is evidenced by voluminous written material by atomic scientists, especially, these men are greatly disappointed over the stubborn fact that an enormous amount of scientific thinking and pure research has been used for the destruction of values that have been accepted modestly by practically all scientists. The Greco-Hebraic-

Christian traditions of decency and a sense of humanity have been accepted by all scientists, and their work has been conditioned by ethical standards. Every scientist recognizes that a community of scientists is necessary to scientific progress and that such a community must be an integral part of a more-inclusive social community with its ethical standards. Scientists have been greatly disappointed to find that they, as scientists, took part and are taking part in a program which, under quite conceivable conditions, would lead not only to the dissolution of their own community but also to the destruction of that wider community in which we find our most cherished values. The physical scientists seemed to have awakened en masse from their dogmatic slumbers, for until recently they had taken for granted that science as science was saving and would save the world from all the catastrophes such as in the past had been lurking in every corner. They were greatly disappointed to find that something had gone wrong. Actually what they discovered was that pure research without its proper application and direction is hopeless and lost. They discovered that a choice of proper ends for which science is to be applied is essential to the welfare of both the scientific community and the community at large. They discovered, also, that scientists in their laboratories cannot discover ends.

Physical scientists have never rebelled against the basic ethical principles of a culture, which prescribe in broad outline how men should treat their fellow-men. Furthermore the atomic scientists did not put in question the beliefs that peace is better than war, that knowledge is better than ignorance, that socially minded and socially integrated behavior is more satisfactory than self-centered behavior, and that, if possible, we should feed our fellow-men. In short, these scientists did not question values that had been given to us through religious, ethical channels. Rather these scientists, implicitly or explicitly, accepted these basic values as support for their thesis that something must be done about science in relation to society and, more particularly, in relation to highly culturalized values. It was indeed a great disappointment to the scientists to find that sheer knowledge does not of itself lead us automatically to more satisfactory conditions. They had never suspected that the accumulation of basic knowledge would bring new and vastly greater social problems nor, least of all, that scientific information would call for a transvaluation of values.

The confusion of the physical scientists was exhibited in the reaction of the members of the Federation of Atomic Scientists immediately following World War II. Members of this Federation assumed the task of informing political leaders of the social and political implications not only of atomic energy but also of basic knowledge in general. Here for the first time in history we find pure scientists and so-called "disinterested" men concerned over intrinsic values. In this case it meant that they were concerned with the problem of the application of basic knowledge toward particular ends.

In 1945 scientists began making value judgments of all kinds. They were concerned not only with value judgments concerning means-end relationships, but they were concerned also with ethical value judgments. They were concerned with such questions as these: (1) Granted that victory is the end, and granted that technologically speaking the atomic bomb is the better means of effecting that end, are we morally and ethically justified in using this weapon? (After all there are international laws based on human ethical principles which prescribe the limitations of technology during time of war!) When one asks the question: Does the end justify the means? he does so from a moral, ethical view. (2) Should the application of knowledge about nuclear energy be left to a particular organization, such as the military, in our society? This is about the same as asking whether a particular group of persons should have a monopoly on setting up ends, on choosing intrinsic values, for which pure science is to be used. (3) Should war as an end (or any other intrinsic values) determine or, to say the least, condition the direction and the subject matter of research science? In general, is "pure research" conditioned by cultural, social values cherished independent of pure research? (4) Is it possible, short of the destruction of pure research, to censor scientific ideas and to limit the free exchange of information among scientists? (5) Are individual interests and individual initiatives essential to the discovery of new knowledge; can pure science be regimented? (6) Is science, at its best, applicable unless we have the co-operation of all members of a civilian community and, in some cases, the co-operation of the entire civilized world? (7) Is it possible and, if so, is it desirable to control the relationship between pure science and social values? In general, is it possible and, if so, is it desirable to plan the integration of science, national and world economy, personal values, and social values?

If it is possible to plan the integration of science with other phases of civilized life (i.e., if there is no "law of nature" that prohibits such planning), and if it is desirable to make such plans, who in our society should do the planning? The last question entails the most important problem facing us today. I believe it is both possible and desirable, if not imperative, to plan and control the relationship between science and values. The question is: How is it to be done in a democratic society?

The confusion on the part of physical scientists is a consequence of false notions held implicitly or explicitly. They had assumed that pure science is a compartment complete in itself, that it is self-regulating, and that the motivation for pure scientists is pure knowledge. They had assumed, further, that good scientists should be left alone, which implies that they should not be restricted in their research and that they should not be concerned with social values. Naturally, scientists were confused to find that before science with its pure research can proceed, it must reconcile itself with other phases of civilized life—economic, political, and moral-ethical or religious institutions. How is this reconciliation to take place?

A Program for Society

I assume that only democracy can furnish the political matrix necessary for an effective correlation of pure science and social values. Ultimately, a satisfactory correlation of science and other institutions is to be effected through politics, and the life of politics is to be furnished by the people. Not all values are fixed, although certain values, such as the economic necessities of life, are permanent. *That* men survive is a necessary prerequisite to all other values. *How* they survive is the crucial question. New values emerge and many things once valuable now have no value. It is impossible to reconstruct all values at once, or to substitute an entirely new set of values for old ones. Old ends, goals, or values must become obsolete one or a few at a time, and new values must be introduced gradually. The reason for this is that setting up new ends or values can be done systematically and intelligently only if these ends are considered from the standpoint of more basic primitive values. (The extent to which values are basic or primitive may be identical with their universality.) For example, in making value judgments about whether the government should institute conservation programs such as TVA, we would ask such questions as these: Will it interfere with democracy? Will it interfere with our economic system? Will it interfere with civil liberties? Will it interfere with religious liberties? This does not mean that none of the values in our economic system or in other institutions will be sacrificed, but if they are sacrificed it will be because men believe more basic values will be achieved in so doing. In this case the principles of democracy would not be put in question.

If a group were to maintain that there are unchanging basic values common to all people and, perhaps, given to us "by nature," such as "life," "liberty," and the "pursuit of happiness," then a people may set up a means of protecting and guaranteeing the continuation of these values. The unchanging values would then be considered intrinsic values by a people, and an instrument, such as democracy, set up for the purpose of protecting and perpetuating intrinsic values would have extrinsic value only. When, however, a people make explicit to themselves both the intrinsic values and the extrinsic values (ends and means) of their culture, they have taken the first step toward institutionalizing these values. In America, probably the first explicit account made of intrinsic values was the Declaration of Independence, and the next is to be found in the preamble to the Constitution of the United States. Men did not claim to have discovered new values when they conceived and wrote these documents. They were claiming, rather, that these values, presumably given by nature to all peoples, had been made either impossible of achievement or insecure by abuses superimposed by the government of England. What was new in America was the Constitution, which, of course, prescribes the means of protecting and securing basic values. The old cultural, moral, and ethical values were taken over from the Greco-Hebraic-Christian tradition.

To look upon a constitution as fixed and final is to think of means as static and institutionalized. This is to mistake means for ends.

Fortunately, the Constitution of the United States makes provision for its revision and for amendments to it. Through the Constitution, Americans have institutionalized change. In practice this means that things having extrinsic values may be replaced by other means in a systematic manner. But the more basic principles of a constitution for democracy, i.e., the contention that ultimate authority rests in the people, could not be changed short of revolution. Marx to the contrary, wars may be fought over basic values, such as values expressed in religion. If one, like Marx, maintains that all of history, including wars, can be adequately explained from an economic standpoint, then one is assuming that basic or intrinsic values never change. Under those conditions, only the means to ends could change.

I believe there are values that cannot be expressed in economic terms and that many of them are considered basic, intrinsic values. Then there are basic means or basic extrinsic values such as freedom of speech and of the press, and the right to trial by jury. Institutionalized values in a democracy, whether extrinsic or intrinsic, may not be changed without the consent of the people. But there are many different kinds of practices in technology, in economics, and in religion, that are equally compatible with explicitly stated institutionalized values, and for that reason there is freedom of choice between them. This means that in the application of science, in general, in the method of protecting, securing, and achieving values there is room for individual expression, moral judgment, choice, and the use of intelligence. Since the method for achieving values under particular circumstances is not prescribed in the Constitution, there is always the necessity of stipulating the means for particular cases and for particular kinds of cases. Furthermore, the Constitution does not prescribe particular intrinsic values nor prohibit them if they are consistent with the Constitution. Our question is: Who should prescribe these means and these lesser ends demanded by particular circumstances?

Certainly the pure scientists should be included in the commission whose function will be to decide on ends having wide social implications, and to set up the governmental agencies necessary for carrying out those ends. The technician or the technologist must work in conjunction with the pure scientist. Together their function will be to inform the other members of the commission of the achievability of various ends under consideration. For example, if one is considering an irrigation project for a certain region, the scientist and the technologist can judge whether such a project is feasible. Such judgments would be based on geological and meteorological facts. Or if the commission is considering the nature of the subject matter for pure research to be subsidized by government funds, the judgment of the pure scientist in conjunction with judgments concerning the desires and needs of civilian society will be indispensable.

In addition to pure scientists and technicians, it is imperative that we have moral philosophers, humanitarians, and politicians, particularly, who must be statesmen also. A moral philosopher at his best may be a culturalist, for his function is to examine ends and the behavior necessary for achieving them from the standpoint of their consistency with basic cultural values. He must look at values from the point of view of both their mediate and immediate import for society. The moral philosopher is not one who discovers or invents values, nor is he one to whom values are revealed. Instead, he looks at society somewhat as if it were an organism with a relatively long life which exists for the individual parts as well as for its own sake, and in which the individual parts exist for the whole as well as for themselves. In this way he will be able to consider both the mediate and the immediate consequences of accepting certain ends and the means of attaining them. A moral philosopher must pass value judgments with reference to values found in human social and personal relationships. He must have a theory of the nature of culture and a theory of the general conditions necessary for securing and maintaining values. If, as I have maintained, a civilization is founded ultimately on ethical, moral principles, then someone acting in the capacity of a moral philosopher is indispensable to national conservation programs or to any kind of national planning. We may judge that the politician is capable of passing moral judgment on the consequences of legislation, but this is expecting too much, and there is no reason for not making use of expert advisers in this field.

The humanitarian may be a sociologist or a social scientist. His function will be to gather and interpret data concerning the customs of society. These customs would pertain to family life, recreation, religion, economics, education, and all such customs and practices as may be relevant to the formation of national policies pertaining to these areas and for the general welfare. The interpretation of these data will be made with the purpose of discovering the desires of the people. By all means these desires should be taken into consideration in the formulation of social policy entailing a program for society, or in any kind of social legislation. What we ought to have is always conditioned by what we want, and unless people want something they ought not to have it. This does not mean that what we want we ought to have.

Finally, we must have political statesmen, whose function will be to make the final choice of ends and the means of effecting them. This will be done, it is assumed, under advisement of all the other members of the commission. After ends have been set up and after means have been prescribed, then the responsibility for carrying out programs must be left to the President or to the members of Congress, all of whom must answer to the judgment of the people.

Those who would dismiss moral philosophers and humanitarians from the commission, whose function is to formulate policy, would probably argue that in a modern scientific world there is no need, and therefore no place, for irrationalism in our society. They might argue that one can live by reason and that a rational defense for behavior is identical with stating the intellectual or scientific basis for our behavior. They might argue, further, that we should get rid of all irrational elements in our culture and that behavior based on feelings, emotions, *Zeitgeist,* or *Urkulturdrang* are not only uncomplementary to reason and science but are also contradictory to them. A. E. Murphy, in his highly commendable book *The Uses of Reason,* maintains that it is possible to establish ideologies on a rational basis with a sound metaphysics. Murphy points out that many intelligent persons believe they have discovered the *real* motivation for behavior. These persons believe that through the scientific approach we have learned that people act for selfish reasons and, for the most part, for "materialistic" gain. In short, many historians and sociologists think they have discovered that all ideologies are simply rationalizations or false justifications for what men want to do, and that all moral and ethical justifications for behavior are nonsensical. These critics believe science has enlightened us and will wean us from the stupidity of positing ethics and morality as the basis of civilization. They say we are not moral agents, but opportunists and conventionalists. The hardheaded factualist would have us skip sentimentalism and all forms of "ethics" and would substitute the clever, practical psychologist for the moral philosopher. This, I believe, cannot be done.

The most commendable thing about Murphy's book is that, although he argues against mythologies and all sorts of sentimentalism as an adequate basis for behavior in modern society, he does not equate irrationalism and mythology with moral philosophy. It is not *either* morality and sentimentalism *or* a rational basis for behavior. He believes that we must have a rational basis for our ideologies and that such a rational basis will be a moral philosophy. Murphy is correct.

To assume that science, economics, and politics must have a moral basis is not to assume that our moral-ethical values are absolute. If they were absolute, then indeed we would not need a moral philosopher. The function of a moral philosopher is to evaluate ends, not only with reference to the history and the wishes of a people, but also with reference to modern social problems in the light of scientific information. A sound moral philosophy will leave room for moral judgment, and effective moral judgment must be based on scientific information gathered especially from the physical sciences, biology, and psychology. A moral philosophy based on (but not identical with) scientific information amounts to an interpretation of the import of the physical sciences, biology, and psychology for human behavior in a technological world.

Any moral philosophy presupposes a theory of man, but a moral philosophy constructed by the use of reason will have a naturalistic theory of man. Such a theory will depict man as an intellectual, social, biological organism rooted in an environment whose import for us is given in the physical sciences. As science develops and as our scientific understanding of the intellect and the biological organism increases, there will be need for reconstructing our theory of man and, of course, there will be need for reconstructing our goals. This will amount to re-evaluating chief ends, which can be done best by a culturalist or what I have called a "moral philosopher."

A value judgment concerning ends must have at its base, first, a theory of man, and, second, knowledge of whether desired ends are attainable. Science alone and, for the most part, the physical sciences, can tell us whether ends are attainable. Science and science alone can give us an adequate theory of man and prevent us in our value judgments from entertaining supernatural, unattainable ends. Because moral philosophers of the past (as Dewey points out) have been in the habit of substituting the *contemplation* of unattainable goals for behavior leading to attainable ones, this does not mean that a moralist must be a supernaturalist nor, least of all, does it mean that civilization would be better off without the moralist. Morality of some kind is necessarily the basis of any kind of technology.

It is likely that the greatest difficulty for the commission, which must formulate national policy of any kind, will be our failure to insist that experts in the social sciences and in moral philosophy be included. This difficulty will be the result of our inability to see that the physical sciences are not concerned with intrinsic values. Rather we will assume, wittingly or unwittingly, that science discovers *real* values and, therefore, the "natural" scientist should replace the moralist. I have continued to stress the fact that physical scientists are not concerned with intrinsic values and the "ought." They are not concerned with the direction science gives our culture except in so far as it endangers science itself. Only in judgments concerning intrinsic values can we determine the direction of our social behavior, and only when one considers directions from the standpoint of not simply what *is* or *was,* but of what *ought to be,* can we select particular ends. But an intellectual consideration of what ought to be requires a moral philosopher with scientific information. Through this procedure the Hebraic-Christian part of our tradition can be reconciled with the Greek component; values and ethical decisions can be supplemented by reason and science.

CHAPTER IX

Pure Science and the Place of the Individual in the Scientific Method

Introduction

THE AIM OF PURE RESEARCH is to achieve basic knowledge, which is identical with neutral knowledge. The precision with which neutral knowledge is stated is proportional to its communicability without increase or loss of meaning. And since pure-science statements must be applicable but neutral with respect to ends, and communicable to different persons under widely different immediate circumstances, they must have a social dimension.

Sociality and universality are very closely related. Pure-science statements are universally applicable to the extent that they are communicable and to the extent that they may be applied indifferently to alternative ends. The formulation of pure-science statements is conditioned by the fact that these statements must be applicable to ends and also by the fact that they must not be limited to specified ends. Bernoulli's principle, "Where the velocity of a fluid is high, the pressure is low, and where the velocity is low, the pressure is high," may be used in throwing a "curved" ball, constructing the wings of a plane, or in atomizers. The law of inertia is used by all of us in different ways practically every day.

For a law or a principle to be applied, two things are required: first, a problem (which involves a desired end), and, second, factors in the problematic situation that may be assigned as referents of that law or principle. One may have the problem of getting cargo across a lake. This problem involves a desired end, and "cargo" and "lake" may be assigned as referents to the basic terms related in Archimedes' principle. Pure-science statements, then, must be interpretable; they must be testable and, therefore, they must be such that particular referents can be assigned to the terms related in such statements. Now if, in addition to interpreting a general principle, one has a desired end, then the principle may be applied to achieve that end. A factual generalization has a human social component in so far as it will lend itself to different interpretations under different circumstances and in so far as it may be applied therefore to ends, irrespective of place and time. To that extent, also, it is universal.

Statements about the results of pure research do not give us a knowledge of the structure of nature independent of human interpretation and human behavior. If we maintain that the experimental method is necessary for formulating and testing factual statements, we are at once denying that there can be knowledge for its own sake or that knowledge gives us the structure of nature independent of human experience and human behavior. The introduction of the experimental method is in part a return to the philosophy of Protagoras, who said "man is the measure of all things." But the experimental method emphasizes also that knowing is for the sake of practice.

The Sociology of Knowledge

The theory of the sociology of knowledge, as developed by P. A. Sorokin and Émile Durkheim, is based on the assumption that society (or a human social group with its mores, religious beliefs, customs, and rituals, all of which are irrational and do not constitute intelligent conduct based on scientific knowledge) conditions all knowledge and all statements of "fact" which appear to members of the group to be perfectly unbiased and objective in the sense that these statements are thought to be true of a world unrelated to the group. A corollary to this assumption is that society, being temporally prior to language and thought, is also logically prior, because the expression of "ideas" by individuals is at heart an expression of what is deeply felt, though not explicitly known, by the group. According to the argument, these deeply rooted attitudes, though not at first explicit, are made explicit in categories necessary for meanings and for the communication of meanings through language. These categories constitute the basic concepts or the basic ideas by which men communicate and in terms of which the "objective" world is known. But of course, if Durkheim's theory is correct, the objective world, i.e., the world as it exists independent of man, can never be known in its native form. It is known, if at all, through primitive social categories which are of necessity biased by irrational attitudes that were established possibly by accident, for certainly these categories are not the same in every primitive group.

The following examples might explain what is meant by basic categories: The aborigines of Australia think the cosmos is circular because (so goes the argument) the Australians "sit around the fire." Or again, since the behavior of a Navaho Indian is so closely woven into the family life and the behavior of the group as a whole, the Navaho has no conception of an individual soul, as it is understood in Christian circles. Or, to speak of more abstract and, therefore, more universal categories, Euclidean geometry developed out of the land-surveying practices of the Egyptians; had geometry been developed by navigators, say, it would have been non-Euclidean. Similarly, the Babylonians may have been conditioned by social factors in their choice of twelve as the base of their measuring system.

Back of the assumption that all categories (including, finally, scientific categories, systems of weights and measurement) are conditioned by preintellectual social phenomena is the belief that knowledge is not only social in the sense explained but that it is also conventional in that the various isolated groups of people will develop different intellectual and ideological concepts. That knowledge has preintellectual roots and that its basic categories are conventional is used as a defense not only for the thesis that there is a sociological basis for all conventions but also for the more sophisticated theory held by H. Poincaré that all scientific categories are conventions. This belief is further used by some as a defense for the relativity of knowledge as well as for a justification of the relativity of moral practices—the mores.

Durkheim writes:[1]

Every time that we are in the presence of a *type* of thought or action which is imposed uniformly upon particular wills or intelligences, this pressure exercised over the individual betrays the intervention of the group.

Durkheim believes that categories vary with different societies and that the individual becomes cognizant of them only after they have been felt by society. To say that the categories are made explicit by the individual only after they are implicit in that individual's society is to say that "individual experience," as the term is used in modern science, is not the basis nor even a part of the basis for the formulations which give common meanings and make it possible to communicate by use of language. Those who emphasize the sociological dimension of science usually conceive of the individual as secondary and subservient to the group and think of the individual as being inessential in the development of new ideas. Durkheim believes that categories, mental tools, the devices used to conceive of and find order in the world about us, come from the group first and become explicit to the individual later. In this view the individual, although he may be the medium through which the subintellectual attitudes of the group are expressed, cannot use his own individual experience as a basis for formulating these attitudes.

If we press the issue a step further and ask: How do the basic categories first come to the group? there is no clear answer. Some answer this question vaguely, however, by saying that the "rudimentary experiences" of the group serve as a basis for the origin of the categories which, being based on such group experience, are not necessary but contingent. Hence they are also conventional and lack the universality required of objectivity, which is sought by those who employ the scientific method. Durkheim believes the attitudes of the individual are determined by the group. This is quite opposed to the view that the individual is complete in himself and that social organizations were

[1] See Durkheim, *The Elementary Forms of Religious Life,* trans. by Joseph W. Swain (London, George Allen and Unwin, Ltd., 1947), p. 434.

established by a covenant between pre-existing individuals. Yet it seems to me the view that categories are secondary with reference to the individual is quite untenable in the light of the evidence drawn from history and from actual practices in the scientific method.

If one studies "primitive" societies and on the basis of that study alone draws conclusions about the nature of the individual and society with its mores and taboos, it would be easy to conclude that in those societies there are no "individuals" in the sense in which we, as democrats or experimental scientists, use the term. As Dewey has so capably shown—and Dewey emphasizes the fact that there are individuals at least when scientific attitudes are employed—in primitive societies it is practically impossible for a person to stand opposed to the mores and taboos of the group. At the same time the mores and taboos are slow to change, and it is quite likely that despite the fact that they *do* change, the people are quite unaware of it. Furthermore, it is reasonable to assume that if primitives were aware of a change in their behavior, they would not think of it as involving a change in mores or in the true standards of right and wrong. Rather, like many a modern, they might conceive of changes in practice as deviations from the "true" unchanging, eternal standards laid down by the gods. But it is presumptuous for one to conclude that the mechanism by which *new ideas*—new in that they propose behavior contrary to habits, institutional practices, mores and taboos—is not located in the nervous system of the individual. A knowledge of how the modern world was ushered in and of what takes place in modern experimental science, makes it absurd to say that the ideas of famous (to some, infamous) individuals, such as Luther, Calvin, Copernicus, Galileo, Newton, Einstein, to mention only a few, have not changed the practices of society. These men had new ideas in the sense that their ideas were *contrary* to old practices. These men were considered radical because they put in question certain root or basic beliefs and categories. In modern industrialized societies there is no doubt that the locus of the cause of false beliefs, mistaken notions, and invalid hypotheses is the nervous system of the individual. Even Durkheim would not go so far as to maintain that false beliefs amount to an explicit clarification of the group attitudes. Such a view would be absurd, since it would imply that there is no method by which we can test beliefs inasmuch as all of them would be on a par—all would be expressions of group attitudes and "products" of social opinion. Under the influence of modern political theory as well as modern scientific procedures we have come to recognize not only that the individual is the source of error, mistaken notions, and invalid hypotheses but that he is also the source of new, valid hypotheses.

Before we can justify the thesis that experiences peculiar (at first) to the individual constitute the basis for the formulation of new categories, which in turn serve as a basis for the reconstruction of social practices, there must be a method of testing hypotheses to find out whether they are valid or invalid. This is precisely what the experimental phase of the scientific method offers us. If all ideas were "products" of group action and environmental conditions and came from "putting two and two together," it would indeed be difficult if not impossible to test the validity of ideas.

Scientists claim that in testing a hypothesis they are not trying to ascertain whether it is deducible from or consistent with socially accepted attitudes and practices. Rather they are finding out whether what is believed about the world will stand the test of experience— whether or not one can with satisfaction accept an idea as a basis for action. In this manner the scientist is able to bring to test not only *peculiar, radical* hypotheses held by a given individual, but also ideas of long-standing, ideas that have become institutionalized and have been accepted as a basis for action possibly for generations. Science offers a new method for testing the validity of hypotheses. As opposed to the test that is often set up by those who believe certain statements are axiomatic, a priori, and eternally true, and that these statements are to be used as standards to test the truth of new ideas, science has a method of testing "eternal verities" so called, in the same manner as it tests ideas held by an individual.

Science tries to get behind the provincial and behind the conventional because they are limited to a particular group or a particular time, and it purports to offer statements that are true for everyone at all times. This does not mean there are no conventions in science, nor does it mean that science can do without conventions. But it means that scientists are seeking universally applicable principles, which are conventions only in the sense that all knowledge is human knowledge.

The kind of conventions scientists seek to formulate, then, are conventions that may be applied universally.

Convention and the a priori

A convention is a statement accepted arbitrarily as true, and therefore its truth is not necessary; consequently, it is possible to substitute one convention for another. Given two conventions, c_1 and c_2, c_1 may be more satisfactory or more adequate for the purposes at hand, or more conveniently applicable than c_2. And for these reasons experience and the world about us often condition the choice of conventions. The definition of "gram" is conditioned by the density of water; the definition of "poundal" is conditioned by the attraction of the earth for objects; and the length of a foot is conditioned by the fact that it is easy for us to manipulate certain objects not over a foot long. But nevertheless there is no necessity in a "foot" having the length of this particular object rather than that one.

Although there may be a basis in experience for formulating every convention, experience by itself never fully determines any convention. For this reason a convention cannot be tested by experience to find out whether it is "true" or "false," for certainly "false" does not apply to conventions, and if they are said to be "true" it is because of human agreement. Nonconventional statements alone are true or false in the sense that they are testable, and that is because experience determines their truth value quite irrespective of our wishes and our choice. Conventions, then, constitute a priori knowledge, and statements found to be true because of experience constitute a posteriori knowledge. All conventions are a priori. No a posteriori knowledge is conventional.

There are different kinds of conventions, or different kinds of conventional knowledge. First, there are conventions regarding the application of signs to their factual referents. For example, the word "crow" applies to each and every animal in a certain class. Second, there are conventions regarding the interrelationship of signs. For example, "a foot is one-third of a yard." But "yard" also has a factual referent, and we are continually reminded of this by the yardstick in the Bureau of Standards at Washington, D.C. Third, there are what I will term "conventions of perspective": for example, the geocentric world-view, or the Galilean-Newtonian world-view, or the Hebraic-Christian world-view, or the Marxian economic interpretation of history, or the principles of democracy.

The problem of the conventions of perspective has given rise to considerable difficulty in science as well as in other fields, for as a rule they are mistaken for true factual statements. Some have argued that it is a fact that space is Euclidean; others say it is a fact that the earth goes round the sun. Some believe "evolution" is a fact; others believe Marxism is "a fact that has been proved by experiential evidence." No doubt some Russians believed that T. D. Lysenko's experiments in the field of genetics proved that Marxism is a fact. And F. S. C. Northrop argues that social normative theories may be tested by the facts of nature to find out whether they are true or false. He writes:[2]

> The verification of normative social theory is to be obtained not by checking its basic philosophical postulates, either directly or indirectly, against the facts of society either in the present or in the future but by checking them with the postulates of the philosophy of natural science prescribed by the facts of nature. When the relation between the postulates of the philosophy of culture and the postulates of the philosophy of nature is that of identity, the philosophy of culture is true. When the relation is not that of identity, the philosophy of culture is false or incomplete. . . .
>
> It is because normative social theories look to nature for their truth that they do not have to conform to the facts of *de facto* society. Were they to look to culture, the humanities and *de facto* society for their justification they could not measure the humanities or have a prescriptive power with respect to *de facto* society.

It is a mistake to think that the conventions of perspective can be experimentally verified, for after all they constitute the necessary matrix within which experiments become meaningful and significant, and they are necessary, therefore, for testing factual statements to find out whether *they* are true. For example, Foucault's experiment with the pendulum proves nothing about the rotation of the earth unless we assume Newton's first law of motion and its implication that the pendulum will continue to swing in a plane (with reference to absolute

[2] F. S. C. Northrop, *The Logic of the Sciences and the Humanities* (New York, The Macmillan Company, 1947), p. 338.

space). Yet many have mistaken conventions of perspective for proven factual statements, whereas in fact they will always be conventions.

Here we may dismiss a discussion of the first and second kinds of conventions mentioned; namely, conventions concerning the use of signs as applied to facts (the semantical dimension of semiosis), and conventions with regard to the use of signs with reference to other signs (the syntactical dimension of semiosis), since all will agree that these conventions are not testable by experience for their truth or falsity, and since, consequently, they are not mistaken for factual statements but are, rather, clearly recognizable as a priori. Rather, let us confine our discussion to problems involved in clarifying the distinction between conventions of perspective and factual statements testable by experience.

Conventions of perspective may be thought of as posited factual statements or as factual statements accepted for the time at least as a basis for testing other factual statements. Such statements may be considered factual presuppositions or primitive factual statements.

Conventions of perspective are applied in various fields, including religion, economics, politics, and science. One may assume that God has complete control over every happening and that whatever happens is in accordance with His plan and purpose. Granting that assumption, an explanation of floods, famine, or pain requires that we show how these happenings fit into God's plan. And the success with which we reconcile these events with His plan will be considered by many as evidence, if not proof, of the original assumption, which in fact must remain a convention of perspective. And if one assumes that the Marxian interpretation of past and present events is true, then he will set for himself the task of showing not only that all business transactions and all phenomena involving technology can be explained by use of the basic Marxian assumptions, but he will go further. He will defend the thesis that economic forces are primary in that all human behavior, in science, politics, religion, the fine arts, and other areas, can be accounted for only by resorting to the Marxian principles. In reality a thoroughgoing Marxist tries to show not only that his perspective is all-inclusive, but that, *therefore,* it is also true in an objective sense. It is, however, only a perspective, and it seems to me that when one tries to apply it to all phenomena, he can do so only by distorting the facts. Quite often such a distortion of the facts enables him to "save" a convention of perspective, but he can do so only by forcing the facts into preconceived molds which he erroneously assumes are the "true" and only molds for everything. Or, again, one may assume that the earth is at the center of the universe and immobile. In that case it is reasonable to conclude that all celestial bodies revolve about the earth. Or one may assume that the Newtonian perspective is true, and on that basis try to explain all physical phenomena. Or one may accept the theory of physical relativity.

It is always possible to save a convention even if experienced phenomena must be "distorted." I put "distorted" in quotes, because if one is unable to question a convention, then indeed he cannot interpret phenomena except through that convention and they will not appear to be distorted at all. For example, the invention of epicycles in order to explain the motion of planets did not appear to the inventor to be a distortion of the facts. Rather these epicycles seemed to make experienced phenomena intelligible. Only when these explanations grew too involved and after a less cumbersome perspective had been devised, people were able to say: "The old system distorted the facts." Neither "facts" nor "experience" can show us that a perspective is false. How could experienced phenomena show us that a perspective is false if we use this same perspective as a basis for interpreting these phenomena? But neither is the new perspective by which one says, "the old perspective distorted facts," true or false.

How, then, can scientists decide which perspective to accept? The answer is: on the basis of convenience, expediency, and adequacy. A perspective is analogous, then, to an axiom in geometry. It is neither true nor false in the sense in which a factual statement is, for experience cannot disprove it. Rather it is accepted because of its potency in explaining phenomena and because of its simplicity. Early modern scientists and many contemporary ones argue that the simplest explanation (most easily grasped perspective) is the "true" one, but this can mean only that the more convenient explanation is the one that will be used if men are wise.

Conventional Statements vs. Testable Factual Statements

Conventional perspectives do not determine the truth value of every factual statement. If they did, there would be nothing for experience to determine, and this would lead to the belief that statements predicting future events could be tested by the deductive procedure alone. We do not *decide* that the earth rotates on its axis or that an eclipse of the moon must take place, say, at eight o'clock (as if by definition it will be eight o'clock only if and when the moon is eclipsed). Nor do we decide that water is heavier than oil or that sulphur melts at 44° C. We must find the truth value of such statements by actually experiencing these phenomena and by allowing the evidence to support or destroy former beliefs. And since this is the case, we must conclude that both the truth of a testable factual statement (synthetic statement) and the truth of its contradictory are consistent with the convention of perspective with respect to which it is tested.

Suppose the following statement is submitted for testing: "Foucault's pendulum at the north geographic pole will sweep off all the sand on a platform in one day." And suppose, further, that we test this statement and find that it is false. Does this prove that Newton's first law of motion is false? Certainly not. Does this experiment by itself prove, then, that the earth does not rotate on its axis? Certainly not. Finally, does it prove that the plane of the pendulum changes as the earth rotates? Again, no. In fact, without a conventional perspective, i.e., without assuming something about the world, the results of this experiment could not be used as evidence to prove anything beyond themselves. But if we assume Newton's first law of motion, then we have evidence for the truth of the statement that the earth does not rotate on its axis. Or if we assume to begin with that the earth rotates on its axis, then we have evidence that Newton's first law of motion is false. Or if we assume that the plane of the pendulum rotates (which amounts to the assumption that Newton's first law of motion is false), then we have evidence for the statement that the earth rotates also. But in every case we see that if experience is to serve as evidence for the truth or falsity of a statement referring to something beyond the

PURE SCIENCE AND THE INDIVIDUAL

experience itself, we must first accept an assumption, or we must first adopt a convention of perspective.

To consider another example, let us turn attention to the "negative results" of the Michelson-Morley experiment. At first, neither Michelson nor Morley believed that these negative results disproved the theory of absolute space. Nor did they question the existence of the ether. And if we ask: "For one who is unbiased, what are the 'true' implications of these negative results?" we will find the answer to be: "They have *no* implications for anything beyond themselves." If, however, one is "biased," these results may have definite implications regarding the ether as well as absolute space. For example, if one insists on maintaining the Newtonian perspective with its entailed theory of absolute space and time, then these results may have implications regarding the ether, or the motion of the earth, or the effect of motion on the length of moving bodies. But here, again, before one can come to a conclusion about the ether, he must assume something about the motion of the earth and the effect of motion on bodies. But suppose we assume the Newtonian perspective and that the earth is moving and that motion has no effect on the length of bodies. Then it is reasonable to reject the ether-drift theory, and to say that our evidence for this rejection is found in the negative results of the Michelson-Morley experiment. Or suppose we accept the Newtonian perspective and the theory that the ether is fixed and occupies absolute space and believe also that motion has no effect on the length of bodies. Then it would be reasonable to conclude that the earth does not move. There is a third alternative: We can accept the Newtonian perspective, and the motion of the earth, and the static ether theory, in which case the Fitzgerald contraction theory follows.

In each of the cases cited above, further evidence for the final conclusion drawn—whether this conclusion is the Fitzgerald contraction theory, the ether-drift theory, or the theory that the earth does not move—presupposes the acceptance of a convention of perspective, and no "evidence" (or datum) can be used for anything beyond itself apart from such a convention. An entirely new perspective, such as the physical theory of relativity, may be substituted for the Newtonian perspective, and by use of such a perspective the "evidence" (the experiences we have) may be accounted for more satisfactorily. But never can this evidence prove that the perspective is true. It must remain a convention, and its rejection or acceptance must be based on something other than direct experimental evidence—possibly expediency, adequacy, simplicity.

I should emphasize that some sort of general factual statement must be accepted before we can test any other factual statement and that, therefore, both the statement being tested and its contradictory must be consistent with the presupposed factual statement. For example, when we test the statement: "Water is heavier than oil," we must assume either that the principle of the lever or that Hooke's law is true. And either of these assumptions is consistent with either the truth or the falsity of the statement: "Water is heavier than oil."

Or if we test the statement: "The period of revolution of the earth around the sun is 360 days," we assume that the earth revolves; but its period of revolution is consistent with this general assumption, whether it is 360 or 365 days. Or if we consider whether the attraction of bodies varies according to the inverse square law or in some other way, this would not be contradictory to the assumption of gravitational attraction. Or, again, if we test the statement: "All crows are black," both the truth of this statement and the truth of its contradictory must be consistent with our general assumption as to what a thing must be in order to be a crow; i.e., with our definition of "crow."

Meanings and Conventions of Perspective

Ever since the introduction of laboratories and the explicit emphasis on the place of sense data in scientific method, men have felt that there is a close relationship between experience and the meaning of factual statements. The pragmatists have emphasized this point, and, more recently, the logical empiricists have tried to show that there is a necessary relationship between experience and meaning. Some have gone so far as to say that the meaning of a factual statement is identical with the means of verifying it.[3] We will not discuss this particular problem

[3] See C. S. Peirce, *Collected Papers,* V (Cambridge, Harvard University Press, 1934), 258; Rudolph Carnap, "Testability and Meaning," *Philosophy of Science,* Vol. III (1936), Vol. IV (1937); Albert E. Blumberg and Herbert Feigl, *Journal of Philosophy,* Vol. XXVIII, No. 11.

at this point but will work out some of the implications of the main thesis emphasized in the preceding sections. This thesis is: In order for experience to serve as evidence for anything beyond itself, one must first accept a convention of perspective with reference to which that experience can serve as a test for the truth value of a definite factual statement. That factual statement must be capable of being either true or false within that perspective. This requires that one know what must be the case if the statement is true and what must be the case if it is false. But in order for evidence to serve as a basis for the truth (or falsity) of a statement, one must first accept a convention of perspective, which is not by itself sufficient for doing so. Experience also is necessary.

Given the same sense data, then, in one perspective, P_1, they may serve as evidence for the truth of a certain factual statement, F_1, whereas in another perspective, P_2, they may serve either as evidence for the falsity of F_1, or as evidence for the truth of a factual statement, F_2. For example, if we accept the Newtonian perspective and also assume that there is a stagnant ether, then the negative results of the Michelson-Morley experiment will be evidence for the Fitzgerald contraction theory. But if we are willing to put the Newtonian perspective in question and to deny the Fitzgerald contraction theory, then these negative results are evidence for the theory of physical relativity. Again, if we assume Newton's first law of motion, then Foucault's pendulum gives evidence that the earth rotates, whereas if we accept the geocentric world-view, the pendulum experiment gives evidence that the plane of the pendulum rotates. Finally, if we assume that the economic law of supply and demand is valid, then the fact that our granaries are full would be evidence that people are well-fed and that the demand for these products has been supplied. However, if we agree that people are hungry, then the full granaries are evidence that the people have no purchasing power, and the law of supply and demand may be put in question.

"Data" are insignificant apart from a perspective. All of us will agree that data are used as evidence, that as evidence they refer to something beyond themselves, and that as evidence they lend support to the truth (or falsity) of a statement. We will agree also that a factual statement is testable and meaningful only if it is possible (in principle at least) to have experiential evidence for or against it. It follows, therefore, that testable factual statements are meaningful only within a convention of perspective.

There is a distinction between testable factual statements and factual statements amounting to conventions of perspective. This does not mean, however, that there is an absolute distinction between a factual statement's being tested and the conventional statement with reference to which it is testable. In fact, since our conventional factual statements are chosen somewhat arbitrarily, it is clear that a certain statement, F_1, may be accepted as the basis for testing some other factual statement, F_2. In that case F_1 is the conventional statement. On the other hand, F_1 may be put in question by assuming F_3 or even F_2. For example, we may assume that the earth rotates on its axis and then test, through Foucault's pendulum, whether a highly suspended pendulum will rotate with it (which amounts to acquiring evidence for Newton's first law). Or we may assume Newton's first law and then use the pendulum to test the statement: "The earth rotates on its axis." Or we may put in question the theory of absolute space and time; but evidence for or against that theory can be had only if, temporarily to say the least, we are willing to entertain an alternate convention of perspective.

Objectivity and Conventions of Perspective

Since the perspective we select does not force itself upon us by virtue of external conditions but is chosen somewhat arbitrarily, it is sensible to ask: Are the conventions of perspective and, consequently, the truth of factual statements subjective? This question might well be put in a different way in order to emphasize the necessary relationship between the truth of statements and the human social matrix within which pure research is carried on and within which science is applied toward the achievement of practical ends. Consequently, whether these human conventions are limited to a particular group over a limited time, or universalized and thereby extended to the scientific community, we may ask: Is the truth value of a factual statement determined by human conventions?

Now if the truth of a statement is "made by the human mind" through the choice of conventions, then it may be sensible to conclude that truth is subjective, at least relative to the group, in the sense that what is "true" about the external world has been superimposed arbitrarily by human minds. In that case truth would be a priori with reference to the group, and since, according to our thesis, the a priori is relative to choice, truth might be thought of as purely subjective. This would amount to saying that in so far as factual statements are said to represent the external state of affairs, the mind legislates over the facts and dictates what must be the case. Such a conclusion is absurd.

Human minds cannot dictate the truth value of factual statements. We do not settle matters of fact by definitions or by choice. Nevertheless, as Kant so ably pointed out, men specify the formal conditions under which any question put to nature is intelligible. That is, men must formulate questions within a human social matrix and in such a way that what the environment offers to these questions (through experience) may be used as evidence for answering yes or no to them. In that sense the mind prescribes a part of the necessary conditions for the truth or falsity of a statement. The mind prescribes the categories (the forms or the ideological concepts or, simply, the concepts) with reference to which the questions must be answered. If we ask: Is this object longer than that? we must know what we mean by the relation "longer than" before we can find an answer in experience to our question. Or if we are asking for the *specific length* of an object, we must first establish a relatively universal (i.e., widely accepted) system of measurement. But the "true" length—the length given in terms of centimeters or inches—presupposes units of measurement and a mathematical system, both of which are established arbitrarily. Yet once established, the length of measurable objects can be known. "Measurable object" means any object which will submit to measuring devices, measuring conventions.

Knowledge, in a scientific sense, about anything in the factual world must be communicable. Statements capable of being true (or false) must be expressible in terms having the same meaning to each member of the group. Since meanings of words are established arbitrarily, it follows that scientific knowledge depends in part upon arbitrarily, socially established conventions.

If a statement is known to be true in a scientific sense, then its referent is objective. The conventional dimension of factual knowledge does not detract from its objectivity. If, for example, the length of the table is found to be forty-two inches, it is actually forty-two inches long, not just in the minds of men, but in the external world. Once a measuring system has been accepted, then the factual world determines specific answers to the questions: Is the table forty-two inches long? What is the length of the table?

Physical objects are measurable. Phenomena are orderly, but only with respect to orders (conventional systems of measurement and ideological concepts) established arbitrarily. This does not mean that we superimpose order upon the external world and that, consequently, order is subjective and not objective. It means, rather, that nature conforms to our previously established system or, as Whitehead would put it, nature is patient of our system. This does not mean that nature is impatient of all other systems. The length of a table can be measured by either the English system or the metric system. Similarly, one may apply either Euclidean or non-Euclidean geometries in sailing the ocean. Yet surely it is possible to construct geometries that are not applicable at all to certain situations. In that case, nature could not be known by use of those conventions.

A world that would not answer to nor submit to any convention would be forever inaccessible to human knowledge. The same can be said about a chaotic world. Since every convention or every system is a proposed order for the world, it follows that we find chaos in the world only because a certain portion of the world does not answer to a certain conventional system. But if any part of the world answers to a proposed system, and is thereby known and stated, then the statement is true, and the referent of the statement is objective. If, on the other hand, the world of fact will not submit to a certain conventional system of measurement, or to other categories, then the referent of the statement expressing our belief that the world will submit to this convention is purely subjective, even as is the referent of a false hypothesis. If one believes the world, or a portion of it, will answer to a convention in a certain way, whereas it does not, then the referent of the statement expressing the belief is subjective, for the belief is unsupported by the external world. For example, if we believe that we can express the hypotenuse of every right triangle (given the length of the two legs), by rational numbers, our thesis is false and, therefore, its referent is subjective. It is not the convention that is subjective, but the referent of a false statement. The belief that a convention can be applied in a certain way implies that a certain referent exists, and if the statement expressing that belief is false, the referent is subjective.

The subjective always involves an interpretation. To interpret means to assign a referent to a symbol, a system, or sentence. When one says "the table is forty-two inches long," the length of the table is assigned as a referent to "forty-two inches." This is an interpretation of "forty-two inches," for one claims that "forty-two inches" refers to this table. If one accepts a certain interpretation, that is, if one acts as if a certain symbol, meaning, or statement fits or will answer to the external world, and if in fact it does not, then the interpretation is invalid and the referent of the symbols involved in the interpretation is subjective. If, on the other hand, the interpretation is valid, as can be tested by acting as if it is, then the referent of the symbols involved in the interpretation is objective. But what is objective, in so far as we know it, is also relative to our interpretation, by which we bring the a priori (our conventions) and experience together.

From this it follows that objectivity, being related to conventions, has a social dimension. For this reason if the referent of a statement is objective, that statement must serve as a means of communication and it must be accepted as true by all members of the group who accept the same basis for the test of its truth.

Poincaré writes:[4]

What guarantees the objectivity of the world in which we live is that this world is common to us with other thinking beings.

.   .   .   .

Whether we take the moral, the esthetic or the scientific point of view, it is always the same thing. Nothing is objective except what is identical for all; now we can only speak of such an identity if a comparison is possible, and can be translated into a "money of exchange" capable of transmission from one mind to another. Nothing therefore, will have objective value except what is transmissible by "discourse," that is, intelligible.

[4] H. Poincaré, *The Foundations of Science*, trans. by G. B. Halsted (New York, The Science Press, 1929), pp. 347, 349.

Poincaré has emphasized the transmissible (the communicable) aspect of the objective. What is objective must be stated in terms that enable us to talk about it to other members of the group. This, of course, presupposes a common language or symbols with common meanings. And since a language is based in its human society, it follows that the objective, the intelligible aspect of anything about which we can converse, is dependent for its intelligibility upon social conventions. We can communicate only about that aspect of the external world which submits to the meanings necessary for communication. The order or orders we find in nature are in nature, but to know those orders they must be first formulated in the minds of men. These orders do not pass over into the minds by way of sensations. Rather, these orders are in the minds prior to meaningful or intelligible sensations. If experience is intelligible, it either confirms or disconfirms an interpretation, but the interpretation must be prior to intelligible experience. The fact that measuring systems must be established before objects can be measured and, in general, meanings must be agreed upon by a group before communication is possible suggests the rationalistic view that knowledge comes from the mind or from reason. Yet, in fact, only the form, not the content, is furnished by a priori systems and categories.

There may be alternative orders which render experience intelligible. Whether these orders may be contradictory we will not discuss. But two or more of these orders may be "true" at the same time; true in the sense that they can be applied, or used as interpretative systems satisfactorily.

There is no absolute perspective. In other words, the a priori is relative, and our experiences may lend themselves to being interpreted in different ways, yet more or less adequately. The a priori has a social basis and it may vary at different times in the same group or at the same time in different groups.

Conventions in science are such things as the base of our number system, systems of weights and measurements, definitions, meanings, and perspectives, and to this extent they are a priori. But the a priori aspect of science does not give us the content of experience, but rather its form. And, pertinent to our problem, the a priori is not fixed and, consequently, does not demand that experience fall within the present a priori forms. It is precisely when experience refuses to submit to the present a priori forms that we have occasion for the construction of new forms. These new forms are requested by experience which will not fit old forms, and these experiences are had by individuals who, in turn, are responsible for the new categories designed to make these novel, exceptional experiences intelligible.

The Self, Society, and Perspective

The experimental phase of the scientific method on the one hand helps us draw a sharper line between the individual and society, and on the other hand it clarifies the functional relationship between the individual and society. First let us consider the difference between the individual and society.

This consideration will lead to an understanding of the meaning of "individual" or of "self," although "individual" must be conceived so as not to preclude a functional relationship between the individual and society.

Let us begin by acknowledging the fact that a self or an individual is necessary for proposing a hypothesis. It is not known at first whether a hypothesis is true or false. Suppose, for example, it is suggested that there is oil six hundred feet below the surface of the earth at 30° north latitude and 87° west longitude. Such a statement may be tested, and its truth or falsity is not a matter of decision, as are conventions. Such a hypothesis must be proposed by an individual, for it is deducible neither from "public opinion" nor from "known facts." If it were deducible from known facts, there would be no sense in testing it, and if it were deducible with certainty from public opinion, and if it were assumed that public opinion finally determines all thinking, then also an experimental test would be irrelevant.

If a scientific test for the suggested statement is made, public opinion must be laid to one side, and, having made our meanings clear, *experience* (experience not had in the past with reference to the statement, but new experience) will be the final test. But experience, as the term is used in science, happens to individuals, and the "mob experiences," "vague social feelings," and social attitudes are not considered. An individual is necessary for both proposing a new hypothesis and for testing it. He is the source of valid hypotheses instrumental in changing attitudes and behavior, as well as invalid ones. As for public opinion and attitudes that have become socialized or institutionalized, they are expressed in routine behavior, habits, customs, and mores. Science has developed a method whereby these attitudes can be tested and, therefore, changed. But science has done so only by recognizing the indispensable place of the individual and individual experience in both proposing and testing hypotheses.

I am suggesting that the development of experimental science led to the recognition of a significant distinction between the individual and the group, and it has helped clarify the nature of the functional relationship between the individual and society with respect to new theories, new hypotheses, and, in general, new categories, including conventions of perspective. The distinction between the individual and society cannot be understood by a study of primitive cultures alone. Such a study generally leads to the conclusion that society is an "organism" apart from which the individual means nothing, and that an individual is a "product of the group." His behavior, so the conclusion runs, is determined (predetermined) by mores, social sentiments; in short, the individual is merely a mirror wherein the real—society—is reflected, but he has no part in determining what he reflects. A study of the experimental part of scientific method gives us a better understanding of the functional relation between individual, reflective thinking and social behavior. The mechanism by which ideas (leading to new intelligent social behavior) are effected is the nervous system of the individual. One can argue until doomsday to the effect that whatever the individual might think and make explicit by use of language is nothing but a reflection of the mores, and that "new" ideas expressed by individuals consist of nothing but a *recombination* of prevailing notions. But this kind of argument will never lead to a valid distinction between *new* ideas and *old* ones; much less will it give us a basis for distinguishing between a self and a society. The question is: How are new ways of acting effected, how are institutions changed, and how are new habits substituted for old ones? A study of the scientific method will show that the individual is indispensable to the introduction of new ideas which often lead to new ways of acting. The individual is not only able to conceive of the structure of society with its moral and technological practices, but he is able also to evaluate and suggest changes for society.

Those who assume that *society* is primary and that the individual is secondary, and on that assumption try to develop a theory of the social dimension of knowledge, will come out with a distorted view. On the other hand, if we conceive of the individual and society as separate but integrally related, and thereby recognize that the *condition for* (but not the determiner of) reflective thinking may be social behavior but that, nevertheless, the individual is necessary for reconstructing social behavior, we will be free to develop a theory of the functional relation between the individual and society.

The behavior of an individual termite in a colony is conditioned by its biological structure, by its environment, and by the behavior of other members of the colony. If it is to remain an integral part of the colony, the termite must conform to a relatively fixed pattern of behavior, and its behavior must fit into the behavior of other members of the species in such a way as to be conducive to the survival value of the colony of which it is a member. Any changes in the general pattern by which the life process of the colony is carried on must come about by either a change in the environment or a change in the biological structure of the offspring—a mutation. But change in behavior cannot be brought about by symbols or by the communication of ideas which would represent a proposed change. Not only is the individual member of the colony unable to represent to itself the various acts of the other individuals of the group in so far as they answer to each other and constitute group activity, but least of all is it able to present to itself alternative ways of behaving. As a matter of fact geneticists are prone to think of the behavioral patterns of lower animals as inherited. In any case a member of a colony of termites is not an individual in the sense that members of human societies are individuals. Members of a colony have no selves, for they are not only unable to internalize (present to themselves) the pattern of behavior which each carries out, but they are also unable to conceive of alternative patterns of behavior or alternative responses to a given stimulus.

It is because of the ability to entertain alternative responses to a given situation and, as a consequence, to entertain and previse the behavior of other individuals as they enter into co-operative behavior, that members of human society are said to have selves. Common meanings of signs in a language system tend to become fixed in a society, and the corresponding covert responses evoked by these signs tend to become habitual. But even if these responses become habitual, they can be modified or eradicated by a creative act of intelligence.

The mechanism for such a creative act is the nervous system of the individual. If, however, old responses in the form of habits, systems, and interpretive categories can be applied satisfactorily, there is no need for changing them. The basis for the lack of satisfaction with which these responses and habits are applied is found in experience. When our experiences do not answer to these previously established habits or categories, there is occasion for formulating new ones. Not only do these exceptional experiences happen to individuals, but also the newly formulated interpretive categories come from the mind of an individual.

The source of the a priori is the individual and, at first at least, the a priori belongs to a single individual, and it is only after the individual has expressed the new and peculiar way of interpreting experience that it can be entertained by other members of the group also. The a priori is by no means an "expression of public opinion" or an "expression of the subconscious attitude of the group." Rather, the newly proposed prescription for interpreting the novel or exceptional (exceptional with reference to old interpretations) experience must take a chance on being accepted by the group and, until it is accepted, must be considered as a peculiar attitude of an individual. The final test of the acceptability of a newly proposed prescription is to be found in the adequacy or the satisfaction with which it may be applied. This adequacy or satisfaction is social in nature, and consequently, although the a priori is formulated by an individual, it must be formulated with reference to the group as a whole.

Reflective thinking by the individual can take place only in a society of individuals to whom signs have common meanings in the sense that they call out common responses. This implies that the person who "gives" the sign calls out in himself (implicitly if not explicitly) the same response that he calls out in the other.[5] One has control over these

---

[5] See especially G. H. Mead, *Mind, Self, and Society,* Part III (Chicago, University of Chicago Press, 1934).

responses to the extent that he has control over the signs or symbols that *mean* and, consequently, elicit these responses. Control of responses presupposes choice.

Precisely how choice takes place, we do not know; but before choice is possible there must be alternative possible ways of responding to the same objects in a given situation. A response (excluding inherited behavioral patterns—"instincts") to a situation by a lower animal can be accounted for on the basis of conditioning, and such a response is called a "conditioned response." But men, by use of symbols and through reflective thinking, are not only able to entertain, or represent to themselves, alternative possible responses to a given situation, but they are also able to select the objects to which they respond and to control the particular kind of response made to them. The mechanism for selecting the objects responded to, and for controlling the consequent response to it, is the nervous system of the individual. Yet such selection and control would be impossible apart from the development of a language, which is necessarily social in character. Controlling a response to an object involves the acceptance of a symbol or set of symbols that may elicit a certain kind of response. This involves rejecting alternative symbols with the corresponding responses they would elicit.

This process of selection and rejection amounts to conditioning oneself by use of language, and the action proposed by an individual can be accepted by other members of the group only because the symbols used call out common responses. In any case, the individual is the instrument by which reconditioning of both the behavior of an individual and that of the group are effected by reflective thinking. I do not want to leave the impression that the individual as well as the group cannot be reconditioned by things other than the process of reflective thinking. But where the individual conditions himself and, consequently, other members of the group, he does so by employing symbols. As we have explained, symbols by which men communicate emerge within a social group, and for that reason the individual's newly proposed courses of action may be communicated to other members of the group.

Every newly proposed act, whether limited to one individual or applied to several, must be proposed by an individual. The nervous system is the mechanism by which use can be made of experiences exceptional to habits (accepted laws, theories, and mores), and this is also the mechanism for proposing new ways of behaving.

An explicit consciousness of the method by which habitual ways of behaving can be altered by use of intelligence came late in the history of man. A statement of this method—the scientific method—takes into account the place of the individual with his peculiar experiences and his peculiar proposals of new kinds of behavior. But a careful study of civilizations characterized essentially by science and technology will show that changes take place because individuals are able to take cognizance of situations to which old attitudes do not answer satisfactorily. Individuals are able to accept exceptional experiences (experiences one has when the relationship between one's behavior toward an object and the desired goal is unsatisfactory) as a basis for reconstructing behavior and, consequently, the environment.

Men as well as lower animals may be conditioned to respond to objects in new ways, and such conditioning may be due to new experiences with objects. Animals may also inherit new behavioral patterns so that a mutation would respond to its environment in a different way from its parents. But in neither case does the individual have control over the conditioning process, which takes place without the intervention of reflective thinking, and in neither case is the animal cognizant of what is happening to it. But through the proper use of symbols, men are able to condition themselves, and an explicit statement of the scientific method takes this conditioning process into account. Consequently, although there is a social basis for the emergence of newly proposed systems and ways of behaving, they are a priori with reference to the individual and a posteriori with reference to the group of which the individual is a member. Individuals, therefore, constitute the source of conditioning and reconditioning both themselves and the society which they compose. The ability to reshape culture, society, and the environment in which it exists is known as freedom, and the trustees of freedom are individuals.

The Ethical Bases of Freedom

CHAPTER X

Life, Mind, and Freedom

The Nature of Life

A LIVING ORGANISM is characterized especially by (1) the organization and co-ordination of its parts and (2) a life process which maintains this organization and co-ordination. Organization, which has a durational character, implies both spatial and temporal dimensions, for what is organized must occupy different parts of space; in addition, the process by which the organization and co-ordination of the living organism is effected always has a future reference. This process is intelligible to us only if we describe it in relation to what is likely to happen later. Genes are intelligible only with reference to offspring; metabolism is intelligible only in relation to the restoration of a balance in the chemistry of the organism; heartbeat, breathing, and digestion are intelligible only in relation to their effects. Similarly, the symbolic process or thinking always has reference to a future, even if it involves the past and present also.

The distinguishing characteristic of the living form is this: Its present functions and actions take into account what is likely to happen in its environment and within itself later, and in so doing adjustments are made to oncoming events, thereby increasing the probability of survival of the individual member of the species and of the species itself. This "taking into account" of the distant future event by the organism gives rise to much discussion and to many disagreements. The organization involved in living forms is the basis for the controversy over vitalism and mechanism on the one hand and reductionism and emergent evolution on the other. Since the controversy has many ramifications, it would be best to begin the discussion by clarifying the meaning of vitalism.

Vitalism

Every vitalist maintains at least this: A knowledge of physics and chemistry alone is not sufficient to explain the organization involved in the life process. I agree with vitalism in this minimum claim. Although chemical processes are involved in every phase of the life process, this implies neither *(a)* that the life process is identical with or reducible to them nor *(b)* that they constitute sufficient conditions for the life process. A study of inorganic chemistry by itself would not give us the slightest notion that chemical processes could be organized as they are in the living form. And although there are organizations at the inorganic level, there is a new kind of organization at the organic level. In other words, the living organism is an emergent which, by comparison with the solar system, came into existence only recently.

With these facts in mind a scientist must either accept or reject the theory of evolution. If he accepts it, he must acknowledge openly that the life process is something new, something qualitatively different from what is found in the inorganic world. Most biologists accept the theory of evolution with the understanding that the life process came into existence only recently and that in some essential respect it is irreducibly and qualitatively different from anything that existed prior to its emergence. How is this different kind of thing to be described?

First of all, what is new in the life process is not the analytical parts. Rather, it is the organization of the parts into a whole in such a manner that the parts become members of the whole. In the living form, no new chemical elements can be found. Nor are any new mechanical principles involved. In fact, the biological sciences do not and cannot add to the body of knowledge of physics and chemistry. And, conversely, a thorough knowledge of the basic principles of physics and chemistry, with their entailed implications, cannot give us an understanding of the qualitative difference between life (organic processes) and inorganic objects.

At this point some scientists begin to squirm. For if they grant that biology is not fully comprehended within physics and chemistry (or other inorganic disciplines), then they are close to admitting vitalism. On the other hand, if they claim that the inorganic sciences are adequate to describe and understand biological phenomena, in effect they have given up the belief that organic processes are qualitatively different from inorganic. This latter alternative will lead to some kind of reductionism and to some such statements as these: "There is nothing essentially new in the living form." "Chemistry and physics will finally give us a complete understanding of the life process." "When scientists are able to reproduce (from inorganic substances) a living organism, then all this talk about vitalism will cease." In short, the biologist must either accept evolution and some sort of vitalism or reject evolution and accept some sort of reductionism. He cannot believe in evolution and at the same time believe that the inorganic sciences are adequate to account for the nature of life processes.

Joseph Needham says: "It is for us to investigate the nature of this biological organization, not to abandon it to the metaphysicians because the rules of physics do not seem to apply to it."[1] Needham's remark is both an admission of the inability of physics to include biology completely and a recognition that biological organization is novel with respect to inorganic phenomena. Yet he is a naturalist in the sense that he believes there is nothing mysterious about life. Consequently, if Needham can be classified as a vitalist at all, then "vitalism" means for him that the life process is qualitatively and irreducibly different from anything found at the inorganic level. This is a sensible view and I accept it. This view permits one to believe in evolution and yet accept a biological naturalism, which means that although biological organization is not reducible to inorganic processes it is nevertheless intelligible, neither mystical nor supernatural.

It may be that "vitalism" can sensibly mean only that biological organization is an emergent and is novel with respect to inorganic processes. This novel character of life, with an understanding of the sense in which it is novel, is all vitalism means to me. Given this meaning, if anyone still says "vitalism" has no referent in the world of fact, he is by implication denying that life is an emergent.

[1] Joseph Needham, *Order and Life* (New Haven, Yale University Press, 1936), p. 17.

Metaphysics vs. *Methodology*

If a biologist believes with Needham that life is an emergent and that its novel characteristic consists of a new kind of organization, he must decide whether biology can be made into a new science or whether our approach to it must be by way of the principles of the inorganic sciences alone. Until now the only approach to vital organization has been by way of the basic principles of the inorganic sciences, and this may be the only possible approach. Even if the life process involves a different kind of organization from what is found anywhere else in nature, still this new kind of organization may not submit to being stated in terms of new scientific principles, principles effective in controlling biological organization. Furthermore, it may not be necessary to discover new biological principles in order to control biological processes or the organization that is present in every living form, even as it is not necessary to reduce the color experience to chemical and physical elements in order to control that experience by these elements (its physical cause).

Here I submit the thesis that the control of any phenomenon whatsoever, whether it is a color, an odor, an ordinary machine, or the life process itself, is possible only by manipulating physical objects, directly or indirectly, by human hands. Physics and chemistry are fundamental to controlling and producing any kind of phenomenon. It is a mistake, however, for philosophers and scientists to conclude that since physical objects constitute the basic means of controlling and producing qualitatively different objects, the objects produced are, therefore, metaphysically like their causes (physical objects), and that the only difference between cause and effect is a quantitative difference. In order to think correctly on the problems of vitalism, a scientist must accept evolution and, at the same time, recognize what this acceptance involves. It involves the emergence of novel (qualitatively different) forms; hence, their causes are qualitatively different from the new forms, and the difference between cause and effect can never be stated quantitatively. From the quantitative standpoint, cause and effect are always identical.

I believe that the principles of biological organization can never be stated scientifically in the sense in which physical and chemical principles are stated. Yet, biological organization is not found in the inorganic world. This organization can be *recognized* by theoretical, vitalistic principles, and it can be *described* but can never be controlled by them. Nevertheless, it is precisely this qualitative difference which makes life a metaphysically different kind of process from that found in the inorganic world.

The quarrel over vitalism has been a quarrel over whether or not metaphysics is reducible to scientific methodology. The quarrel stems from a confusion—from the mistaken belief that effects are like their causes. The only way out of this confusion and the only way to settle the dispute is to make a clear distinction between metaphysics and scientific methodology. Bergson's great merit consists in his refusal to fall into the trap set by the scientific methodologists and designed by philosophers to engulf metaphysics—reducing quality to quantity. Bergson had no objection to science as a method; his claim was that method cannot engulf metaphysics. Things qualitatively different in kind cannot be proved to be of the same metaphysical structure simply because the control of them is by means of the same basic method. Once this is clear, a person can be both a vitalist and a naturalist and at the same time believe that the only means of controlling vital processes is by way of physics and chemistry.

Can Vitalism Be Disproved?

In order to give further evidence for the confusion stated above, let us consider the attitude of some scientists toward vitalism. Many biologists actually believe it is possible in principle to disprove vitalism by experiments carried on in the laboratory. And although Darwinism is a defense of the thesis that *new* (qualitatively different) forms emerge in time, it influenced many biologists to espouse mechanism with its claim that biology is reducible to physics. As early as 1911 Jacques Loeb said, "I have the feeling that technical shortcomings of our young science are alone to blame for the fact that the artificial production of living matter has not yet succeeded."[2] Loeb sincerely

[2] Ernst Cassirer, *The Problem of Knowledge* (New Haven, Yale University Press, 1950), p. 207.

believed that when these technical shortcomings were overcome, vitalism would be disproved.

Loeb is mistaken. Suppose that a biologist could start with inorganic matter (matter in which the organic process is absent) and by some procedure an organic process would emerge. What would this prove? If it proved anything at all it would prove that the cause of life is found in the nonliving order (life is an emergent), and that life is natural (since its cause is natural). And it would prove that the life process is not an inorganic process, for certainly the scientist who got life out of the nonliving objects would claim that he had something different from what he started with—recognizably different and irreducibly different from what is found in inorganic matter.

Should a scientist start with inorganic matter and end with a living process, would he have produced life or would he have released it? Those who believe in evolution would have to conclude that he produced it, and that he produced something qualitatively different from what he started with (effects are qualitatively unlike their causes). Those who believe he released it need not accept evolution, but they would be forced to conclude that inorganic objects contain within themselves the life process also. Consequently, the success of the experiment would show that vitalism cannot be refuted, and it would bring us to another basic question: Is evolution possible? In other words, must effects be *in* their causes, or, is there anything new under the sun?

There are three possible answers to this question. (1) To produce life artificially is to show that life is reducible to inorganic processes. This answer is self-contradictory. (2) All objects have both a physical and a vital aspect and the two are inseparable in fact. This view is not self-contradictory, but it is inconsistent with the theory of evolution. (3) Life is an emergent; the biological organization is new; it represents a different level of reality from the level of matter as expressed by physical and chemical principles alone. I accept the third alternative. It is consistent with the general theory that nature is creative, that human minds are creative, and that there is, consequently, human freedom. It is opposed to analytic determinism or to the Greek thesis that the effect is found in its cause. I do not believe there is more in the effect than in its cause; they are qualitatively different. Quantities are found through analysis and through abstraction. Qualitative differences can be recognized and sensed; quantities can be thought only. Quality is a metaphysical term; quantity is a methodological term.

Is Mind Characteristic of All Objects?

In *Cell and Psyche,* Edmund W. Sinnott argues that the same kind of organization manifested in the symbolic process or in mind is found also in every living cell. He says that "biological organization and psychical activity *are one and the same thing.*"[3] And in the "development" from cell to psyche he says "it is hard to see anything qualitatively new, however." Also, "at no point is there a sudden break, a radical innovation."

Had Sinnott gone one step further and argued that atoms too, like cells and minds, have a "forward look" in their organization, he would be a second Ernst Haeckel.[4] But Sinnott, like Haeckel, in trying to explain evolution, finally argues himself out of believing in it at all. For if there are no qualitative differences in evolution, then all differences must be quantitative ones, and, as has been shown, new forms cannot be expressed quantitatively. Sinnott, also, argues from the hidden assumption that "effects" are in their causes and that the results of a process are qualitatively like the process itself; ends are like means. This kind of reasoning is borrowed from rationalism which came from the Greeks. If nature is rational (or intelligible), so the argument goes, then it must be like a syllogism in which the conclusion (effect) unfolds from the premises (causes). Strictly speaking this is a kind of reductionism which will not permit evolution with its qualitative differences. To try to subscribe to both this rationalistic metaphysics and to evolution is to confuse methodology and metaphysics, quantities and qualities.

I believe that the organization in cell and psyche are similar in the sense that both take into account what is likely to take place later, but there is a qualitative difference in the way in which they take the distant event into account. Whereas the nonthinking cell does so un-

[3] Edmund W. Sinnott, *Cell and Psyche* (Chapel Hill, University of North Carolina Press, 1950), pp. 48, 68, 73.

[4] Ernst Haeckel, *The Riddle of the Universe,* trans. by Joseph McCabe (New York, Harper & Brothers, 1900).

consciously and without the employment of symbols, the mind does so by use of symbols, and the symbolic process is an emergent, qualitatively unlike the organization found in the individual cells. As shown earlier in this chapter, the symbolic process emerged only at the human social level, and although cells are necessary for its emergence, they are not sufficient.

Biological Organization vs. *Cell Division*

In *What Is Life,* Erwin Schrödinger offers a plausible explanation of the origin of new genes, which are presumably responsible for new forms, mutations. He presents the view that quantum physics is basic to an understanding of genetics and that the discontinuous "all or none" processes which characterize quantum phenomena are causally related to sudden (vs. smooth and continuous) changes that result in a change in the genes of the organism with their ensuing consequences, mutations. His excellent account of the relationship between quantum phenomena and genetics does not do justice to the title of his book, however. Schrödinger stops short of completing his task. It is one thing to explain the origin of new genes with their tendency to superimpose their image on daughter cells, and another thing to explain the *organization* of the many cells into a well-co-ordinated whole, the organism. Schrödinger does not explain biological organization, and quantum physics cannot help at this point. The basic characteristic of life *is* this organization of the parts. Consequently, Schrödinger does not help us to explain *life*.

We must give Schrödinger full credit for making one point clear; namely, evolution is not a continuous process and we cannot, therefore, express new forms in quantitative terms. There is only a correlation between the quanta entering into the cause of new genes and the genes themselves. Genes are not reducible to quanta; rather quanta are causes of something qualitatively different. Quantity belongs to methodology, quality to metaphysics.

Schrödinger describes the gene as a sort of code script having certain powers and functions with a futuristic bent. He says:[5]

[5] Erwin Schrödinger, *What Is Life?* (London, Cambridge University Press, 1946), p. 21.

But the term code-script is, of course, too narrow. The chromosome structures are at the same time instrumental in bringing about the development they foreshadow. They are law-code and executive power—or, to use another simile, they are architect's plan and builder's craft—in one.

From this it is clear that genes have two functions: (1) They superimpose their chromosomal image on every daughter cell and (2) they organize the daughter cells so that they constitute a unified living organism.

Schrödinger does an excellent job in explaining the physical basis for the origin of new genes and in explaining how, in the new cells, the same internal structure is duplicated. But when it comes to explaining the differentiation of cells, he has nothing to contribute.

In its beginning, the embryo is a single cell. After one division, the two cells are alike, yet after several divisions, somewhere along the line, differentiation sets in. If it were not for this differentiation and organization of the cells, the embryo would result in a mere accumulation of organically unrelated cells. Physics and chemistry are successful in accounting for cell division and what amounts to *accumulation,* but they have no explanation whatsoever for the differentiation and organization. Hans Driesch believed an explanation was necessary, and he, like many others, believed there is a nonphysical cause for biological organization. He called it a vitalistic force. Bergson calls it *élan vital.*

What can these terms mean? Cognitively they refer to nothing other than the organization itself. If we think of these terms as referring to causes or forces they cannot be thought of as physical causes or physical forces. At best the term "vital force" can mean the cause of biological organization. It may even be defined meaningfully to the satisfaction of both the operationalist and the positivist by saying: "All we mean by vital force is the observable biological organization." It may have other meanings, but, as far as science is concerned, I believe it is impossible to discover and state vitalistic principles in such a way that they will give us control over vital processes. These processes can be recognized and described, but control over them must always be by way of inorganic, manipulatable objects.

A Science of Vital Forces Is Impossible

It is possible for scientists to enter into the biological processes, to direct them and control them in many instances, but in no instance can it be done by employing a nonphysical, spiritual force.

This is not to say that no vital forces are present in biological organization. Rather, "force," when applied to the life process, has nothing in common with physical forces, and there will never be a "spiritualistic," supernatural way of controlling biological organization. To believe that new biological, vitalistic principles can be found and used to control life would be analogous to believing that the science of color (an understanding of color) consists of knowing how to control and produce colors by other colors, not physical objects.

Life is a different kind of thing from what is found at the inorganic level, even as colors, tastes, and odors are emergents and are not characteristics of atoms and electrons. Different methods of procedure are used in producing color and taste, and, in general, there are different laws for each. But in every case of control the scientist must fall back on physical objects that can be manipulated. Confusion arises when scientists and philosophers begin to think that the things controlled and produced are reducible to and identical with the means of controlling and producing them. The confusion becomes more firmly established when the word "understand" is used in two different senses. Yet despite the two different senses, each of which is legitimate, many philosophers and scientists claim there is only one proper sense, the scientific sense, in which "understanding" can be used.

Scientific Understanding vs. Empathetic Union

Thomas Edison knew about electricity from the practical, controllable standpoint. Yet he kept insisting that he did not "understand" electricity. Obviously "understanding" was used in both a practical sense and in a metaphysical sense. Probably Edison wanted to say that although he had considerable control and practical knowledge, he still could not "take the attitude" of an electric current, or he could not "feel" like an electric current must feel, or he could not enter into an empathetic union with electricity.

This same ambiguity about the meaning of "understanding" is entertained by philosophers and scientists. The pragmatists, operationalists, and positivists are ready to clear up the confusion, but they try to do so by claiming that "understanding" has no metaphysical meaning whatsoever. Its only meaning, they say, is a practical, operational, sensible meaning, completely identifiable with scientific meaning. In short, some groups have been trying to bring all meaning and, consequently, all understanding over into the camp of scientific methodology.

Although Edison (and others) may be mistaken in believing we can understand things by some sort of empathetic union with them, I believe it is also a mistake to try to identify all meaning and understanding with the scientific dimension of understanding. For just as the color green can be known, and the meaning of the word "green" understood, quite apart from a scientific understanding of how to produce and control it, so the "metaphysical" meaning of things cannot be equated with the scientific. All "metaphysical" may mean, however, in many instances, is a recognition of the sense in which an object or process is qualitatively different from other objects or processes.

Consequently, if "biological organization" has a meaning that cannot be equated to the scientific method of controlling it, that meaning is confined to what can be recognized and observed as a process qualitatively different from what is found at the inorganic level. I think it has this nonscientific meaning. Whether we call it a metaphysical meaning or not is of no consequence. What is of consequence, however, is an acknowledgment of the fact that we cannot exhaust meanings by recourse to scientific methodology. The attempt to do so justifiably provoked many good philosophers to protest against the claim that science teaches us the nature of things and that it tells us what things "really are." This protest is not just against the positivistic claim that science is all-embracing. On its positive side it maintains that values are outside the sphere of science and that science can be justified only as a means to ends selected on ethical grounds. To identify metaphysics with methodology is to smother values and human freedom in a sea of techniques.

Scientific understanding is confined to the means of controlling and producing ends. It includes the know-how of science. If pragmatists had made it clear that the kind of knowledge and understanding they are talking about is scientific knowledge only, then they would be completely correct in their contention that knowledge (scientific knowledge) is for the sake of practice and that the locus of understanding is in action—in behavior. Pragmatists went awry in suggesting that behavior is the locus of all values and that the act is for its own sake. Dewey could not distinguish clearly between means and ends and, consequently, he confused scientific methodology with metaphysics.

The pragmatists, however, are not guilty of confusing scientific methodology, meaning, and understanding with sense experience or sensibilia. This the positivists did, and in doing so they left the know-how, the means of attaining values, out of scientific methodology altogether. "Understanding" is left with neither scientific nor metaphysical meaning. Sensibilia are instrumental as guides to the manipulation of physical objects and are often enjoyed as ends in themselves, but they do not constitute know-how and are not in themselves the methodological devices necessary to control and produce. One may *have* a sensation, but it cannot be handled and used to control the order of events. Sensibilia are indeed secondary qualities from the standpoint of scientific method.

Biological Organization vs. the Symbolic Process

Sinnott's attempt to show the similarity between cell and psyche is interesting and well known. But we must not mistake description of an awareness of the future dimension of biological and mental organization for scientific knowledge or scientific understanding. Such description enables us to recognize these processes and to comprehend the differences between them and inorganic phenomena. It also helps us to understand the meaning of the terms "biological organization" and "mental organization." These descriptive terms help us recognize their referents if we experience them. This is the same sense in which we understand the referent of the term "blue" by being able to recognize a blue object when experienced.

All arguments between "vitalists" and "mechanists" are at heart nothing but arguments over whether or not the full meaning and understanding of the referents of all terms (such as mind, biological organization, and life process) can be expressed through scientific-methodological concepts alone. The mechanists say yes, and the vitalists say no. The vitalists are correct, and their argument rests on the simple fact that a distinction must be made between the know-how of science and the ends reached by applying that know-how; between means and ends, quantity and quality, methodology and metaphysics, and between extrinsic and intrinsic values. Just as the operationalists made the mistake of identifying the full referent of a term with the operational procedure of measuring it and as the positivists mistakenly identified the full meaning of a proposition with the means of verifying it, so mechanists are mistaken in identifying the entire meaning of "biological organization" with the only possible means of controlling it.

As indicated above, three different approaches have been made to the explanation of the evolution of new forms. (1) Forms are new in appearance only, but fundamentally they are nothing but combinations of inorganic processes. (2) Every object has both its organic and its inorganic aspect (both spiritual and material) and the "evolution" of life and mind is nothing but a concentration of the inherent organic nature of objects; such concentration only makes the organic aspect easier to recognize. Accordingly, evolution is believed to be a process which makes explicit what was implicit from the beginning. (3) Evolution means the epigenesis of new forms. These forms did not exist or subsist in any manner prior to their emergence. They are, therefore, qualitatively different from anything that existed prior to their emergence, including their causes, the conditions for their emergence.

Only (3) is consistent with the belief that there are genuinely new types of things or new forms that emerge in time, that time is essentially one-directional, and that qualitative differences in the world are not reducible to quantitative differences. Despite the unacceptability of (1) and (2), let us explain why these two views are still held by many scientists who claim also to accept the theory of evolution.

Those who accept (1) fail to distinguish between means and ends, between the history or past of a form and the form itself, between the necessary conditions for the emergence of a new form and the form itself, between scientific method and ends produced by it. For these scientists and philosophers there is only one meaning to "understanding"—knowledge of the means of control. I believe this is the only *scientific* meaning of understanding, but, in addition, there is understanding in the sense of comprehending the qualitative difference between cause and effect and of knowing a thing by direct acquaintance. Bergson emphasizes this distinction in kinds of understanding in a slightly different way. He says one way of understanding is through analysis, the other is through intuition.[6]

By intuition is meant the kind of *intellectual sympathy* by which one places oneself within an object in order to coincide with what is unique in it and consequently inexpressible. Analysis, on the contrary, is the operation which reduces the objects to elements already known, that is, to elements common both to it and other objects. To analyze, therefore, is to express a thing as a function of something other than itself.

Those who accept (2) above have ignored the creative aspect of nature as well as the fact that the one-directional character of time implies the emergence of qualitative differences. Also, they seem to accept the medieval dictum that effects are *in* and *like* their causes and that nothing comes from nothing (nihil ex nihilo). They recognize that life is a metaphysically different kind of thing from inorganic matter, but do not, therefore, recognize that inorganic elements may be the cause and constitute the conditions for the emergence of life without actually containing life as an inherent property. This view fails to distinguish between scientific method and ends produced by it, and it maintains essentially that there is nothing new under the sun. Ernst Haeckel, a typical exponent of this view, argues that every atom has both its physical and its psychical pole. Edmund Sinnott holds essentially the same view in his contention that the difference between cell and psyche is a difference in degree only.

At this point let us describe the life process, first at the biological level and then at the mental level with the purpose, finally, of understanding the meaning of the freedom of human individuals.

By continuous use of the term "survival value" biologists implicitly

[6] Henri Bergson, *An Introduction to Metaphysics,* trans. by T. E. Hulme (New York, G. P. Putnam's Sons, 1912), p. 7.

acknowledge the future, temporal dimension of biological processes. Also, they strongly suggest that the term explains these processes and gives us a scientific understanding of them. "Survival value" is, however, a purely descriptive term and is not scientifically explanatory; i.e., a knowledge that the color of a moth has survival value is of no use as a means of controlling the life process. But, as used by biologists, the term strictly implies that some of what has taken place in the past and what is taking place now in the living form has significance or is intelligible only with reference to what is likely to take place in the future. This temporal (future) dimension of the behavior of living forms clearly distinguishes the living organism from the nonliving. The physicochemical-electric processes in the living organism are so organized as to enable the processes themselves to continue, thus allowing the organism and the species to survive. The particular way in which these processes are organized may be made clearer by use of the term "survival value," which means that these processes somehow take into account later possible conditions.

The Future Dimension of the Gene

The genes determine the genotypic form of the offspring, and presumably they begin this determination in the early stages of the development of the embryo. The very concept of "gene" makes sense only by referring to its function, which can be described only by referring to the future stages in the process of the development of the organism.

Although one may see chromosomes by aid of the microscope, and although one may know the chemical make-up of the germ plasm, we can never hope to see at a given time the way a gene functions nor the referent of "gene" in so far as it refers to function. The mechanism by which the function of the gene is carried out can be isolated but we cannot sense what determines the form (or nature) of the offspring, namely the gene, and distinguish it from the chemicals involved. Looked at from a slightly different angle, no scientist could possibly have arrived at the concept of "gene" through the most meticulous scientific analysis of a germ cell, nor through the analysis of each and every stage in the development of the embryo, taken individually or collectively. Rather, one comes to the concept by understanding an unsensed and an insensible relationship between the parent-form and the offspring. The basic meaning of "gene," therefore, is not something that can be directly sensed. It is a metaphysical meaning which refers to a determining factor that has a temporal dimension lacking what can be directly sensed by use of the most powerful and most helpful instruments conceivable. The gene is able to take into account, through its functioning, the temporally distant possible circumstances and events in such a way that it enables the living form and the species to survive, or, at least, it makes it possible for them to take a chance with survival.

Some may be inclined to argue that there is nothing but inorganic processes in the living form. But let us remember that if that were all that is involved there would be no basis for distinguishing between the living and the dead. Nor could we accept the thesis that living organisms actually *emerged,* since there would be nothing to distinguish them from the nonliving.

A second argument may be: But the only difference between the living and the dead is the manner in which the "inorganic" processes are organized. Yes, that may be *the* difference and the only difference. Now let us try to state this difference more significantly. It amounts to this: the processes in the living form are so organized as to take into account later conditions and circumstances.

The functioning of genes presupposes the offspring, and "what they are doing" makes descriptive sense only in relation to what is likely to happen later.

The Future Dimension of the Mutation

Whereas control by the gene somehow provides for the organization and development of a single individual member of a species, giving it what are called its genotypic characters and thereby increasing its chances of survival, the mutation is the means by which new species are brought into existence, thereby increasing the chance of the survival of life on earth through the introduction of new forms capable of surviving in new environments.

The origin of a new kind of biological organism (the epigenesis of form) cannot be predicted by applying the Mendelian law. A mutation is a breach of the law, and the specific nature of every mutant form is unpredictable. The mutation is a sort of unlawful phenomenon, at first at least and with respect to the Mendelian law which is the only basis for predicting the nature of the offspring. Yet if it were not for mutations, life could not continue on earth very long, considering the fact that no species in its present form existed five million years ago and that most if not all species of five million years ago could not survive under present environmental conditions.

These facts make it clear that evolutionary processes take into account, by way of mutations, later possible environmental conditions, and that if they did not do so, life on earth would soon become extinct. This taking into account need not be a conscious affair, and as far as I know there is no evidence whatsoever that it is. It is quite clear also that it is not a purely mechanical affair. Although mutations have their physicochemical, mechanical bases, and could not emerge without them, their significance lies in the fact that they enable life to continue on earth. The import of mutations for biology is that they have survival value, and, consequently, we can understand and explain them from that standpoint as well as from the standpoint of scientific control. This means, finally, that an understanding of mutations, and a significant statement of their implications for biology, amounts to an understanding of the fact that through them the living form takes into account oncoming, future environmental conditions.

The Overt Behavior of Individuals and the Future

Every animal must assimilate food, and the first stage in the process of digestion is intelligible only with reference to its value in sustaining the living form. One can "explain" digestion in the chemical-mechanical sense by simply describing the chemical processes involved, but that these processes result in sustaining life and thus have a future temporal dimension cannot be so explained. A Darwinian would be inclined to say that the digestive process simply *has* survival value, and so it does. But we should hasten to point out that the term "survival value" cannot be assimilated to a sheer mechanical description of the process involved. The Darwinian might reply: "All I mean by 'survival value' is that if digestion did not take place, the form could not live." Precisely so. And when properly translated this means that if what is taking place now did not somehow take into account what is likely to take place later, the organism could not survive.

If one were to speak loosely he would say, "What is going to take place later, or what is likely to take place later *determines* what is taking place *now* in the living form." Obviously this is a teleological statement, if not an explanation, and I do not subscribe to it. When, however, a biologist purports to explain life processes by referring to "survival value," he is assuming that explanation must include reference to certain probable future conditions or circumstances, and this is identical with assuming that what is now taking place in the life form becomes intelligible or can be understood and made significant only in relation to some probable future condition. Is this tantamount to saying a future condition, since it determines the significance of a present process, also determines the *nature of* that process? I think not, for a description of a present phenomenon in relation to a future condition does not mean that the future condition enters into the phenomenon in a causal way. Hence, it does not causally determine the phenomenon. Teleology found its way into biology simply because of a confusion between two kinds of understanding; understanding by comprehending the nature of a thing as distinguished qualitatively from other things, and understanding by knowing the cause of the existence or emergence of a thing. Anyone who offers a teleological (final cause) explanation of biological processes mistakes the first kind of understanding for the second; he mistakes metaphysics for methodology.

Involvement of Probable Future Circumstances in the Behavior of Lower Animals

From among the multifarious objects in the wider environment of an animal, it selects very few as stimuli to which it responds. This selection of stimuli means that the animal is determining its environment (that to which it responds—or what stimulates it) in such a way that the responses of the animal enable it to survive. The stone, a piece of dead wood, a string, each will lend itself to being swallowed by the bird, but the bird rejects them as stimuli and swallows the seed, the grub, the worm instead. One cannot say *why* the bird swallows the seed instead of the stone by stating *how* it swallows. Obviously it could swallow both by the same procedure. This is why the biologist speaks of *survival value,* which, he presumably believes, explains why the bird selected the seed and rejected the stone.

The problem is not to explain why a bird lives, but why it eats seeds; why it selects certain stimuli and rejects others; why it determines, by its selection, the nature of its environment. Can that explanation be framed in pure mechanical terms, thereby ignoring that for the sake of which the bird eats seeds? To date it has not been so explained, and it is my contention that the behavior of living forms, and life itself, must be described essentially with reference to oncoming, future conditions.

If the squirrel did not gather nuts in the fall, it could not survive the winter. Why does the squirrel store nuts instead of stones? Does the squirrel *know* the nuts contain food? The wisest of men can have only practical certainty of that. Every living form must take its chance with the future, but what the squirrel does in the fall increases its chances of surviving the winter. Although we may not be able to explain the behavior of lower animals, or even much of human behavior, by mechanical principles nor yet by a teleological principle, it is clear that the living form through its present behavior somehow takes into account oncoming events or circumstances and thereby increases its chances of surviving.

The Conditioned Response and Future Circumstances

The response of an animal to an object by way of a stimulus not attached to that object is called a conditioned response; e.g., a dog may learn to respond to meat through hearing a bell. What is immediately sensed is the sound of the bell, but the response is to the meat.

One can "explain" the conditioned response in two different ways. First, he can state the simple fact that the sound of the bell causes the saliva to flow in the dog. This amounts to a statement about the sensed conditions that serve as a basis for the response of the dog to the meat. But the sound waves do not cause the saliva to flow in same sense that, say, heat causes a metal to expand. Given the dog and the sound waves, still the dog must be hungry and his response is to a distant object, the meat, which, if eaten, increases the dog's chances of survival.

Every conditioned response is a response to a temporally (and often spatially) distant object by way of present stimuli. Such a response always involves the survival of the individual making it, and it can be described only by reference to its consequences.

The "reason" the bell initiates the response to the meat is not found in the physical strength (loudness) of the sound waves coming from the bell. Nor does it make sense to argue that the bell, as a stimulus, is aesthetically more attractive, since any other stimulus would serve as well. This is a case in which the animal, by way of a present stimulus, responds to the future oncoming, unsensed object.

I may add that if conditioned responses were impossible, then the behavior of all animals would be determined (predetermined) by inheritance alone. Then, all responses would be automatic or mechanical and could be thought of as inherited behavioral patterns carried out instinctively. But the fact that animals can be conditioned to respond to objects by stimuli not physically related to those objects is evidence that the behavior of animals is not completely determined in advance of a particular environment. This implies that in the development and growth of an animal, future possible alternative environments have been taken into account; and of the many actual things in the presence of an organism to which it could respond, only those are responded to that have survival value. To say that the dog is stimulated by the bell because it is hungry presupposes a disposition in the dog prior to the ring of the bell. It presupposes a selection by the dog, and this selection makes sense only with reference to survival.

First, then, conditioned responses can be described in terms of the "good" of the animals involved. Second, the fact that an organism is flexible and is able to develop new habits and, in general, to learn by experience, seems to have been "built into" it in advance of the actual conditioning. Consequently, even before an animal encounters an environment in which it may be conditioned and reconditioned, that environment has been taken into account in this very general way.

Mind, Future Objects, and Events

Through cognition men take into account oncoming (future-distant) objects. When one's action is controlled by a symbol for the consequences of the act, he is acting both intelligently (out of cognition) and purposefully. Also, in that case, he is taking into account, through the first part or parts of the act, the final stages of the act, and thereby the chances of the completion of the act are increased.

It may be assumed that purposeful action—action controlled by symbols for things not present—not only increases the chances of the completion of acts but also increases the chances of the survival of individual men and the human species. Consequently, the taking into account of oncoming events by lower animals, although quite unconsciously on their part, is strongly analogous to the taking into account of future events by men through the use of intelligence. The reason many people believe that lower animals act out of purpose and not blindly in taking into account oncoming events is that when *men* take the future into account they often do so consciously and purposefully.

The point to be made here, however, is not that there is purpose in the behavior of lower animals but rather that cognition and reflective thinking in men constitute an improvement over the kind of behavior carried on by lower animals which, although without purpose, nevertheless has survival value. Consequently both lower animals and men have the ability to take oncoming events into account through present behavior. The basic difference is that this taking into account is conscious, cognitive, and purposeful, and is carried on symbolically in men, whereas in lower animals it is not.

Evaluation, Choice, and Freedom

All purposeful behavior involves the use of symbols and symbols are used by human beings only. An act is purposive only if it is controlled by a symbol (or set of symbols) which stands for a future eventuality toward which the act is directed and to which it is causally related. Whether there are genes or vital forces that *direct* biological processes toward certain ends is very doubtful. At least genes are not conscious of the ends involved. But in men there is no doubt that the ends reached in behavior are often represented by symbols even before the activity required for reaching these ends is completed.

Since future eventualities can be represented in a present by symbols only, and since the symbolic process, although carried on by human individuals, emerged at the human social level, it follows that purposive behavior is confined to human beings. All evidence for the existence of the symbolic process is confined to language, and a language exists when one individual, by use of an observable gesture, is able to elicit in himself the same response that he evokes in another member of the group. Proof that a person has done such a thing is always partly introspective, for a person must know on subjective or introspective grounds alone that the response he initiates in another member of the group is the response he *intended* to initiate; i.e., that it has the same form as the response which he initiated in himself implicitly. The response *intended* by one who makes a gesture is known introspectively to have the same form as the overt response of the person stimulated by the gesture. The evidence for the existence of the symbolic process rests finally on introspection, and there is no completely objective (or operational) test for determining its existence. Regardless of the observed behavior of chimpanzees, we can never conclude that they are symbol-users. Since they have no language and since their behavior can be accounted for without assuming the existence of the symbolic process in them, it would be a violation of the law of parsimony to attribute symbolic behavior to them. Hence, it would be fallacious to assume that the behavior of lower animals is purposive.

It would be futile to give assent to behavior that is inevitable and to the consequences of such behavior. If all behavior were inevitable, purposive behavior would be impossible, for when one acts with a purpose he gives assent to both the act and its consequences. Thus the existence of purposive behavior, i.e., behavior to which one gives assent and which is controlled by symbols standing for the consequences of it, presupposes alternative possible ways of acting with their ensuing alternative consequences. To say there are alternative possible ways of acting means these alternatives are equally rational. From the standpoint of descriptive law it is impossible to act irrationally. Consequently, to say a person acts *rationally* means that the act he commits is effective in bringing about a *desired* and *desirable* consequence. From the standpoint of descriptive law, all behavior is rational. From the standpoint of ethics and the good, some behavior is irrational simply because its results are undesirable, i.e., bad.

If men had no choice, if they could not act out of purpose, their behavior would be like a falling stone. We would never say: "The stone falls irrationally; the stone's behavior is unlawful." To control behavior by symbols is to act out of purpose. To act out of purpose is to give assent to or to choose the act with its consequences. To choose is to select from alternative possible and equally rational (from the descriptive standpoint) acts, one that is actually committed. This selection requires evaluation, and evaluation results in the selection, in the actual determination of one out of a number of possible acts.

Since evaluation is not a purely deductive procedure, (inasmuch as it is creative and to that extent nonrational) neither is it deterministic in the rational deductive sense of the word. Evaluation is a comparison of equally rational and equally possible ends or goods. The result of evaluation is a choice or a selection of an end, but this selection means also giving assent to it. To give assent is not simply an intellectual affair. It is also an attitude toward an end, i.e., a disposition to act in such a way as to effect the end selected.

Choice eliminates many possible ends and determines what particular end or ends will become actual. There is nothing extranatural about choice. The symbolic process enters into the determination or the shaping of the future, and it does so simply because a symbol for the distant possible object or event controls an act that is the cause (or a part of the cause) of actualizing that object.

Purposive behavior involves evaluation and choice, and choice is a part of the cause of the actualization of preconceived ends—many of which were never experienced in fact but are, nevertheless, presented to the individual by symbols.

If perchance some philosophers believe there is scientific evidence that choice and purposive behavior do not exist, but rather that everything in the future is determined by past and present physical objects not symbols, I am confident they would muster such evidence from experiments carried on scientifically. What does such an experiment involve? First of all, it means that the scientist had control over the experiment; i.e., he was able to synthesize objects and direct events (at will) in a way they would not have been synthesized and directed if left to themselves. Such experiments could not be carried out unless men had the freedom to control them. Consequently, far from disproving the existence of freedom through experiments, experiments presuppose freedom and choice. Controlled experiments have shown us that many things in nature can be controlled by man, but it does not show that nonthinking objects in nature control men. The most conclusive evidence that men are free is found in the fact that through science men have been able to reach goals quite unattainable otherwise and that science makes possible the achievement of alternative goals, which increases the number of possible ends from which selection is made.

CHAPTER XI

Individualism, the Human Mind and Ethics

Introduction

THE HUMAN MIND is different from the minds of all other animals because it is social in nature. The social dimension of the human mind is possible because men can communicate with each other by use of symbols, signs, words. Ideas are what is communicated, loosely speaking. But scientific symbols enable men to communicate attitudes, or tendencies to act or respond in certain ways, which is the same as the logical structure of responses and behavior patterns. Such attitudes and their corresponding responses are toward physical objects which are known by the scientific symbols employed in communication and, consequently, known in relation to responses. Scientific understanding, which is communicated by scientific symbols, is for the sake of action, and action, in turn, is for the sake of attaining ends freely chosen by men who employ science as a means to the attainment of these ends.

Science is and ought to be a slave to human freedom which, when exercised, sets up ends, goals, values, on other than scientific grounds but which may be attained in part at least through the employment of science as a means. Pure science, i.e., scientific knowledge devoid of ends and of its application, is an abstraction. Pure science presupposes applied science, and applied science presupposes ends for whose attainment it is applied, and the attainment of ends involves human behavior.

It is my contention that the ends to be attained by science are selected on ethical grounds, and human freedom as ordinarily conceived is an ethical freedom in contrast to the freedom of lower animals. Science increases our freedom to the extent that it increases the means of attaining selected goals, but it does not create freedom even as it does not create the responsibility accompanying freedom. Ethical freedom rests finally on the nature of individuals. Integrity, responsibility, conviction, a sense of duty, a sense of decency, all depend on the individual, and I shall defend the view that the nature of individuals cannot be reduced to cultural, environmental, or social factors, nor is its meaning exhausted in terms of them. Rather, each individual is unique, each is creative, and each can assume the responsibility of setting up ends as well as the responsibility of devising scientific means of attaining those ends. Individual persons are also social, and probably everything one does or thinks is conditioned by that culture and society in which he lives. Yet he cannot be assimilated to society, the group, or culture, nor can his thinking and behavior be explained by tradition, the mores, or custom. Tradition and culture represent general social patterns of behavior in society, but they do not account for actual changes that take place. I contend that individuals are responsible for innovations, good or bad, in social action and that these innovations depend on the ethical freedom of individuals. Human freedom is necessarily teleological in character, for freedom means first of all the ability to select ends, and neither pure science nor applied science can tell us whether an end is good or bad, desirable or undesirable, satisfactory or unsatisfactory.

To explain ends, freedom, and individuality in relation to science and society does not mean reducing the former to the latter. Nor does an explanation of the relationship between natural laws and the exercise of freedom imply that freedom can be reduced to law nor that, consequently, ethical choice is determined by forces outside the individual. Many sociologists, anthropologists, and psychologists believe that we can understand completely the behavior as well as the thinking of individuals by recourse to objective laws of behavior. They seem to say, "If we knew enough about the *laws* of thinking and of behavior,

we could *control* the thinking and behavior of individual persons."
This is a contradiction. If the thoughts and behavior of those who are
not social scientists are determined by something over which they have
no control, so are those of the social scientists. Consequently, social
scientists would not be *free* to set up goals; much less would they be
free to attain them.

The assumption that science will empower men to accomplish goals
implies that there are alternative possible goals no particular one of
which must be accomplished. If a particular goal had to be reached regardless of science, then science would be superfluous. If only one goal
or future were possible, then freedom would be impossible. This assumption implies also that the particular goals accomplished would not
have been accomplished without the intervention of science (applied
science). Consequently, science as science does not determine the goals
and is neutral with reference to whether or how science is applied.
Goals are selected by human beings and are always first thought of and
proposed by individuals, not by the group.

The truth of the foregoing remarks may seem obvious to many, but
because of recent developments in the social sciences and because of the
remarks of many interpreters of science, there is the prevalent view that
science is a way of life, an end in itself, that it gives us a comprehensive
understanding of man, and that science, like education in general, will
somehow save the world. Science is not self-corrective nor is it self-
directive. It is a tool, a means devoid of ends, justified if at all on
ethical grounds, on the ground that the ends achieved through its use
are freely chosen and better than ends that would have been effected
without the intervention of either free choice or science.

Reason as a Component of Ethical Judgments

In the process of evolution, animals emerged with the capacity to adjust to variations in the environment. Adjustment implies the ability
to carry on the life process despite the existence of peculiar circumstances and environmental variations that may arise during the life of
the animal. Such adjustment is usually made by conditioned responses.
This means the animal responds to the distant (spatial or temporal)
object by way of a present stimulus, or a stimulus, *s,* evokes a re-

sponse, r, to an object neither directly nor necessarily related to s. The owl is stimulated by twilight to go to the mouth of the cave and "wait" for bats. All conditioning in lower animals or in men that takes place apart from human intelligence and choice takes place accidentally, without plan, purpose, or trial and error. Nevertheless, in every case of such conditioning the response is directed toward the future object and in general increases the chances of survival of the animal.

Reflective thinking is an extension of the process of conditioning. It is internalized conditioning, or conditioning by the symbolic process. Human beings have the ability to condition themselves by means of symbols. In part human freedom means self-conditioning; i.e., the ability of the organism to select the stimuli to which it is going to respond prior to the advent of these stimuli. But responses made to objects, and actions on objects, have their effects also, and consequently the selection of the stimulus entails the effects of the responses made to it. The selection of the stimulus entails controlling the effects of the response made to it and, in general, the spatiotemporal order of these effects. The sole justification for the scientific method is that through the application of it we can effect desirable consequences and prevent undesirable ones from happening. Through the use of symbols we can present to ourselves alternative possible future consequences of various responses, and a symbolic representation of these alternative conditions is what is involved in choice.

Research scientists often remind us of the fact that they have no concern for how their findings are to be applied and that pure science is devoid of ends. Yet basic knowledge will lend itself to the accomplishment of various ends indifferently. Also the alternative ends that a person can present to himself symbolically are equally possible. The lumber will lend itself to being made into a desk or a chair, and the tools at hand are equally useful in making either. Neither the material nor the tools determine the end; both are neutral. A desirable consequence or a selected end is necessary for all behavior, with its ensuing consequences, conditioned by and controlled by intelligence, the symbolic process.

Choice, then, depends on the symbolic process, a process that emerged at the human social level, for symbols are found in languages only, and languages emerge out of the co-operative behavior of human beings.

George H. Mead[1] has given a naturalistic account of the origin of the self as arising out of the co-operative behavior of members of the group. For the organism to have a self requires that the organism, by use of the symbolic process, be able to take the role of another member of the group, which means to represent to one's self that part of a social co-operative act which will be carried out by the other organism (or person). Role-taking, then, means calling out in one's self (symbolically) the response that will be made overtly by another organism in a social act; that is, by use of symbols a person can present to himself the entire overt act *before* it takes place. The ability to symbolize an overt act is the basis for all planning and for all purposive behavior.

Symbols are also the means by which analysis of the act is effected. An overt act often becomes habitual with men even as it does with lower animals. But whereas a habit can be broken and a new one set up in lower animals only through the mechanism of conditioned response, in the human being it may be effected by means of the symbolic process. This self-conditioning by human beings is a reorganization of the parts of one act or several acts into a new act which may effect a goal unlike any that has occurred previously.

By virtue of the symbolic process (a process carried on by individual organisms but only in relation to human group behavior) human beings are able to condition and recondition themselves and in that sense are both creative and free. If men did not employ the symbolic process they would be neither creative nor "free" in the sense in which we apply the term to men; i.e., freedom means self-determination, and self-determination refers to the determination of one's behavior by a process inside the organism and not by processes outside it or in its environment.

Although the symbolic process emerges in group behavior only, it is carried on by individual organisms. There is no group mind, no corporate mind, no group opinion, but minds and opinions of individual organisms only. Consequently, individuals, not the group as a whole, devise (create) new ideas, new plans of action. Individuals con-

[1] See *Mind, Self, and Society* (Chicago, University of Chicago Press, 1934).

stitute the source of novel proposals for actions. Individuals only can be radicals; they can be antisocial, but the group as a whole cannot be so. Individuals can tell lies and have new ideas that are false. But they can also have new ideas that are true. The attempt to account for the thoughts and ideas of the individual by showing that they are consequences of mores and public opinion breaks down when it comes to explaining lies and false ideas. All will agree that their source is the subject and the subjective. Behaviorists have not succeeded in stating the nature of erroneous beliefs by recourse to stimuli in the environment. Rather, every behavioristic approach to an understanding of the subjective results in a discovery of something unlawful about each person, and the psychologist attributes the unlawful to "individual differences."

These individual differences, manifested in the unanticipated, unique responses of individual persons to a given situation, are the sources of unique creative symbolic representations of overt action which leads to a modification of custom, culture and habitual social behavior. Consequently, human beings enter into the creative advance of history because of the ingenuity of at least some members of society. In so far as men behave intelligently they determine custom, culture, and the structure of institutions; and to the extent that they do so, they are free. Statesmen in every democracy know that the freedom of their country depends upon the freedom of individual citizens. A country cannot give freedom to its people. A country lacks freedom when its citizens are not free, and only people can suppress other people, and if they are suppressed, only people can free them; only men can throw off the unwanted chains of custom.

Although the individual is the source of new ideas, before these ideas can be put into social practice or become institutionalized in a democracy they must be accepted by the group. Freedom of speech and press are recognized as essential to the democratic manner of calling on the people for the solution of contemporary social problems. The recognition of the rights of minority groups is an implicit acknowledgment of the necessity of calling on these groups, and finally their individual members, for proposed solutions of political, social problems. Even with the knowledge that false beliefs and improper proposed solutions come from individual members of society, still a democracy must take its chance with radicals and subversives in order to reap the beneficial rewards of individuals with constructive, though novel, ideas.

Any attempt to account for the creative, novel ideas by assimilating them (as effects) to such things as culture, heredity, or environment (as causes) fails to take evolution into account and unwittingly falls back on a rationalistic, mechanistic conception of nature and the individual. Just as the general theory of evolution implies the innovation of novel forms of things the like of which never existed prior to their emergence, so language is an emergent, a novel way of communicating, and language with its accompanying symbolic process lays the basis for the emergence of the human individual with its capacity to create new ideas. These ideas have conditions or causes, but in accordance with the theory of evolution, as opposed to rationalism, they cannot be assimilated to their causes. If minds were purely passive, though receptive, there could be no adequate account of false beliefs and errors. Only by assuming that mind is creative can we arrive at the concept of falsity. Similarly, it can create new and constructive ideas. Since individual men can and do have new ideas that cannot be reduced to the conditions necessary (but not sufficient) for them, it is clear that culture, including science, does not make the individual what he is. Individuals determine culture and the course of history.

Science (including applied science, technology, and industry) does not determine the behavior of free men. Rather men direct and use science in order to achieve goals selected from a number of alternative possible, equally rational ones. Those who hold that the thoughts and behavior of individuals are completely explainable in principle, if not in fact, in terms of forces and factors outside the individual must acknowledge finally that, according to their own doctrine, freedom and ethical responsibility are meaningless terms.

Ethics and the Individual

Early modern physical scientists, such as Galileo, Kepler, Boyle, and Huygens, clearly recognized and openly acknowledged the difference between science and ethics. Science was considered by them to be a study of nature with an attempt to find and state its laws. They recognized the difference between the status quo in society and what ought to be. In fact they made a covenant with ecclesiastical authority to the effect that as scientists they would not meddle with social affairs. At that time there was widespread agreement in Europe that values, ends, and the purpose of living were prescribed by the Hebraic-Christian tradition. The conflict between science and religion from that day to this has been over the question whether the Greek tradition with its emphasis on reason and science is adequate to account for the ethical nature of man, for "goals" and "values." Can purposes, final causes, be assimilated to reason and efficient causes? Is the Hebraic-Christian tradition, or something like it, necessary? Many have suggested, after the Greek stoics, that there are natural, objective, civil laws and that the distinction between conventional law *(nomos)* and natural law *(physis)* should be abolished. Some say science is self-directive and self-corrective. Others speak of natural laws in economics, and still others say that that government which governs least governs best. These attitudes rest on the implicit if not explicit assumption that the rationalistic component of the Greek tradition is adequate for society and that discussions of freedom and the unique character of individuals is nonsense.

Auguste Comte made the suggestion that theology, including the Hebraic-Christian, was really an alternative to science, that its purported function was to explain phenomena. He held that science supersedes theology (and metaphysics) and that because of the advent of science we should forget theology. He would not grant that the Hebraic-Christian tradition could be reconciled with the Greek. They are, according to him, incompatible, competitive, alternative ways of accounting for phenomena. Comte could not understand that the direction and the application of science requires an evaluation of goals and that these goals are not furnished by science itself. He was confused. He could not distinguish between means (science) and ends (values). He could not understand that since science is neutral regarding ends, it does not determine how or whether it is applied in achieving them.

This Comtian confusion has infiltrated into contemporary social science. Many social scientists today assume that the Greek tradition is adequate to encompass external nature and human life. This does not mean that social scientists believe freedom, ethical responsibility, and the creativity of the human mind can be explained rationally or scientifically. Rather, it means that since these terms cannot be so explained they are meaningless and refer to nothing. They speak of determinism in a pre-evolutionary, rationalistic sense; cultural determinism, environmental determinism, institutional determinism, technological determinism.

The reason for the revolt against theology by the social scientists is clear. They think not only of theology but of ethics also as disciplines competing with science. For them it is either science or final causes, which amount to purposes, spiritual direction. Consequently, in order to save science with its determinisms, they must deny the existence of things talked about in ethics—freedom, choice, responsibility, final causes, purposes. Yet these same scientists turn around and say "Science will save us, it is the messiah, and when we know enough about how the behavior of individuals and society is controlled, we can use science to achieve our goals."

It may be that the Hebraic-Christian tradition is subject to criticism, that it has at times misled us and presented us with ideals and values that need re-evaluating. But even if it were discarded altogether, *some* ethical system and some set of values would be necessary for directing and applying science. Science per se does not select the ends for which it may be applied as a means to achieving them. (Neither do values and goals select the means of accomplishing them.)

Some have argued that evaluation characterizes deductive arguments and logical analysis in the same manner and to the same extent that it does ethical decisions. Both the true and the false conclusion are presented to the mind in argument, and drawing a definite conclusion requires evaluation. They argue, then, that no distinction can be made between ethical judgments and rational judgments and all ethical judgments are reducible to rational evaluation. But granting that there may be evaluation in both logical argument and in ethical judgment, still they are different kinds of evaluation. Ethical judgment requires the evaluation of alternative possible ends each one of which can be attained in a perfectly rational way. (In fact no end can be attained by irrational means.) In logical evaluation, however, the end or conclusion is accepted because its contradictory is irrational with reference to the premises. Knowledge of fact resulting from pure science is neutral and there is nothing in it that compels its use. Nevertheless it, like a craftsman's tools, lends itself to being used in alternative equally rational ways, but the ends achieved thereby are not equally ethical or moral.

Now even if men set up certain ethical objectives as basic, such as happiness or survival, still the question arises; what in the future will give us happiness (or the greatest amount of it or the best kind), and not whether, but how, do we want to survive? There are alternative ways in which to be happy and alternative ways in which we can survive, each of which is as rational as the other. This cannot be said for the conclusions of arguments. Hume says reason is and ought to be a slave to the passions. Even if he were right we would still have the ethical problem of deciding which passions are to be gratified and when and where, and reasons would not move us to use reason, even as science cannot move us to employ it as a slave.

Finally, the alternative possible courses of action are all present while we consider and compare them. They are equally rational in the sense that, if our reasoning is sound, they present to the thinker equally correct ways of achieving alternative ends. With the same money one can buy a coat or a gun and with the same gun one can kill a deer or a man in a "very scientific way." These alternatives are present in thought; symbols for them are here now. But in practice they cannot all be achieved at the same time if at all. The achievement of one may completely eliminate the other, and certainly they cannot be achieved simultaneously. Ethical judgment or evaluation, then, results in eliminating some alternative possible ends and determining which others will be actualized; consequently, the spatiotemporal order of the achievement of ends is thereby determined also.

In ethical evaluation we do not judge the rationality of an act and thereby judge that certain means will accomplish a certain end. Rather we lay the means-ends problem to one side, inasmuch as it belongs properly to science and the factual studies, and judge that certain ends should be accomplished at certain times and places despite the fact that their actualization will eliminate alternative ends that could be accomplished by equally available and equally rational means. Ethical evaluation, like rational evaluation, is for the sake of practice. But whereas reason (and pure science) ends in contemplation and in giving assent to conclusions that are true and rejecting false ones, ethical judgments give assent to ends with their entailed method of achievement at the expense of other ends. Ethical decision, then, eliminates certain possibilities from being actualized and determines the actualization of certain others, all of which are equally possible and attainable by using science and the materials at hand as means. We do not eliminate ends on the basis of truth and falsity but on the basis of good and better. An ethical judgment leading to assent initiates the act that accomplishes the end. Pure reason and science neither initiate nor motivate.

Whether or not ethical evaluation is conditioned by the passions, pleasure, or a sense of duty, is irrelevant to the practical problem of which pleasures and which duties have priority over others in their competition for the practices of men. The important fact is that there are genuine alternatives as envisaged by the use of the symbolic process and as equally realizable by means of scientific knowledge and factual materials at hand, but not all can be realized at the same place and time, and in many cases the realization of one possible alternative excludes all others. If, then, ethical assent to an end initiates the scientific means of actualizing what was previously only possible, it also eliminates other ends. And although ethical responsibility consists of the responsibility for eliminating as well as determining ends, no purely logical argument eliminates anything. Reason, in that sense, leads to nontemporal, nonspatial ends, or, as some say, to pure possibilities and eternal truths.

It may be pointed out that one could start with certain arbitrary assumptions in ethics (even as all formal and factual disciplines must do), in which case ethical judgment would then consist of drawing conclusions in a perfectly rational way from these assumptions as premises. If killing is bad and if a particular act will lead to the death of a person, then it is bad; i.e., it should be eliminated as a means since the end is bad. But evaluations of this sort do not constitute crucial ethical problems. Crucial ethical problems involve a choice between (1) whether we should give assent to one or more particular basic principles (with reference to which particular acts may be judged good or bad), and (2) what particular good ends should we give assent to though other good ends must be eliminated in doing so (i.e., which of the good ends is better or best?). This does not mean, which end is good or better or best under all circumstances and in general. If it did, ethics could be settled either deductively or by command. The question of best and better has a practical and unique setting in actual circumstances that change continually. Ethics is a matter neither of indoctrination nor pure reason. It is concerned with actualization, but also with the spatiotemporal order of actualization. We can make neither an experimental nor a deductive science out of ethics. To make it into a deductive discipline is to ignore the particular circumstances that call for ethical judgment (vs. routine, customary behavior) in the first place. To make it into an experimental discipline is to ignore the fact that the acceptance of one end, and the consequent experience of it as an accomplished fact, means the elimination of others, which precludes a comparison of actualized alternative ends by experience. The comparison takes place at the symbolic level only, and a contrary-to-fact condition cannot be compared experientially to a factual situation. From which we must conclude that ethics is not a science despite the fact that it deals with practice and the world of fact. One cannot gamble with his life. There are no odds.

Individualism is expressed in practice and its expression is initiated by ethical judgments which terminate in assent. The practice based on ethical judgment is often a departure from ordinary practice, custom, and the mores. John Dewey points out that among primitive people individualism is at a very low ebb. Primitives believe the ways of conduct are pre-established and eternal, and, consequently, the business of the individual is to conform. This attitude is not altogether lacking in our own society. There are many who believe that the ways of practice and all "moral" conduct have been stipulated by eternal truths. Other less theologically inclined ethicists hold that ethics is a rational discipline and that how a person should act under given circumstances, even though these circumstances are unique, has a universal form. But rapid changes in our society help us to understand that changes in the external world call for changes of custom and of culture itself. These changes are proposed by individuals and not by the group, nor are they suggested by public opinion. During a crisis there is no "public opinion" capable of meeting it. During a disaster we do not ask: "What is the customary thing to do?" Much of governmental policy in America today would have been meaningless one hundred years ago, and much of it will be inapplicable one hundred years hence. New economic, social, political policies are not deducible from previous policy or laws nor from the Constitution of the United States, which is itself subject to change. Every case brought to the Supreme Court for decision is looked at not only from the point of view of the intent of those who proposed and agreed to accept the Constitution but also from the standpoint of the new situation giving rise to the case. Every interpretation of the Constitution is, therefore, a new interpretation, and intepretation is not a deductive matter. If it were, there would be no split decisions, no minority reports.

Not only are new governmental policies first proposed by individuals but so are all the other, less inclusive, institutional policies. Every policy, when carried out, determines the order of events and the nature of ends reached, and it also excludes other possible alternative practices and ends. In a democracy ends and policies are made for men, for free men, and not men for ends, custom, culture. New conditions call for new policies and the individual is the source of them. Many new policies proposed by individuals are unacceptable to the group, and some of them are said to be radical, absurd, treasonable, unpatriotic; but some policies are accepted, and their individual authors are often rewarded to the extent of having their names attached to the plans. Every democracy recognizes the value of individuals and minority groups as the source of new constructive proposals designed to meet new situations, and in so doing every democracy has institutionalized change.

Individuals do not think in a vacuum. Their ideas and proposals are related to the behavior of the group, to custom, culture, and mores, but by no means identical with nor deducible from them. Pure science is one of the basic factors conditioning the thinking of individuals as they make new proposals for action. Science increases the freedom of individuals to the extent that it furnishes the method of attaining new and a greater number of ends. Raw materials or "natural" resources also are necessary for ethical judgments; and with the combination of know-how and materials, both freedom and responsibility are increased, but neither raw material nor know-how will direct itself toward the attainment of goals. Only a drunken driver will permit the horses to take him home, and then "home" is where he came from, not where he intended to go.

An ethical judgment, like an emergent, is novel and, therefore, unpredictable. But whereas an emergent such as a new biological form (mutation) may produce others like itself and whereas it is possible for the scientist to reconstruct circumstances similar to the ones that produced the emergent form originally, it is impossible in fact to reconstruct conditions that serve as a basis for ethical judgments. In this sense, then, every ethical judgment is unique, unpredictable, free, and if the word "determined" applies to it, it applies in the sense that the conditions for it are necessary, but not in the sense that these same conditions would lead to the same ethical judgment. This does not mean the same conditions would not lead to the same judgment. The point is that there can never be the same conditions since the ethical judgment itself, being not of the nature of giving assent or consent to an established, habitual, customary way of acting, determines a new future (or a part of it) by selecting certain as yet unrealized ends thereby precluding the realization of alternative but equally possible ends achievable (at the time of the judgment) by equally rational means. Ethical judgments, then, determine the course of history, and there is only one history. In this sense Bergson is correct in holding that there is a necessary relationship between time (in the nonspatialized sense) and free will. That part of human behavior known as the history of a people or a culture is precisely that part in which ethical judgments were necessary ingredients in the determination of it. For that reason, also, that part of history is irrepeatable and unique. Also, for that reason, it may be possible to state the necessary conditions for historical events, but one can never state the just-sufficient ones. There is no experimenting with historical events. A people's history is unique, even as the process of evolution is unique, and the determination of the order of events is by way of individuals, each of whom—in so far as he enters into the determination of history by ethical judgments—expresses his own individuality and uniqueness.

From the standpoint of descriptive law all behavior is rational. Even the behavior of an insane person can be accounted for. No physical laws are ever suspended or broken. No conduct is irrational from that standpoint. Yet much of it is immoral. All we can ever mean by saying "That person's conduct is irrational" is either that he is not employing the proper means to effect desired ends or that what he is doing is not controlled by symbols for an end. Ethical judgment, then, is not a matter of acting rationally or irrationally. It is a matter of determining which ends are to be achieved. The means of achieving ends, i.e., rational procedure, is left to science, and the method employed never becomes an ethical problem unless it accomplishes ends judged on ethical grounds to be good or bad. It is clear that a method quite efficient in accomplishing a major end may produce in its wake many undesirable ends. Whether it will be employed nevertheless is an ethical problem.

Those who would deny the existence of genuine ethical problems would have to prove that there is only one possible order of events, that the goals to be achieved are already determined, or that there is only one possible rational order. This would imply that the ends for which pure science is to be used as a means are entailed by pure science, that it is not neutral, that freedom and responsibility are meaningless terms.

CHAPTER XII

The Social Sciences, Freedom and the Individual

Human Societies

BECAUSE OF FIXED GOALS and means of attaining them, the societies of lower animals have no social problems. Human societies, too, have both goals and manners of achieving them. But unlike other societies, members of human groups are conscious of their goals (values, ideals) and of the means of attaining them (norms, institutionalized behavior patterns, mores). And, by using the symbolic process, men can change both the norms, the ways of achieving goals, and the goals themselves. Without this consciousness and the ability to change both values and norms, there would be no social problems.

Men are not only interested in surviving but also in *how* they survive. Since there are alternative ways of surviving, both the freedom and the responsibility of each member of a human society is increased beyond that of a lower animal by virtue of the ability of men to use symbols both to indicate to themselves values and norms and to control behavior in achieving values (ends).

Every human society is distinguished from every other human society primarily by (1) its values, objectives, goals, ends, and (2) its behavior patterns, institutionalized manners of acting, its norms. Furthermore, the fact that different societies are usually separated geographically is accidental, despite Radcliff Brown's contrary contention that all norms are determined by the environment and that survival per se is the fixed end of each.

Any social scientist who proposes either environmental, social, or cultural determinism will end with the conclusion that both values and norms are determined by factors outside individuals and, consequently, that there are no such things as social problems. All such advocates would interpret the behavior of human societies exactly as they interpret that of lower societies. Accordingly, they would be forced to conclude that all changes in "norms" take place unwittingly and accidentally and, as Radcliff Brown suggests, the only end would be unadulterated survival, a biological value pure and simple.

Social Problems

Fuller and Meyers say, "Social problems are what people think they are."[1] Although it is true that people must be conscious of social problems before they can do anything about them, nevertheless, the situation of which they are conscious has objective status whether thought about or not. Actually, there are two basic causes for social problems: (1) disagreement among members of a society (under the same government) over values to be defended or achieved—this implies that the consequences of avoidable practices by some members of society are opposed to the general welfare; and (2) disagreement over the means of achieving values—often caused by cultural lag in which the ends or values are not put in question but rather the norms or practices used to achieve them do not employ the best available technical means. Cultural lag is inevitable since the means furnished by pure science necessarily precedes the application. All social problems caused by cultural lag are concerned with changing the attitudes (and patterns of behavior) of people so that their values can be achieved more efficiently. The prevention of smallpox through vaccination required both legislation and the substitution of new techniques of prevention for old ineffective ones, such as magic or prayer. Often social problems are solved by community discussion—members of a community may agree to build parks and gymnasiums to prevent juvenile delinquency.

[1] R. C. Fuller and R. R. Meyers, "Some Aspects of a Theory of Social Problems," *American Sociological Review,* VI (1941), 24–32.

But in no case can social scientists as scientists solve social problems.

Social problems are not to be confused with technical ones. Techniques are confined to means alone and are neutral regarding ends. Einstein writes:[2]

Science, however, cannot create ends and, even less, instill them in human beings; science at most can supply the means by which to attain certain ends. But the ends themselves are conceived by personalities with lofty ethical ideals and—if these ends are not stillborn, but vital and vigorous— are adopted and carried forward by those many human beings who, half unconsciously, determine the slow evolution of society.

The fact that social problems necessarily involve values not discovered or questioned by pure science is recognized by some sociologists today. "It is exactly this disagreement in value-judgments that is the root cause of all social problems, both in the original definition of the condition as a problem and in subsequent efforts to solve it."[3] I must add that all value judgments, all considerations for what is good either as means or as an end, is conditioned finally by a theory of the worth of either some or all individuals. According to Kant, no way of achieving an end, if it is good, will use another person as a means. And even in a social system where it is considered good to use men (as slaves) to achieve the good of the exploiting class, it would not be considered good to use one member of the exploiting class to achieve the good of another member.

In principle, in a democracy no person shall be used as a means to the accomplishment of the ends of others. It follows, therefore, that an end or objective, regardless of how good it may be, cannot justify every means of attaining it. In other words, the method of achievement, the norms themselves, have value or are of value, and this is precisely why norms become institutionalized and, in some cases, are transformed into ritual, a pattern of social behavior that exists for its own sake divorced from ends for which it was originally designed. Pure science itself is subject to the same danger, and often a pure scientist, like a religious priest, unthinkingly declares pure research to be a way of life—an end in itself.

Although there is an international "code of ethics" supposed to be

[2] *Out of My Later Years* (New York, Philosophical Library, 1950), p. 124.
[3] Fuller and Meyers, *op. cit.,* p. 27.

employed even during war, these codes are often forgotten and the end, victory, often "justifies" any means whatsoever of achieving it. Often heroes are made, not in accordance with the technological niceties employed in killing members of the enemy group (sportsmanship is laid to one side) but in accordance with the number of enemies killed. But among members of a group held together by bonds stronger than the values engaging them in social conflict, the actual resolution of the conflict is of no higher value (if as high) and is no more important, than the method used in resolving the conflict.

It is no accident that the sense of sportsmanship is emphasized especially in the democracies. It is common to hear that both the games for children and for adults teach the contestants how to be fair and how to consider other contestants as equals. As much value is placed on good sportsmanship as on good athletes. In general, anyone who insists on attaining ends regardless of the means of attaining them has a distorted sense of value and has not solved in the least the problem of the co-ordination of values.

Conditions for Social Problems

The recognition and actual presence of social problems came late in history. Slavery to the Greeks and Egyptians was not a social problem, nor was exploitation of laborers by aristocratic groups in ancient and relatively recent times. Whenever individuals are forced to adhere to the mores and social practices in a society, no social problems are recognized.

1. Before there can be social problems a group of people must be held together by certain political bonds, regardless of how loosely woven or how strong they may be. Such a group constitutes a society. Their unity, because of these governing bonds, distinguishes them from other human societies.

2. A human society, regardless of size, held together by political bonds, must recognize certain objectives or goals as basic to the good life. These objectives are believed by these people to be of the highest value, and all lesser values are oriented with respect to them. Without these values no social problem could arise, yet by themselves they are not sufficient to give rise to problems.

In Western culture basic values have been bequeathed to us through the Hebraic-Christian and Greek traditions, and inevitably they are defended on ethical grounds, not on scientific grounds. The locus of these values is in individual members of a society and is neither in institutions nor in science.

3. An explicit acknowledgment that changes in social practices can be made through the use of intelligence is necessary for every social problem. What is inevitable cannot be a problem, and whatever takes place without a plan takes place without choice. Consequently, there are no real alternatives to it, and it cannot constitute a social problem.

4. Social practices (or the behavior of individuals in a society) cannot become social problems unless society recognizes (a) that the individuals, whose practices they are, have a legal and ethical right either to willfully object to these practices or give assent to them, and (b) these rights are to have consideration in reforming these practices. This implies: i) The domination by one individual or a group of individuals in society over another individual or group of individuals cannot have legal or social approval. If there is legal and social approval of slavery, then slavery cannot be a social problem. This applies also to "problems" of segregation or the "ownership" of children by parents. ii) Social problems cannot arise in a society where there is complete dictatorship or complete domination (legally and socially recognized) by one group over another. iii) Put positively, social problems can emerge only within the framework of democracy and in those areas in society where democracy is recognized. The absence of a democratic form of government does not imply the absence of democracy in all areas in that society. But if democracy is absent in all areas, then no social problems whatsoever can arise.

5. A recognition of the responsibility of society to try to solve a social problem is a prerequisite for its existence. This implies that individual members of society must believe (or recognize) that they are partly responsible for the attitudes and consequent practices of other members of society. In a representative democracy the duly elected representatives should assume the responsibility entailed by the explicit recognition of such responsibility.

6. There must be recognition of the fact that new kinds of social problems emerge from time to time and that new norms or social

practices are necessary to solve these problems. Without this recognition, the proposed solution to so-called social problems (i.e., adultery, stealing, divorce) would be that we return to eternally fixed mores and ideals. In that case the sole responsibility would be on the individual violator, and his fellows would practice the hands-off policy. That is, problems would not be social. "Where there is temptation there is grace sufficient to overcome it."

7. It must be realized that basic values do not come from science but that science is a means of solving social problems resulting from a conflict over values as ends and values as norms. The social sciences do not give us or discover for us basic social values. Rather they offer information, based on facts, that may help solve social problems caused by conflicts in attitudes and values.

8. When social problems are solved each member of society, in so far as the problem affects him, must give assent to the new social practices necessary for solving them and each will shape his behavior accordingly. This implies: (a) If members of society are forced to conform against their will, the social problem has not been solved. The prohibition amendment did not solve the social problem of drinking. (b) Acting out of fear of consequences cannot be a motive for behavior if the social problem is solved. (c) Punishment, in the traditional sense of the word, is not a means to the solution of social problems. If the reason for not stealing is fear of punishment, then the attitudes of the thief (i.e., his personal proposed plan of action to which he willfully gives assent) are in conflict, for he does not subscribe to the property rights of others, and does not willfully assent to defending these rights. No social problem can be settled by threat, duress, or physical force. The control of lower animals is often effected by force recognized as expedient, but no social problems are involved. To get the chimpanzee to go into his cage and to behave is not a social problem, but if the chimpanzee had any rights, it could become a social problem.

9. If certain persons or distinguishable groups of persons in a society have no recognized rights in a certain area or areas, then no social problems can emerge within those areas. If Negroes had no right to an education, then even if they did not and could not get an education, there would be no social problem. If the state had no right to interfere in the treatment of children by parents, then whatever the parent did

to his children would not be the basis for a social problem. Under Hitler, the attitude of Jews toward their treatment in camps was not a social problem for the Nazis. In America, until recently, the attitude of prisoners toward their treatment did not give rise to social problems, for it was assumed that prisoners have no rights, and that control of their behavior had to be by force, even as with lower animals.

10. Unless it were assumed that the institutions and approved social practices of a society could be changed for the good of society, no social problem could arise. Wherever a social problem exists, it must be assumed that its solution involves more people than the person or persons whose behavior gives rise to the problem. Its solution requires that society change external conditions or laws or practices so that behavior can be changed also, and so changed that it is conducive to the welfare of the entire group.

This implies, (a) The solution of a social problem cannot be made through preaching, with the assumption that institutions are good and fixed and some individual members of society are evil and must change their attitudes. If this were the case, such social problems as juvenile gangs would involve police force and "correction" homes only, but not improvement in such areas as parks and play supervision. (b) To recognize any problem as social is to assume that the mores or values (the institutional structure of society) are at fault, not the individual directly concerned in the problem. A person who steals bread (for his children) is not at fault if his stealing constitutes a social problem. Children without supervision are not to blame for their mischievous conduct. The more serious question: Is the individual or society immoral?

11. Social problems are not religious problems. The social sciences must justify their existence by the claim that the problems of society cannot be solved by exhortation and the subjective approach. This claim is far-reaching and even revolutionary. Where can we draw the line between the responsibility of the individual and the responsibility of society with its institutions, mores, and values? The answer to this question is confusing to many social scientists. Once the claim is made that environmental circumstances are a condition for crime, social scientists tend to go the whole way, and many of them end with a determinism in which the individual purportedly has no responsibility. If

that were the case, how could any individual, sociologist or other, be responsible for changing social institutions? On the other hand, if the individual directly involved in a social problem had to assume full responsibility (the traditional religious attitude) then institutions need not be changed, and the "social problem" would disappear. This is why I said, in the introduction and under (4) above, that social problems came late in history and require a new approach to their solution. Also, this is precisely why the approach to the solution of problems by the social scientist is in conflict with the traditional theological approach.

I believe individual responsibility must be assumed by every member of society. This is the locus of freedom and responsibility emphasized by the Hebraic-Christian tradition. Since, however, a person is also an integral part of society, the institutional practices can be changed for the good of both the individual and society. An overemphasis on the religious tradition—on the morality of institutions and the immorality of individuals—leads to the belief that values and norms are fixed. A defense of this view in its extreme form is responsible for the fact that many social practices degenerate into ceremonies, and often the individual is sacrificed for the good of "the state." Similarly the extreme view that society alone is responsible for how individuals behave leads to social, cultural, or environmental determinism. Neither view, in its extreme form, makes sense.

Norms and Values

Roughly speaking, a norm is a social act approved and accepted by at least some members of a group; e.g., driving in the right-hand lane, defending the rights of others at court, respecting and defending property rights, marriage ceremonies. All norms are conventional and are conditioned and limited only by basic biological, social, religious, and economic needs. These basic needs are considered to be ultimate and unchanging for men, or they are said to be basic values. By some they are considered to give motivation and direction to all behavior, and in that sense they help determine and give form to all norms. In many cases, then, norms are means of attaining basic values. Food has basic value and the means of acquiring it is a norm. Stealing food is

wrong. But norms cannot be considered mere means to the achievement of ends. Often they have intrinsic value or are valuable for their
own sake as well as for the attainment of ends. A quilting bee, a husking bee, shopping at the store, building a bridge, tilling the soil, all
may be of both individual and social value in themselves as well as
means to acquiring other values. Pragmatists have emphasized this
fact by insisting that action is good in itself and that the rewards of
living are found in the process of living and not in a hereafter. If life
is for its own sake, then norms (means) also have intrinsic value. There
is nothing wrong or inconsistent about rituals and ceremonies if it is
clearly understood that they exist for their own sake or as symbols for
other things and that they neither preclude nor are a means to the accomplishment of anything beyond themselves. People sing for the
sake of singing, dance for the sake of dancing, enjoy art for art's sake,
and often find satisfaction in the act of attaining another value.

Consequently, norms cannot be judged wholly from the standpoint of their technical efficiency. They must be judged from an ethical
standpoint also. From a strictly technical standpoint it might be better
to have individuals separated from each other while husking corn,
but this would preclude the achievement of social values that are
found in the social act per se. An act is ethically wrong if it is not
necessary to commit it and if it interferes with the attainment of maxi-
mum value for the group. To test the accuracy of my gun by shooting at
a tin can in my neighbor's window may be technically proper and even
good for my immediate purposes, but morally wrong. Even if an act is
the most technically efficient for achieving an end and does not interfere with the attainment of other values, it may still be unsatisfactory
on other grounds. Utensils for eating should be aesthetic as well as
practical. And every particular act has its social significance inasmuch as
it indicates an attitude toward life and toward other members of society. Marriage ceremonies, commemorating services, inaugurations,
burial ceremonies indicate atttitudes and one's respect for social values
beyond these particular acts. Even the clothes one wears indicate his
attitude toward others.

Social problems arise when attitudes of different members of the
group prevent co-operation in carrying out a social act which admittedly
would result in a common good, or when the co-ordination of indi-

vidual acts and the consequences thereof lead to conflicting goals. Hence, all social problems are concerned with the co-ordination of norms as well as the co-ordination of values.

Often the achievement of a certain end makes it impossible to achieve what was once an alternative end; one cannot both eat an egg and hatch it, nor can one make a table and a bookcase with the same lumber. An end should not be selected simply because it is desirable in itself but because one believes it in turn will be conducive to the achievement of other desirable ends. In other words, selection may be conditioned by a consideration of the harmony of ends. Before such co-ordination can be made, one must think not only of the ends isolated from other phases of the process of which they are a part but also, and especially, of the manner in which those ends are to be achieved. This requires that the various processes existing independent of men be so organized that their confluence will occur at the proper place and time in order to effect desired ends. Men can organize these processes only by first organizing their own bodily behavior, for it is through behavior alone, controlled by symbols for desired ends, that men can bring other processes in nature together so that the result is satisfactory. To organize an act means to order its parts not only with reference to the immediate environment necessary for executing it but also with reference to its consequences.

If one takes into consideration not only the immediate end which the act is designed to achieve, but also possible mediate consequences, then he is planning with reference to a more general principle (or principles). These are ethical principles, and a socially accepted plan of co-ordination is called a social norm.

Norms are guiding principles formulated for the purpose of securing ends harmoniously and securing harmonious ends. A norm is based on a principle—an ethical principle—which is a different kind of principle from what is formulated by scientists when they are confining their statements to unalterable relationships in nature. The principle of the lever states how things, under specified conditions, will behave inevitably. Such a principle is concerned with what of necessity was, is, or will be, but not with what *ought to be,* or with what might better be. Often scientists simply want to know what kind of end (or result) follows from a particular kind of process. To desire an end is a different matter, and to desire a harmony of ends is a still different matter.

Nature offers us no law or principle according to which we can arrive at or deduce the norms which, if applied in achieving ends, would guarantee a harmony of these ends. Neither the pure scientist nor the technician can, through his research, discover the goals we "ought" to seek, nor, consequently, can they discover the norms that might best be employed in achieving those goals in order to guarantee a harmony of ends. The reason for these limitations is clear, for even if an end is agreed upon, there may be many equally rational technical ways of achieving it, and a choice of a particular way, then, must be made on other than purely technical grounds. Consequently, it will be impossible to state a law according to which the means must be chosen. This being the case, there can be no "natural" norm that is to be followed in the achievement of ends.

Values that are not norms are ends or goals co-ordinated and integrated with other desired ends. Such things as health, peace, security, friendship, and eating may be values. If these and other things are values, it is because they are desired *and* because they have been compared or *evaluated* with respect to each other. In fact, desiring is a kind of evaluation which involves selection. To evaluate ends is to order them with respect to other ends, and this requires that these ends belong to a system. Values, then, are confined to means and ends that have been systematized and are believed to be in harmony with each other. Once we accept a few ends as basic, such as life, liberty, property, the pursuit of happiness, and friendship it becomes much easier to evaluate other ends with reference to these basic ones. No end need remain fixed in a system, but it is doubtful that the entire system of values can be changed all at once. In practice we change one or more values (or deny that they are good) by appeal to the inconsistency (disharmony) with other universally accepted values, i.e., universal with respect to a group of persons.

Albeit values and norms are correlative terms, they are, nevertheless, distinguishable, even as ends and means are distinguishable. Norms do not refer to ends directly but refer to the means of acquiring ends, and they specify the moral form, as opposed to the technical form, of a particular means of acquiring particular ends. The technical aspect of the means is left to the pure research scientist and the technician. Norms are concerned, rather, with that aspect of the means which will have its effects and repercussions on mediate ends. Consequently, they are concerned with behavior in so far as that behavior, which is designed especially to reach a particular, immediate end, affects the attainment of mediate ends. Norms concern the social implications of the immediate technical act, and their function is to control one's behavior in applying technical knowledge toward the achievement of certain values without interfering with the achievement of other values. They inform us also that if a specific value cannot be achieved without interfering with the achievement of certain other desired ones, then there is no rational defense for achieving it, for its achievement would lead finally to something undesirable.

Here we see that if one is to defend his belief that a certain end is good, he must show among other things that it is harmonious with other generally accepted ends (or values), and if he is to justify his behavior in reaching that end, he must show that such behavior is consistent with established norms. Thus, starting with generally accepted ends and norms as the basis for argument, one can argue that his end is *good* and that his way of achieving it is *moral*. Neither the generally accepted ends nor the norms prescribe either our particular ends or the particular (technical) way of achieving them. It is assumed, rather, that there are many alternative possible achievable ends, some of which are consistent with what, for the time, are our basic values, and that there are many alternative possible ways of achieving ends, some of which are consistent with accepted norms.

A technical act has reference to the achievement of particular isolated ends only, without consideration of their impact on other ends and on society. Both the burglar and the lawful keeper of the vault may use the same key in the same way to open the vault, but the implications for mediate social ends may be quite different in the two cases. Persons are not moral or immoral because they are skillful. Rather they are immoral if their behavior leads to ends that are disapproved by the group because they are a hindrance to the achievement of desired (desirable) ends, either mediate or immediate. A particular end, or achievement, such as opening a vault, may not be bad in itself, but only as related to other ends. And many other particular kinds of acts may be good or bad depending on *when and where* they are committed, e.g., taking off one's clothes.

Both the moral and the immoral act are necessarily continuous with technology. Still there is a difference between behavior looked at from a technical standpoint and from a moral standpoint. In our society the desirability of ends freely chosen determines the particular technical knowledge that is to be applied, for technical knowledge that gets into practice is conditioned by the ends chosen. This does not imply that morality and social norms determine either the nature of pure science or the most efficient technical way of achieving particular ends. But it does imply, first, that choice of ends precedes the intelligent application of pure science and technology and, second, that ordering chosen ends with reference to place and time (or harmonizing ends) precedes and conditions the order in which technical acts are to be carried out.

Moral and ethical principles, norms, conditioned by values, are emergents dependent on a society having a language and upon a society in which the behavior of individuals is conditioned by symbols of events which, if they happen, must happen in a future. An insane person is not held to account for his behavior, not because he is unable to carry out certain acts efficiently from a technical standpoint but for the same reason that a lower animal is not: he is unable to take cognizance of the implication of immediate means and ends for mediate ends. And if mechanical efficiency were the test of morality, the highest morals would be those of some lower animals and some machines. But this is not the case, and I am defending the thesis that moral tenets and social norms are emergents in human society, and that when one acts from moral principles he is employing something in addition to technical principles and skills. Such emergents are necessary if one's behavior is to be conditioned by ends chosen from among possible alternatives. Social norms may not only require that we commit an act with technical efficiency and by use of the best information pure science offers us, but also at the proper place and time. "Proper" has significance here only when ends (and means) are co-ordinated with reference to each other so that the prevised outcome will be continuously satisfactory.

An end is good and is of value only if it contributes in a functional way to the achievement or preservation of a system of desirable ends.

Similarly, an end is bad if it interferes in some way with the preservation or achievement of one or more ends in a system of desired ends. Assuming that means and ends are continuous, it may be a question whether or not any end is unrelated to other ends.

Institutions, Values, and Norms

Can there be a science to determine the norms to be followed in applying our technical knowledge toward the achievement of specific ends or values? Can the social scientist prescribe the norms for society? Science is not a direct way of arriving at norms. Scientific information is useful in formulating norms, but such information does not include them. Although a wise person may use scientific information in formulating norms, he need not do so; but he cannot, by the very nature of norms, exclude a consideration of ends and the harmony of ends. And since scientific information is devoid of a consideration of ends, but may be applied indifferently to alternative and possibly incompatible ones, it is obvious that norms are not included in factual statements. Rather science must be considered a means to ends, and in a free society it must remain subservient to human purposes. Furthermore, in a democracy every person has the right to express his likes and dislikes, and if a person does not care to consider what science has to offer him, no one can force him, as a voting citizen, to do so. By voting we may decide whether or not children should be vaccinated against smallpox, but the voter need not consider scientific information when he votes, nor can the scientist as scientist decide the issue. You may say that the voting citizen *ought* to take cognizance of science when deciding on issues, but the "ought" which you stipulate does not come from science. No scientific statement of fact has included in it "I *ought* to be considered." For better or for worse, democracy precludes a stipulation of both motives and means of effecting ends from any particular area—science, religion, or aesthetics.

Not only is it impossible in a democracy for scientists to prescribe norms, but it is impossible under any form of government to arrive at them on a priori grounds, nor are they handed to us by revelation, nor yet can we arrive at them directly on the basis of observation. The source of norms is found in the creative judgments of individual members of society. We cannot learn how men might better behave by reference alone to how they behave in fact. It is as fallacious to assume that "right" and "wrong" are nothing other than what is practiced and what is not practiced, respectively, as it is to assume that the most efficient technical way of effecting an end (e.g., picking cotton) is the actual method used. To say the least, since the many artifacts, scientific techniques, and raw materials at our disposal do not compel us to behave in any predetermined way, but rather give us freedom by making alternative futures possible, it is evident that before we can take advantage of freedom, we must accept responsibility for evaluating not only the particular ends (among alternative possible ones we want to attain) but also what effect their attainment would have on other ends. This is a moral responsibility to be assumed by every individual member of a society.

William Sumner says that every institution is characterized essentially by its idea and its *structure*.[4] In other words, every institution has both goals, or a set of values, and norms which control behavior as men work toward them. One may have ends and the means of achieving them, or values and norms, without their being institutionalized (that is, without being ordered with reference to the values and norms of others), but there can be no human society nor an institution without norms and values. When an institution has been established, certain values become social and certain prescribed practices are proposed as universal with reference to a particular society.

Since science makes it possible for us to attain not only desirable ends but also undesirable ones, we cannot learn through science alone which ends we ought to seek. Our political freedom is a guarantee against the possible dictatorship of *scientists,* not science. Science, or scientific information, is neutral with reference to ends, but citizens, including scientists, are not. Social scientists, even as physical scientists, are obligated to submit information to the public through the proper channels, and they may submit proposals also for the solution of social problems, but in a democracy no norm should or will be accepted on scientific grounds alone.

The basic conflicts in the contemporary world are not conflicts over ends as values, but conflicts over norms. As a rule, men speak loosely

4 See *Folkways* (Boston, Ginn & Company, 1906), pp. 53 ff.

and say that if we had the same values or if our scale of values were the same, there would be no conflict. Many writers, of course, contend that our social problems emerge out of a conflict of values. For example, we read:[5]

Similarly, value-judgments which deny social acceptance to the mother of a child born out of wedlock not only contribute causally to such conditions as abortions, infant mortality, and abandoned children, all of which are socially disapproved, but such value-judgments also obstruct efforts to solve the illegitimacy problem by impeding free discussion of it.

Doubtless the sociologist has ignored the value-judgments of people because he feels he cannot be objective about them and hence will lose his scientific detachment. The danger of subjectivity should not deter him from studying social values; if he leaves them out, he has not a complete concept "social problem"; he is dealing with only fragmentary and partial data. He must bring these value-judgments into the arena of scientific study before it can be said he is obeying one of the first rules of science, which is to study all, not part, of the evidence pertinent to his problem.

A common sociological orientation for the analysis of all social problems may thus be found in the conflict of values which characterizes every social problem. These conflicts are mirrored in the failure of people to agree that a given condition is a social problem, or assuming such agreement, failure to reach an accord as to what should be done about it.

Even if all of us evaluated things the same so that each of us wanted the same kinds of things, that would not insure us against a conflict in attaining them. Often we are led to believe that other persons and other nations want bad, evil, debasing things, and that if we could but convince them to want good, upright, or even "spiritual" things, we would have peace and co-operation. But if others should want precisely what we do not want (including the means of attaining those wants), then there would be no conflict, and possibly no co-operation. Which means the conflict is due partly to the fact that we *do* want the same kinds of things and often the same thing. The conflict is a conflict in the moral (vs. technical) procedure involved in attaining ends.

It is an implicit assumption by all who try to reconcile norms that if we operated from a common, proper set of norms then the goods

[5] Fuller and Meyers, *op. cit.,* pp. 26–27.

that are valuable would be distributed equitably. "Justice" in economic matters has meaning only with reference to norms and values. In our capitalistic system, philanthropy and benevolence correspond to mercy in the Hebrew-Christian tradition, and they may be exercised as a sort of indirect defense of the basic rules of our economic system. Yet it is assumed that, if we follow the proper norms, the goods will be divided justly and equitably and that dissatisfied persons have no firm grounds for complaint.

It is not wrong for two different persons to want the same property. What may be wrong, however, is the method by which they try to get that property. It was not wrong for Germany to want to become well-fed and wealthy in every way. The conflict was between their norms and ours, for each prescribed a different way of attaining and maintaining those values. Our conflict with Russia today consists of a conflict of the norms or principles from which we and they operate. We want bread; so do they. Apparently both we and they want industrialization; we like the results of machinery, the pleasure of automobiles, good music, painting, sculpture, as well as the fruits of science in general. It would be absurd to say that we like spiritual things (or have spiritual values) and the Russians do not. If it were as simple as that, there would be no conflict, for we could have *all* the spiritual values and be satisfied, since Russia would want none. Probably those who criticize Russia because of her "lack of spiritual values," really mean to say that Russians do not have the same norms as we have and that the norms they employ in the distribution of goods ignore personal values and persons and consider only technical expediency. This, indeed, is a proper criticism to be made of any political system that uses persons as means to attain values which are purportedly higher than individual worth. Because of her disrespect for personal freedom, we cannot co-operate with Russia in what we recognize as the just and equitable way of distributing valuable things, such as food, coal, oil, music, art, or whatever else we consider desirable. It is utterly impossible to do away with the stubborn fact that often different people want the same things or the same kinds of things. But it is possible to operate from the same set of norms in attaining ends or values.

In order to illustrate what is meant by a conflict in norms, we may suppose that certain people in a community, despite the fact that they would like to get rid of typhoid fever, are opposed on religious grounds (and politics defends their religious rights) to being vaccinated, whereas others in the community believe it is proper to eliminate the disease by vaccination. Here we have different persons acting from different norms, and in that case the realization of the commonly accepted goal—good health—is precluded because of a conflict. If, however, the scientist successfully argues that vaccination is not contrary to the will of God, or if the theologian convinces all members of the community that science *is* contrary to the will of God, then the conflict of norms is resolved and the social problem disappears, though if the theologian succeeds in his argument, the disease does not disappear.

Again, two economic systems may be in conflict, such as communism and capitalism, and in that case the goods acquired and distributed in accordance with one system will be said by those who accept the other system to be distributed and acquired *unjustly* and *inequitably*. And if two persons or two groups of persons try to acquire certain specified goods, such as oil in Iran, and if they try to acquire such goods by contrary economic norms, then the one that is not successful will accuse the successful one of acting unjustly. Unjust behavior often justifies "righteous" retaliation and a redistribution of goods "justly" and "equitably" according to the "correct" norms.

If every time certain socially accepted needs were not being fulfilled, despite the fact that they could be fulfilled from a technical standpoint, there would be ready at hand an accepted social norm which could be employed in fulfilling them, and there would be no social problem. In some cases where values are not being achieved (despite the technical means and the raw material available) there is no norm present at all, and a norm has to be formulated, whereas in other cases there is more than one norm, but they conflict in some way. In the less civilized societies, where change takes place slowly, there are few if any conflicts in norms, and there are few if any emergencies for which there is no norm ready at hand. Consequently, there are few if any social problems in these societies. But in a civilized society, where frequent change is normal and often necessary, the contrary is true.

If a group would insist on superimposing old norms on new situations at the expense of a satisfactory solution of social problems, they would be substituting mores and established practice for moral responsibility and moral judgment. In that case they would be making a bow not only to ceremonies at the expense of technology (as C. E. Ayres so capably points out),[6] but they would be making a bow to moral complacency as well. A corollary to the conclusion that fixed norms lead to stagnation and ceremonies, or a worship of means at the expense of the accomplishment of ends, is the conclusion that dogma, finality, and creeds are substituted for the democratic process in which the people as a whole decide what, for the time, are the chief ends of society, and what will be the means of achieving those ends.

Technology is concerned with the application of pure-science statements to particular ends without reference to the implications of the achievement of those ends for other or mediate ends. The technician is interested in the know-how. The social scientist is concerned with problems emerging out of a conflict of norms; that is, out of behavior, whether of a single individual or a group of individuals, which precludes the achievement of mediate desired ends, or which precludes the harmony of ends.

Is There a Science for Determining Norms and Values?

If we ask when a discipline becomes a science, the traditional answer is: When we can state the principles (axioms, assumptions, primitive statements) by which we can solve problems within that discipline by the deductive method. Every science must have some principle or principles at its roots. A set of principles in any science must enable us both to explain and to predict phenomena. Presumably the principles of mechanics enable us to explain and predict such events as the eclipse of the moon or the movement of tides. And if we could discover a set of principles by which we could determine the proper direction and goals of society, or, which is the same thing, by which we could determine what we ought to want and how we ought to proceed in fulfilling those wants, then we could use these principles deductively and there would be no need for ethical judgments.

It seems obvious that we cannot arrive directly at social normative principles by stating the results of a study of the status quo. Despite

[6] C. E. Ayres, *The Theory of Economic Progress* (Chapel Hill, University of North Carolina Press, 1944), see especially Chapter VIII.

the Sumnerian thesis, held by many sociologists and anthropologists, that one can learn how men ought to behave by studying how in fact they *do* behave, and that ideologies express accurately the actual practices of a people, we commit a cultural fallacy[7] if we believe that the principles from which we judge that behavior is good or bad are derived directly from social phenomena and the facts.

In order to co-operate with others effectively, peaceably, and intelligently, a person or a group of persons must act from common meanings and from a common set of moral principles. Two persons or two groups of persons using contradictory sets of norms can co-operate only as rivals. For this very reason social scientists today are giving attention to a program which has long concerned religious reformers and moralists—they are interested in trying to resolve the conflict of norms. And apparently many educated persons have looked to the social sciences for an answer to how this conflict is to be resolved. Of course, two nations can operate from contradictory sets of norms short of conflict, provided neither has traffic with the other; and if it is impossible to resolve the conflict of norms short of war, then possibly the next best plan would be for each to try to "contain" the other; that is, each should try to build a wall around the other. There is an obvious difference in attitude and behavior between building a wall around ourselves and building it around another nation. It is the difference between isolationism and cold war. "Containing" a rival nation makes sense only if one is willing to stand by his own normative principles and if the other nation has a program of aggression endangering those principles.

The major difficulty which precluded and is likely to preclude a satisfactory resolution of conflicting norms lies in our inability, either as individuals or as organized groups, to apply the basic principle involved in reflective, creative thinking. This is the principle of taking the attitude of the other with the implicit assumption that more satisfactory goals can be achieved through peaceful co-operation than through isolation or conflict. Conflicts in norms can be resolved satisfactorily only if these conflicts are approached rationally by applying

[7] For the meaning of "cultural fallacy," see F. S. C. Northrop, *The Logic of the Sciences and the Humanities* (New York, The Macmillan Company, 1947), pp. 70, 279 ff.

scientific information to them, and only if the various persons involved in the conflict are permitted to exercise the democratic principles of freedom of expression. No conflict of norms can be resolved satisfactorily outside a democratic matrix which, in the last analysis, guarantees the individual the right to help select the common goals of the group and to help determine the norms by which these goals are to be reached.

There is no deductive science for solving conflicts of norms and values. Every solution requires ethical, moral judgment, and every conflict arises because of some novel situation. Laws of nature are not good or bad, moral or immoral. One cannot reasonably hate the solar system or the law of falling bodies. One can justifiably praise or blame, call moral or immoral, only what could be otherwise—only what does not happen of necessity, but of free choice. There is no law for an act that could have been otherwise; hence social scientists cannot discover it. Where scientific information stops, there is room for freedom, responsibility, and changing the status quo.

The social scientists should be careful in advocating a system of values and "scientifically tested" social practices. The subject matter of the social sciences is unlike that of the so-called "natural sciences," since the social sciences deal with problems that arise, in part, from a conflict in attitudes. Finding the proper norms is by no means like discovering a law of nature. Norms would be altogether meaningless without human purposes and ends. And since there are many different possible ends men may achieve, no one of which is necessary, men must first select them and then formulate hypothetically what they believe to be not only the most technically desirable way of attaining them but also the most ethically desirable way. In a democracy every voting citizen has a right to help determine the common ends of the community as well as the right to help formulate the norms to which we conform in achieving those ends.

The Function of the Social Sciences

The function of sociology as a science is to study and describe the uniformities of human behavior, the relatively repetitive sequences of human events. Those who argue that sociologists in their research on human cultures and societies must push beyond this function to evaluate the uniformities or sequences of sociocultural events which they discover are saying in effect that sociology is not a science, that it is a philosophy.[8]

In a democracy the business of evaluating, of selecting both the goals and the means, must be left to the people. In fact a society is free precisely to the extent that its members are permitted to engage in the social act of agreeing on values, and the individual is responsible to the extent that he is capable of entering into social acts requiring his co-operation in order to preserve or attain values agreed upon through democratic procedures.

Social scientists may discover conflicts over values and they may propose solutions to these conflicts, even as the physical scientist proposes solutions to technical problems, but they should not and, as unbiased scientists, cannot determine what the values ought to be. There is no science that can discover for us the chief end of man nor is there a science that can inform us directly how we ought to behave or how we ought to treat our fellow-men in a particular situation. Evaluating, even as living, is an art. Just as every individual must live his own, and only his own, life, he must also do his own evaluating in so far as he lives intelligently. In the process of evaluation lies both the freedom and the responsibility of the individual.

Both the social sciences and the physical sciences are used in solving social problems. The former show us how to resolve conflicts in values and norms, and the latter furnish the means of attaining and preserving values. No absolute lines can be drawn to separate the physical from the social sciences in the solution of practical problems. Nor can a sharp line be drawn between means and ends, norms and values.

If it were the function of the social sciences to discover the "laws of our being," that is, to discover how men would act if not controlled by external forces, such as institutions, then the only function of science would be to help us distinguish between "natural" social practices and "institutionalized" practices, so that we could do away with the latter. Or, again, if we were to assume that there are unchanging principles and unalterable human nature at the base of a social science and that, consequently, "true" human values are fixed, then inevitably we would

[8] Edwin M. Lemert, *Social Pathology* (New York, McGraw-Hill Book Company, Inc., 1951), pp. 5–6.

come out with a laissez faire doctrine, and the hope that we will be able to solve social problems by the aid of the social sciences would be forever precluded.

In contrast with physical laws, norms are man-made and, therefore, conventional. Even if there were a natural, unconventional, social law which it would be the business of social scientists to discover, it would be folly to do so, since men could not act otherwise than according to such a law anyway. There is no such thing as two or more conflicting laws of nature. But two or more norms may conflict, inasmuch as they are prescribed by men.

What has been demanded of social scientists is something in the nature of a contradiction. They are expected to find out how men behave naturally—not controlled by institutions and their accompanying norms and values—in order to control them *by* an institution. In the back of the minds of those who demand of the social scientists that they discover the "real" principles and laws of social behavior is the hidden assumption that institutions are artifacts and conventions and that the "true" laws of social behavior are natural and nonconventional. Some seem to want a "true" science of man in order to make him behave unscientifically; that is, unlike the way he is behaving. Or, they want to discover the principles according to which uncontrolled men behave, in order to control them. Obviously these demands are self-contradictory. Social scientists are asked to subscribe to the cultural fallacy of mistaking a statement of the facts for a statement of norms; they are asked to define what *ought to be the case* in terms of what is in fact the case.

From the fact that our national government gives financial support to pure research, it is clear that our representatives believe our goals can never be reached if things are left to themselves. Furthermore, it is obvious that even those who believe institutions are a drag to social progress or to the technological process, believe also that through sufficient understanding we can control processes leading to desirable, satisfactory ends. In the first case, some believe that desired ends can be reached by setting up the proper institution; in the second case, others believe these ends can be reached by doing away with institutions. Both views imply that control is possible.

Before we can decide what social science is, we must consider the fact that men have goals, ends, values. Men act with reference to future events. Men control their behavior by symbols for events away from them both spatially and temporally. And those who contend that the values or ends we work toward are those to which we have been conditioned by mores, ignore the fact that science is not a means of perpetuating the *status in quo datur,* but a means of getting away from it. *Men study human social phenomena in order to control processes leading to desired goals.* But can a dispassionate scientist discover how men ought to behave in working toward desired goals? Can a physical scientist, through studying falling stones, discover how they ought to fall, if he means by "ought" anything other than the way in which they *do* fall?

A dispassionate, disinterested scientist must study things as they are, not as they ought to be. A good social scientist, some argue, must stick to the facts, teach the facts, but never ask *why.* He must never pass value judgments—*that* is being biased and it means breaking faith with the scientific priesthood. Yet a statement of actual overt behavior or of the actual practices of a person or a group of persons does not contain a statement of a conflict, for conflicts are in attitudes—tendencies to act in different ways—many of which may never express themselves directly in practice. On the basis of a statement of the overt behavior involved, one could not distinguish between "stealing" and simply appropriating certain material goods for oneself. But behind the act of stealing there may be conflicting attitudes entertained by the thief, and certainly the norm which he employs conflicts with the explicit moral principles known to and accepted by the group as a whole.

What one intends to do or would like to do is not directly observable but must be known, if at all, indirectly. The social scientist can discover these attitudes best by conversing with people and by analyzing what they say. Strictly speaking, an observation of the overt behavior of people may reveal an inefficiency of skills and techniques, but it will not reveal attitudes and motives.

The basic difference between social problems and the problems of the pure-research scientist is that the former emerge only because the way of achieving certain desired ends precludes the achievement of other desired ends. Hence, the problem of the social scientist is to show

how society can resolve the conflict in attitudes or norms which precludes the harmony of ends. A proposed solution to the conflict must take into consideration not only behavior now taking place (things as they are—the status quo) but also things that may possibly take place.

The fact that social problems emerge because there is either no adequate norm present or because of a conflict in norms implies that if we could agree on norms, there would be no social problems. All problems would then be technical. We may say in general, then, that that which prevents the solution of any problem is either a lack of technical knowledge or else the absence of an accepted norm. The one who exploits labor may justify his behavior by economic principles, saying he has done nothing contrary to the rules of the game, whereas another may say the exploiter is doing something contrary to religious principles. We may know *how* to prevent smallpox or *how* to cure "moneyless no-accounts" of syphilis, but is it good to do so? Can we justify such behavior by appealing to values, whether they are religious, economic, or aesthetic?

If democracy holds, no science will ever be able to tell people directly what they ought to want or what principles they should live by in getting what they want. If freedom of individuals amounts to anything at all, it must include the privilege of establishing the norms by which they live as well as the privilege of selecting goals for which they are willing to work. There can never be a scientific formula signifying the "correct" direction for human behavior.

If we say we do not believe in coercion, but rather that values and goals should be chosen freely by the people, we see immediately that social science as a science cannot concern itself with a formula for choosing ends, nor can it be concerned with propaganda devices for making people want certain things or for making them choose certain values. In a democracy we must go to the grass roots for our values. This means that ethics cannot be drawn into the scientist's laboratory nor can democracy be delegated to the wisdom of the bureaucrat. What, then, is the function of the social sciences?

The proper function of the social sciences is to study social situations involving a conflict in norms and to state the results of these studies so that they can be used by the people to resolve these conflicts. But conflicts in a democracy cannot be resolved directly by social scientists any more than the physical scientist can determine when and where guns are to be used. It is easy enough, however, to see that there are certain conflicts between the attitudes of labor and capital, or between the property owner and the thief, or between the communist and the capitalist. Sufficient data may help people with conflicting attitudes to agree on a program in which both parties can participate willingly.

If social scientists hope to contribute to the solution of social problems, they must stop trying to justify the relativity of norms and mores. They must quit saying that everyone can see from practice that right and wrong are relative matters. Instead, they should be working to get rid of this relativity in order to make room for co-operation. In so far as science has had an influence in any field—aesthetics, medicine, agriculture, industry, religion, or any other—it has succeeded in doing away with the relativity of norms and of establishing common principles that enable us to co-operate effectively. Science at its best, as the implications of nuclear energy forcefully remind us, requires the co-operation of the entire world. If all that the social scientists can tell us is that what is "right" in Guatemala is "wrong" in Timbuktu and what is "right" in Russia is "wrong" in America, and vice versa, they should close the books.

Where co-operation is desired there can be no basis for justifying the relativity of norms, for in the last analysis, if a norm is peculiar to and therefore relative to a particular group, it is also a limitation, for it prevents co-operation with other groups. And although all norms (and mores) may be relative in the sense that they are conventional and are designed to meet certain present demands and effect certain desired ends, it is not true that one is as good as the other as a basis for co-operation. Co-operation between groups with regard to the attainment of common values requires common norms and the dissolution of relative ones.

As we understand Northrop's main contribution to the problem of world co-operation, made in his three books,[9] it amounts to a clarification of the norms by which different people and different nations carry

---

[9] F. S. C. Northrop, *The Meeting of East and West* (New York, The Macmillan Company, 1946); *The Logic of the Sciences and the Humanities* (New York, The Macmillan Company, 1947); *The Taming of the Nations* (New York, The Macmillan Company, 1952).

on their group activities (often en masse). Such a clarification, it is hoped, will make it possible for the various nations to agree on a common norm so as to insure peace, security, growth, and stability in human society. Probably there will be compromises here and there by all nations, and it is hoped that the final result will lead to common norms and the absence of relativity. The absence of the kind of relativity of which we speak does not imply that there is such a thing as absolute right and wrong, nor that within common norms there will be no room for the gratification of individual needs and the selection of various peculiar ends. It implies, rather, that co-operation, peace, security, growth, and stability presuppose common norms, and that it is because of the relativity of norms that conflicts arise.

Social scientists can act in good faith by presenting to the students and to the public the various possible ways in which conflicts in norms may be settled; and in the information given out, they can include the alternative possible consequences of following certain procedures. In general, the social scientist can do what the physical scientist has done —lay his information before the public, and as a citizen exercise the art of persuasion in trying to get people to consider such information in selecting goals and in formulating the norms according to which they will seek those goals.

This is not to suggest that *the* base of ethics should be science. It suggests, rather, that science may well become *one* of the factors employed or taken into consideration in the formulation of ethics and the norms. Religion, aesthetics, and economics may well be other components taken into consideration. And if, after the scientist has done his work, there still remains a conflict in norms, it will not be because we are unscientific or evil-minded or unaesthetic or irreligious, but rather because men do not care to utilize information in the same way. After the social scientist has offered his information, and as a citizen has exercised the art of persuasion, he must then go to the grass roots for an answer to the question: What ends will we work for; what means will we employ?

CHAPTER XIII

Freedom and Ethical Judgment

Introduction

THERE ARE THREE BASES for freedom and ethical judgments: the psychological, the physical, and the physiological. If any is lacking, men are not free. In order to make ethical judgments a person must have the intellectual capacity to evaluate ends and to understand the relationship between science as a means and the ends to which he gives assent through ethical evaluation. But this is not sufficient. The physical world must lend itself to being acted upon by men, and, finally, men must have the capacity to manipulate objects in the environment.

Quite often physical scientists use the word "free" in connection with physical phenomena. They speak of freely falling bodies, of the free expansion of gases, of free vibrations, etc. A body or a substance is said to be free only with respect to a certain law which expresses the behavior of that body "when it is free." A freely falling body is one whose motion is expressed precisely by the law of falling bodies. Or, conversely, if the behavior of a falling body is expressed by this law, then the body is falling freely. If, however, there is a restraining force, such as the friction and buoyancy of the air or any other medium through which a body is falling, then the law would not express its behavior and it would not be free.

According to the Aristotelian concept of freedom anything, including men and physical objects, is free in so far as it behaves unrestrained according to its nature or its form. A stone is free when it acts according to φύσις (*physis*—its nature or form), when it is not moved from its natural place, or when it is not prevented from moving to its natural place. But if one throws a stone upward, then the stone is in unnatural (violent) motion by virtue of causes external to its form (end, nature). If one were to ask Aristotle *why* the stone falls, he would be asking essentially: Why is a stone a stone? For after all a stone behaves as it does because it is a stone—because *that* is its nature. It is sensible, however, to ask: Why does the stone *not* behave according to its nature if it moves upward? And the answer is: There are causes contrary to its nature acting on it. Aristotle held that the freedom of inanimate and animate objects is limited by their forms, which were thought to be that for the sake of which an object moves; i.e., form defines (*de finis*, de-limit) or sets an end for action.

According to Aristotle, men, unlike inanimate objects and lower animals, are conscious of their form (the end, the good). This does not mean that men can choose their end any more than they can choose their form or nature. Rather men can deliberate (Latin, *libro*, to weigh, balance, and *libero*, to free) about *means* for achieving ends. A man was considered free when he could exercise deliberate choice (προαίρεσις; see Aristotle *Ethics* ii. 2) over the means of achieving his nature; but the ends were fixed. Since the stone is not conscious of its nature, it cannot deliberate about the means of achieving it, and hence it cannot counteract violent, extraneous forces, but must submit to them. In a sense, then, the freedom of man means for Aristotle that man need not submit to extraneous causes that would prevent him from being or becoming what he is (or ought to be) by nature. How could man will to be other than what he is?

Aristotle makes a distinction between voluntary action (ἑκούσιος) and involuntary action (ἀκούσιος). One may will to conform to the wishes of another who has a gun in his hand, and in that case the involuntary means of the one conforms to the voluntary means of the other. But in no case can men, according to Aristotle, will the ends, for that would be willing the nature or forms of things. Rather they are free in willing means only; i.e., in selecting particular means for given ends and in preventing extraneous forces or causes from interfering with their fixed ends, or that for the sake of which they act.

Similarly medieval Christian theology maintained that the ends of man are fixed. They are two in number. Man, however, was said to be a free moral agent, and by virtue of his "freedom" could say "yes" or "no" to the will of God or to the ways of Satan. But here again it was not believed that men have the capacity to create ends. Contrary to Aristotle's view, Augustine believed men are born in sin and have been saddled with a burden (through Adam). This burden can be thrown off if we exercise freedom and thereby conform our will to the will of God. One's "true" nature is divine, but since Adam fell and we inherited his sins, we can achieve man's true end by searching and finding the key to God's favor. Freedom, according to Augustine, lies in this quest for God, but man is not free to set up ends—they were prescribed by God Himself.

The basic fault of both the Aristotelian and the medieval Christian conception of freedom is that they do not make room for the establishment of new ends and the reconstruction of old ones. A corollary to this is that they separate absolutely the means and the ends. Since ends were believed to be fixed, choice concerned means only, and this, when analyzed, implies that means are fixed also. The Roman Catholic Church has worked out the means presumably necessary for achieving man's "true" nature, and these means are as fixed as the ends.

Modern science has opened a new perspective for us. We are beginning to see that civilizations, cultures, institutions, customs, fashions, mores and folkways are man-made. And although Aristotle believed free men are free by nature and slaves are slaves by nature, and although the medievalists believed that man's "true" institution is the City of God on earth, established by divinely inspired men, science is helping us to see that freedom is something to be acquired, protected, and developed, and that institutions are set up by the people for the sake of ends freely accepted on ethical grounds. When new ends are accepted and when old ones are reconstructed, this calls for the reconstruction of the means of accomplishing them, namely, scientific knowledge and institutions. Consequently, we must put a hyphen between means and ends and recognize that they, like terms in an equation, vary concomitantly. Which is the dependent and which the independent variable will be determined by present circumstances. C. E. Ayres[1]

[1] See especially C. E. Ayres, *The Theory of Economic Progress* (Chapel Hill, University of North Carolina Press, 1944).

and others have aided us tremendously in seeing that if institutions are fixed, then ends are fixed also, but if ends change, institutions change accordingly. Applied modern science, technology, involves changes in both means and ends, both institutions and values.

The lack of a sense of freedom in Greek civilization was expressed in their tragedies, which took on the form of fate—that which happens to all men alike and of necessity. The more fearful, if possibly wider, perspective offered by the medieval theologian presents a supernatural interpretation of man and places values or ends in the world to come. The early modern humanistic reaction to the narrowness of the medieval perspective was based on the assumption that the world is man's home. This reaction was followed by the scientific mechanistic interpretation which not only conceived of man as a citizen of the world but also as a victim of natural law and the external environment. According to the mechanistic interpretation (which I believe is in error), there is no purpose in man's behavior, for whatever he does can be accounted for on the basis of unthinking laws of nature. Man is "free," so the argument goes, in the same sense in which a stone is free when it falls "freely." In effect this means that "freedom" is a perfectly meaningless word.

In what follows I hope to show that men are free to the extent that they can determine the form of things to come by controlling what is present.

Quite often when men try to state the nature of human freedom, they conceive of it as absolute liberty and the absence of all causal relationships between the environment and human beings. In fact some writers believe a person is free only to the extent that he "overcomes" external influences, and goes "against the grain" of the "natural" environment. Others, such as Arthur Compton,[2] believe that "necessity" and "human freedom" are contradictory terms and that men are free because of the absence of causal relations and by virtue of the principle of indeterminacy. Still others, such as Spinoza, conceive of freedom in rationalistic, deductive, necessary terms. For example, just as two premises, such as "all a is b," and "all b is c," are free in the sense of being able to yield certain definite conclusions, and just as the axioms

[2] Arthur H. Compton, *The Freedom of Man* (New Haven, Yale University Press, 1936).

of geometry are free to yield only valid theorems, so God is free to act only in a necessary way as predetermined by His nature and, finally, men are free in so far as their behavior conforms rigidly to certain ethical laws.

In the sequel I shall develop the thesis that human freedom consists not in behaving according to "human nature," nor in behaving according to the "law of our being," nor in overcoming the laws of nature, nor, yet, in following rigidly fixed ethical principles. Human freedom depends on the capacity of men to set up ends and to devise the means of achieving those ends. This implies that there are alternative possible goals and alternative possible means of achieving them.

Freedom presupposes that some future events are not determined, that thinking conditions our behavior and determines, in such cases, the specific form of behavior. We can control our behavior, and thereby, indirectly, the environment, through the use of symbols. The free individual, through behavior, can use his environment to shape future events according to a preconceived pattern. But in order to do so, three things are required: (1) He must have the mental capacity to predict, to entertain alternative possible future ends, and to state the conditions under which each will occur. (2) The physical world must be amenable to change so that alternative future events may possibly take place—present conditions must serve as a basis for alternative future events. The intervention of reflective thinking leading to controlled behavior will, then, determine what specific events, among alternative possible ones, will become actual. (3) The individual must be able to select the stimuli to which he responds, which requires that the human body be able to store up energy, releasing it at particular times and directing it toward particular prevised ends.

The Psychological Basis for Freedom

If a standard were set up which would measure the extent to which a person is free, this would be a means of measuring the extent of that person's control over his behavior, directing it toward specified ends through bodily behavior controlled by reflective thinking. Every living organism, man or lower animal, is free if it can act as a whole. A bloodhound is free when it can roam about and use its keen sense of smell.

But if the nostrils of a bloodhound were closed, then it would not be free. In general, each kind of lower animal has its particular kind of environment, which is, of course, coextensive with the biological form. And if an animal can act as a whole, with no sensitivities restricted and all parts of the organism co-ordinated, it is free.

This conception of freedom applies also to men; but men are distinguished from lower animals by being symbol-users. Through symbols men can stimulate themselves to act in ways that lead to prevised ends when only the symbol for the ends and the physical means of achieving them are present; i.e., here-now. If one's behavior is under the control of symbols for ends, then immediately present, possible physical stimuli become actual stimuli and are responded to only if they are instrumental (or believed to be instrumental) in achieving the prevised end. The symbol for the prevised end controls the act of achieving it. Reflective thinking is not superfluous baggage appended to men but a part of each man; therefore if a man acts as a whole, it will be an integral part of his action. A person is free in so far as his biological organism, his physical environment, and his reflective thinking are integrated in action that leads to predicted ends. One may be sound of mind but restricted in behavior by an infirm body. Or one may be sound of both mind and body but, nevertheless, restricted in behavior if the physical environment will not surrender to his requests.

Before one can use symbols to indicate things away from him in space or in time, he must have both a language and a calendar. One can "hold on to" past events and recognize them *as past* only by employing both symbols and a calendar. By use of a calendar we make a distinction between past, present, and future events, whereas without it, behavior would involve only a present. Lower animals may have images, but the images they have, although caused by past experiences, can never be referred back to their original causes; the images will be present but none will serve as reference for the animal to anything beyond them. Lower animals have no calendar.

A calendar cannot be constructed on the purely qualitative phase of events; it is based, instead, on the repetitious factors or on the recurrence of events of a certain kind. The recurrence of the summer solstice, the new moon, or the morning sun may serve as a basis for a calendar, but unique events will not. We can say significantly that the "big flood" came *after* the earthquake and *before* the plague only if we already have a calendar. The establishment of a calendar requires a considerable degree of abstraction, and, of course, the actual use of and request for it emerge when men try to regulate their behavior in conformity with oncoming events.

Possibly the earliest use of calendars was in connection with storing uncultivated food in season, and later in connection with herding, and still later in connection with agriculture. We find proof of fairly accurate calendars devised by ancient peoples, especially the Mayans and the Egyptians, whose calendars were based on the recurrence of the vernal and autumnal equinoxes. But among more primitive peoples the year was indefinite and marked by the time animals brought forth their young, or the time of planting and harvesting. Quite often the years were not numbered, but were marked by some special event, such as a war, a flood, a drought, or the ascendancy to power of a certain ruler, or the death of a king. In many cases the calendar was used as much for determining the time of social or religious festivals of a group as for regulating its occupational behavior. In its practical function, a calendar enables men to regulate their behavior with reference to a future.

Remembered events are secondary and have a bearing on behavior only in so far as they are useful in predicting oncoming events and in regulating behavior. Past events, whether remembered or not, must get into present behavior before they are significant. Just as our knowledge of past ages helps us to carry on present behavior that will terminate in a future, so memory helps us to regulate our behavior; either to adjust to uncontrollable oncoming events or to change conditions and bring about events that would not happen at that time and place without regulated behavior. If the weatherman predicts a blizzard, which at present is uncontrollable, we may nevertheless prepare for it. But through the use of artifacts and technological devices in the modern world, we are able to prevent the occurrence of many events (that would take place without regulated behavior) and to substitute other events in their places. We no longer accept the plague of smallpox, or famine, or floods as inevitable—acts of God. Our freedom has been increased tremendously through our ability to determine the nature of the future that lies before us.

One cannot respond to a future event now, but he can control his act by use of a symbolic representation of a posited future event—or the event symbolized—which will be the terminus of the act and will be present symbolically in every stage of the act that requires controlling, or in every stage of the act not carried out through habit. It is in this sense that a posited future event is operative in present behavior; but without symbols, which involve a language, this would be impossible. When behavior is not controlled by symbols, man acts either instinctively or out of habit. In such cases his response is to what is either there-now or here-now, and a symbol for it is quite unnecessary since the presence of the sense-stimulus will suffice. The consummatory phase of an act always takes place with reference to what is here-now; it represents the terminus of the act; and except for possible physical disability, it takes place automatically and without the use of symbols.

Action that takes place without the control of symbols is conditioned and determined by the present physiological state of the organism on the one hand, and by the character of the immediate environment on the other. The hungry dog does not eat stones, and unless the dog is hungry he will not eat at all, despite the presence of "food." If there is such a thing as the "selection" of the stimuli to which a lower animal responds, it is determined automatically on the basis of the present physiological state, but there is no conscious selection or rejection. For there to be conscious selection of the stimulus, a symbol of the terminus of the act must be present, in which case selection amounts to responding only to those present stimuli or objects that enter into the act and lead to (or that one thinks will lead to) a prevised effect.

If one is to use a calendar one must first be able to use symbols and a language. In other words, symbols are the basis for language and language is the basis for a calendar. This implies that a calendar is a chronometer that emerges only in a society, and it can belong only to a group of animals with a language. There is little doubt that language arose out of the co-operative behavior of human beings and that its first function was to control the concerted effort of a number of individuals and direct individual behavior toward a common end. There was, of course, co-operation among the ancestors of modern men long before the emergence of language and significant symbols; and co-operation among our languageless ancestors, even as among lower animals today, was carried on through the responses of the co-operators to immediately present stimuli without these stimuli having cognitive reference to anything beyond themselves. In that case, present stimuli controlled the co-operative behavior of individuals, and responses to these stimuli were conditioned only by the physiological state of the individuals.

A sign used in a language system indicates to its users physical stimuli or sense stimuli that are not present but are actually away from them both spatially and temporally. As Mead has shown,[3] the test of the common meaning of a sign is found in the responses it elicits in the members of the group. What goes on within the mind of an individual by way of images, wishes, and emotions may be private in the sense that it is confined to the individual, but the meaning of a sign can be common to various members of the group, as behavior will show.

John Dewey and others have shown that the significance of all symbolic processes lies in overt behavior involving the co-operation of different members of the group. Dewey argues that a conflict between the organism and the environment, which arises in what is called a problematic situation, is the basis for reflective thinking; i.e., the basis for carrying the act of adjustment over into the organism in symbolic form. The function of the symbolic process is to permit the conduct of individuals to proceed unimpeded and this is possible because, through the use of symbols, the individual is able to reconstruct the impeded act (and, thereby, the external environment), with the result that the life process in the organism continues through an effective co-ordination of the biological form and its environment. This pragmatic emphasis on the nature of mind, which I accept so long as it is confined to scientific method, is consistent with the belief that the prime function of scientific thought is to free the temporarily impeded behavior of men in accordance with the demands of new situations to which old responses or old habits will not answer. The symbolic process is, then, a means of establishing new patterns of behavior in us which, if successful, may become habitual. Reflective thinking would indeed be superfluous if we could live by old habits.

The significance of the symbolic process is to be found finally in the

---

[3] G. H. Mead, *Mind, Self, and Society,* ed. by C. W. Morris (Chicago, University of Chicago Press, 1934).

fact that it frees our behavior from old habits, customs, and institutions by setting up new patterns of behavior which answer more effectively to our need or, in general, to the requests superimposed upon the form by the ever changing, external environment—requests that must be met if the life process, including social and cultural values, is to be carried on satisfactorily. Freedom depends on the symbolic process but it depends also on whether or not the newly released act (conditioned by the symbolic process) answers to the present exigencies and promotes a satisfactory relationship with the (newly created) environment.

Not any newly formulated act will meet these exigencies. A degree of confidence that the proposed act will be satisfactory can be had only if one is able to represent to himself (symbolically) the outcome of the act prior to committing it. If, of course, one's responses were always with reference to (not simply to) what is either here-now or there-now (i.e., either within the manipulatory range or within the range of sensitivity), it would be impossible to control the act by a symbol of what is there-then (i.e., by a symbol of what is beyond the range of immediate manipulation and sensitivity). The bloodhound simply follows his nose. The child is "restless" and the pap answers to its restlessness and stimulates the child to suck. The cattle low without a consciousness of their need for salt, and the caribou at times turn seaward and drink sea water, but they have no symbol for, nor can they indicate to themselves or to each other, what is away from them and finally answers to their restlessness. Nor does the squirrel plan for the winter, but rather the behavior pattern of "storing nuts for the winter" has been inherited as a part of its repertory.

Any conceived future event that is contradictory to the laws of nature and to the status quo is dismissed from consideration, temporarily at least, and unless it is believed that certain statements of "laws" are false or that our statement of the status quo is incorrect, symbols for these contradictory events will not control human behavior. Freedom, then, does not consist of simply allowing the symbol of *any* conceivable future event to control behavior. Rather the controlling symbols must conform to both the method of achieving their referents (which method is given by science in the form of laws) and the means at our disposal. This is why there must also be a physical basis for freedom, for we are not made free simply by thinking, or even, finally, by knowing the laws of nature and the status quo. It is necessary also to be able to release stored up bodily energy toward a certain, prevised end.

The capacity to entertain alternative possible ends and, through symbols, to allow some, at the exclusion of others, to control our behavior is a condition for selecting the immediate stimuli to which we respond. In that case the symbol whose future referent is posited hypothetically determines which particular objects among alternative ones become stimuli or objects to which we respond. Under these conditions man is said to "select" the stimuli to which he responds. This means that the "strength" of the immediately present "stimuli" (i.e., the loudness of the noise, the pungency of the odor, or the brilliancy of the color) is not the primary basis for man's response to them, but, rather, the symbols of hypothetically posited events determine which present objects are stimuli and which are not. Indeed, that to which one responds delineates his environment. The control, therefore, of behavioral responses through symbols is a way of determining the nature of the immediate environment through the concept of a reconstructed environment which, one believes, will be made actual by means of the present environment. Just how one comes under the influence of *this* symbol instead of *that* one is a moot question, but in ordinary language we say that there is a choice of ends, and the choice determines which end we strive to attain.

Freedom is exercised in various particular acts, but this does not imply the absence of causes or even of factors that determine the particular nature of these acts. It means, rather, the control of one's behavior by what traditionally has been called "final cause" or "purpose." "Final cause" involves behavior controlled by symbols, but the symbolic process has its roots in the more primitive process involving the interaction of the form and its environment. It is when this interaction of form and environment is carried over into the higher nervous system that we have the symbolic process. Once the symbolic process is begun, it is more or less automatic and needs for its stimulation only the smallest variation in the environment to become instrumental in reconstructing one's environment; or, as Dewey and others have said, the checking of an old habit furnishes the basis for creative thinking leading to a new kind of act. In creative or reflective thinking, either more than one possible end or more than one possible means of accomplishing a proposed end are symbolized. The symbolic process, which may be considered the essential part of a self, is one of the factors determining the form of the oncoming events.

Free behavior, then, is partially self-determined behavior. Consequently, human freedom has one of its roots in the symbolic process, the psychological character of man, for symbols become ingredients in that behavior which frees men from an established restraining environment and enables them to determine by choice and on ethical grounds the form of many things to come.

The Physical Basis for Freedom

Contrary to the writer's view, the most generally accepted meaning of "freedom" in modern times is practically the same as that held by the early Greeks and by the medievalists: it is generally believed that one is free only in so far as his behavior cannot be expressed by physical laws. Almost all of the early Greek writers made a sharp distinction between *nomos* and *physis,* between laws of society (positive laws) which are purely conventional and are formulated by men without reference to the structure of nature, and laws of nature, which are the opposite of convention in that they are universally valid and are, therefore, characterized by necessity. In general, it is believed that whatever is orderly is not free but follows from pre-established principles. If these pre-established principles have been designed consciously, then all that ever takes place according to them is predestined; but if these principles are nonthinking and impersonal in character, then all that follows from them, including our behavior, is mechanical, fated, and blind. In other words, predestined behavior is prevised, whereas mechanical behavior is blind and unplanned.

The medieval Christians argued against fate and held that things happen according to the will of God and that individual men are free moral agents because they have a peculiar faculty, namely a free will. Free will traditionally and today is conceived by many to be an extranatural faculty and it purportedly enables man to escape the rigid laws of nature or transcend the compulsions of external laws that rule over all other things. We find Descartes accepting this same general theory. He located the physiological mechanism for freedom in that gland which is single—the pineal gland.[4] But all other things, including lower animals, are, according to Descartes, under the governance of law and necessity. And yet, confusing as it might appear to us, Descartes believed that the will and reason are antithetical at points and that although men should live according to reason, they become unreasonable when the will outruns the intellect.

Two great contemporary physicists, Max Planck and Arthur Compton, are much troubled over the problem of "free will," as they put it, and both assume uncritically that the principle of causation is antithetical to human freedom. Planck expresses the opinion held generally by fairly well-educated people of our day when he writes:[5]

And is all conduct in the last resort to be attributed to the causal activity of circumstances, such as past events and present surroundings, leaving no place whatsoever for an absolutely spontaneous action of the human will? Or have we here, in contradistinction to nature, at least a certain degree of freedom or arbitrary volition or chance, whichever name one wishes to choose? From time immemorial this question has been a source of controversy. Those who hold that the human will is absolutely free in its act of volition generally assert that the higher we go in the scale of natural being the less noticeable is the play of necessity and the greater the play of creative freedom, until we finally come to the case of human beings, who enjoy the full autonomy of the will.

Although Planck and Compton are in agreement on a definition of freedom, Planck is of the opinion that the operation of the mind and the will can never be studied scientifically or from the standpoint of causal laws and that, therefore, as far as practice is concerned, men are mysteriously free. He writes:[6]

The fact is that there is a point, one single point in the immeasurable world of mind and matter, where science and therefore every causal method of research is inapplicable, not only on practical grounds but also on logical grounds, and will always remain inapplicable. This point is the individual

[4] See Descartes, *The Passions of the Soul,* Articles XXVII-XLIII.

[5] Max Planck, *Where Is Science Going?* trans. by James Murphy (New York, W. W. Norton and Co., Inc., 1932), p. 151.

[6] *Ibid.,* p. 161.

ego. It is a small point in the universal realm of being; but in itself it is a whole world, embracing our emotional life, our will and our thought. This realm of the ego is at once the source of our deepest suffering and at the same time of our highest happiness. Over this realm no outer power of fate can ever have sway, and we lay aside our own control and responsibility over ourselves only with the laying aside of life itself.

Planck believes that although in principle it is possible for us to state in a lawful way, and in accordance with the principle of causation, the basis for every act, in practice it is impossible. He says:[7]

The law of causation is the guiding rule of science; but the Categorical Imperative—that is to say, the dictate of duty—is the guiding rule of life. Here intelligence has to give place to character, and scientific knowledge to religious belief. . . .

Planck is drawn between two opinions, the principle of causality and freedom. But he holds tenaciously to the principle of causality, and winks at it in human behavior only for the sake of responsibility and character.[8] Yet he believes a superhuman mind could state in the minutest detail the causal principle operative in what we take to be the freest expression of mind; i.e., the mental behavior of the genius.

Arthur Compton, like Planck, shares the view held generally by most others under the influence of mechanism, namely, that lawful phenomena are not free, or that law and order are antithetical to freedom. But unlike Planck, he has given up the principle of causation in all fields and has accepted in its stead the principle of indeterminacy as formulated by Werner Heisenberg. Compton has, then, a "scientific basis" for his belief in "free will." The principle of indeterminacy is based especially on the fact that we are unable for a given time to predict with accuracy *both* the momentum and the position of an electron in its orbit around the nucleus of an atom. And the indeterminacy principle is the very antithesis of the causal principle. According to the causal principle, whatever is predictable is caused, and whatever is unpredictable is uncaused or indeterminate. Consequently, since we cannot predict for a given time both the momentum and the position of an electron, they are uncaused. And since Compton assumes that quantum physics is the basis of all the sciences, or that all nature con-

[7] *Ibid.,* p. 167.   [8] *Ibid.,* pp. 164–165.

sists of objects like those studied in quantum physics, he believes we are justified in generalizing on our "electron" experiences and in accepting the principle of indeterminacy. According to Compton, because this principle is applicable to the atoms of the nervous system and the brain, the brain does not operate as a machine, for the future positions of the electrons in the brain are unpredictable. The will, therefore, is free.

What a strange spectacle, and what a victory for Hegelian dialectics! The physical sciences, which were largely responsible for the belief that man is a machine and, consequently, for showing that men are anything but free agents, contained within their seeds the very negation of determinism and the basis for freedom. So one might argue in Hegelian fashion offhand. But the conclusion is too easy and by no means valid. The physicists (indeterminists) have not yet made fools of psychologists.

What Compton has said in effect is that a search for a religious or a psychological basis for freedom is fruitless. The only basis for freedom lies in what has traditionally been held to be the only obstacle to freedom, namely the physical world. Religion and psychology, he believes, must be rooted in physics alone. But as we have pointed out several times, freedom must be rooted in psychology and biology as well as in the physical world. And above all else, it is folly to assume that freedom can be defined as the absence of physical necessity; i.e., as indeterminacy. Compton labors, probably unconsciously, under the assumption that the "will" is a psychical entity which has its chance to operate in the physical world because of the loopholes in nature—because the causal principle, at times at least, is not operative. At last, through a study in physics, we are able to prove, so Compton believes, what philosophers and theologians for thousands of years have accepted on faith—namely, that man is a free moral agent and that there is such a thing as "man's place in God's world." In fact this principle of indeterminacy, revealed finally to the physicist, serves as the intellectual defense of our belief in the agelong, most cherished values and aspirations—God, Freedom, and Personal Immortality.[9]

After reading Compton's account of how, presumably, we can justify the statement that freedom is a fact, even though we cannot

[9] Arthur Compton, *op. cit.*, Chapters IV and V.

prove it, read Philipp Frank's little monograph, *Interpretations and Misinterpretations of Modern Physics.*[10] There one may learn how several other outstanding scientists, including Sir James Jeans, A. S. Eddington, and A. Sommerfeld, have used quantum physics to "prove" the validity of unrelated spiritualistic points of view.[11]

One thing is certain: Freedom is impossible if we cannot make predictions about physical phenomena. In short, we cannot rest our case for freedom on the presumption that there is no such thing as a law of nature or that there is no such thing as necessity in the external world. Put positively, in order to have freedom of behavior we must be able to depend on the external world; it must be lawful, and we must be able to state its laws and make predictions from them. One cannot build freedom on either indeterminacy or chaos. To behave intelligently is to behave reasonably in a world that is intelligible and can be reasoned about.

Ever since the Stoics tried to unite *nomos* and *physis* and formulated the thesis that the positive law (conventions constructed arbitrarily but tempered by reason) should be formulated in accordance with natural law (necessary nonconventions that are universal), many thinking men have been willing to defend the belief that one can live a life guided by reason and in conformity with natural law. But such a statement is confusing if used to answer the questions: Are men free? If one lives according to reason and law, is not anything he does necessary? My answer is: of course. Whether a person's conduct is controlled by symbols through reason, or whether his behavior is not conditioned by symbols and reasoning, there are reasons and causes for whatever he does and, therefore, whatever he does is necessary in the sense that there is a sufficient basis for it from the standpoint of descriptive law.

If symbols are a part of the basis or cause for an act, then physical laws and the external environment do not constitute the entire cause. Reflective thinking and reasoning furnish something admitted by all mechanists and "naturalists" to be lacking in universally valid laws of

[10] Trans. by Olaf Helmer and Milton B. Singer (Paris, Hermann & Cie, 1938).

[11] See R. S. Lillie, *General Biology and Philosophy of Organism* (Chicago, University of Chicago Press, 1937), Chapter XI.

nature: namely, future reference. The symbolic process, or reflective thinking, has a temporal dimension lacking in nonmental behavior. What is often forgotten is that human behavior and the symbolic process are parts of nature. Would we say it is unnatural to carry water in milk pails? Yet it is not necessary to do so, for other things or nothing could be carried in them. Similarly, human behavior could be of this, that, or the other sort, and just what it will be like will be determined by the nature of the immediate physical environment, scientific information, and symbols indicating what is not in the immediate environment. An insane person may perchance throw stones if there are stones to throw, or he may throw wooden blocks, but for what reason? One may answer, because the stones or blocks stimulate him to reach for them and physical energy is released in the form of "throwing," and that's all there is to it—everything is lawful and necessary. Or, again, a person may walk in his sleep, and he may manipulate objects in his sleep, but one cannot walk on "nothing" nor can he manipulate "nothing," and all behavior is at the expense of (physical) energy; every act must conform rigidly to physical laws.

What, then, is the difference between the behavior of a rational person and that of an insane person or of one who acts in his sleep? From a purely physicochemical standpoint, the answer is: none. This amounts to saying that all behavior can be expressed by use of the laws of physics and chemistry, and that if we analyze an equation which expresses the behavior of an insane person, it will be the same, except for possible numerical differences, as the equation expressing the behavior of a sane person. Consequently, a physicochemical analysis of the behavior of an individual will not serve as a basis for classifying behavior into "rational conduct" and "irrational conduct," or "necessary behavior" and "free behavior." It would follow, also, that if one insists on explaining freedom and necessity by resorting to physical and chemical principles alone, or if he insists on grounding the explanation of freedom and necessity in the physical sciences alone, then all behavior will be alike—either free or necessary or possibly, through a confusion, both free and necessary. To a "pure" physicist or a "pure" chemist, the behavior of the insane will be different from that of the sane in degree only, not in kind. According to our original definition of human freedom, one is free when he can act as a whole, and this implies that the symbolic process must be co-ordinated with the physiological process as well as the physicochemical processes.

The physical world, or the physicochemical processes within the environment of one whose behavior is free, must be *continuous with* the symbolic process and with the organic processes of that person's body. The fact that the symbolic process, including reflective thinking, is an accomplishment made possible only through the behavior of an individual *in* and *with respect to* its environment guarantees that the symbolic process is continuous with both the organic behavior of one's body and the external environment. The symbolic process does not take place independent of organic processes, which in turn do not take place independent of environment. Free conduct involves the three kinds of processes mentioned, and if we consider a free act of an intelligent organism, then "symbolic process," "organic process," and "environment" are abstractions from it. If one were to live by habit or out of custom altogether, the symbolic process would be superfluous indeed. In that case one's behavior would not be free, and he would not possess his behavior, but rather his behavior (habits and institutions) would possess him.

In order to condition behavior by the symbolic process, the environment—the physical world—must be subject to different kinds of human responses. The physical world must be such that we (through our bodies) can respond to it in different ways. The stone, for example, must be something that can be thrown, broken into pieces, used as a weight, or put to other uses before we can react to it in different ways. And, of course, our own bodies must be of such a mechanical structure that we can throw, break, or use the stone. In fact the human body, especially the hands and arms, consists of a very complicated, highly co-ordinated system of levers. Furthermore, the forelimbs of the human being have been freed from supporting the weight of the body. Consequently, the senses of sight, smell, taste, and hearing are co-ordinated with the intricate analytic and synthetic manipulations of the hands and arms in the process of acting on physical objects.

The symbolic process is continuous with the processes of analysis and synthesis that take place by use of the hands. No doubt there is a genuine causal relationship between our ability to arrive at abstract concepts, such as "point," "atom," "electron" (all of which refer to objects at the converging end of the analytic process), and our ability to tear down and dissect objects with the hands or with tweezers, knives, scalpels, and other instruments, including the microscope, that aid in the extension of the analytic capacities of the hands. But these dissecting instruments presuppose physical objects that surrender themselves both to dissection and analysis and, in turn, to synthesis or the reconstruction of objects in accordance with alternative patterns and, especially, in accordance with planned behavior. A physical world that will fit into a preconceived act, or into an act controlled by symbols, must be orderly in the sense that at least many of the oncoming events are predictable and in the sense that bodily activities can be co-ordinated with processes in the environment. The possibility of co-ordinating bodily activities with environmental changes rests on the capacity to predict oncoming events with respect to which these activities are co-ordinated; and if we carry the matter of co-ordination of human behavior with the environment by use of symbols far enough, we will find that the significance of prediction lies in the fact that it is instrumental in effecting the co-operation of form and environment in carrying on the life process.

Parenthetically, it is rather paradoxical on the part of mechanists and certain behaviorists of the Watsonian type to state that we have no freedom because our behavior is predictable on the basis of present conditions (and therefore caused *by* present conditions), when in fact the significance of prediction in the science laboratory and in ordinary life is that it enables us to make adjustments to oncoming events and, in many instances, enables us to determine the specific nature of future events. In scientific method it is trite to point out that factual statements must be tested for their truth value by what they predict. But testing by means of prediction is not a purely passive affair on the part of the observer. In order to test by prediction, one must regulate his behavior so that it will be co-ordinated spatially and temporally with the anticipated event. In cases of prediction-test situations, the behavior of an individual is controlled by symbols standing for the event predicted.

If we are to give objective meaning to the concept of prediction, we must include the fact that it implies behavior that is adjusted to the predicted event. If one's behavior (including prepotent responses to sense stimuli), although controlled by a symbol for the anticipated event, turns out to be unco-ordinated with events that actually take place, then we can say that our prediction is incorrect or that the statement from which we made the prediction is false. Contrariwise, if behavior controlled by symbols is co-ordinated with the actual predicted event, then our prediction is correct, and the statement from which we made the prediction is true or verified to that extent. But to try to define prediction without including co-ordinated behavior controlled by symbols is like trying to define truth apart from experimental verification. Consequently, to argue against freedom by arguing from the standpoint of the experimental scientist is inconsistent.

The verification of a factual statement is not a passive affair, nor can it take place at the purely symbolic level. Rather, verification requires a special kind of behavior—behavior co-ordinated with environmental processes through the use of symbols. And unless the statements being tested are about processes and events with which we can co-ordinate our bodily behavior, there is no sense in talking about the possibility of testing any factual statement, nor is there any sense in speaking of prediction as a test for statements. To say, then, that an event is predictable is to say that one can, on the basis of planned conduct, co-ordinate his behavior with physical events that are external with reference to the symbolic process. Such co-ordination implies freedom.

"Testing-behavior" is always controlled by symbols of what *might be* and not by what *is*. Even if the assumed event actually occurs, its occurrence did not control the "testing act," for it was not present during the act. We anticipate a flood and build a levee to control it, but the flood did not stimulate us to build the levee. The flood may never come. One's judgment may condition his behavior, whether the judgment is valid or invalid; which is to say, something other than present mechanical factors may control one's behavior.

In the illustration given, we have referred to a predicted event which presumably takes place whether we predict it or not. But there are cases in which behavior is itself instrumental in effecting events, and at the same time the symbol indicating effected events controls the act. There are cases in which men control not only their behavior but also, and thereby, the nature of the effects of that behavior. These are cases in which men are exercising freedom to effect ends that would not take place, at least not at that time, without behavior controlled by symbols. Here we have in its clearest expression the exemplifications of human freedom. For the function of knowledge and of science is to enable us to reform and transform our environment or to make parts of it, at least, other than what it would have been if left undisturbed. We find through experience that the physical world yields to the symbolic process in many cases and that, therefore, it is possible for us to control our environment to a certain extent, although in many ways the environment in turn conditions the symbolic process. Under human freedom one acts for the sake of things to come, and in many cases by doing so he can determine specifically what does come.

The case for freedom of human conduct may be stated in a slightly different way. We know, for example, that the Mendelian law applies to biological phenomena but not to inorganic processes. This law, which is applicable only to organic phenomena, has its basis (partly at least) in inorganic phenomena. On that account, however, no one is so foolish as to say that the Mendelian law can be explained on the basis of inorganic processes alone, nor do biologists try to "reduce" organic phenomena to inorganic phenomena. In fact the Mendelian law of inheritance teaches us something about inorganic phenomena; i.e., at least it teaches us that the inorganic world lends itself to being used in the life process, which is to say, inorganic phenomena are *continuous with* organic phenomena. But that was learned by studying organic phenomena and finding that inorganic processes were carried on within the life process.

A consideration of the symbolic process in relation to the living organism and the physical environment shows that it is continuous with and functionally related to both the organic and the inorganic processes. Many contemporary psychologists, particularly those influenced by the Darwinian theory of evolution and the experimental method used in laboratories, have recognized that an increased understanding of the symbolic process must be reached by studying the nervous system in relation to both the physiological structure of the human body and the human environment. Aside from the work of extreme behaviorists, such as John B. Watson and K. W. Spence, and certain operationalists, such as Kenneth MacCorquodale and Paul

Meehl, there have been no other attempts to deny the existence of an unobservable process called reflective thinking. To locate and analyze the mechanism necessary for thought, however, has been a major problem.

Every emergent makes a difference in and to the world, whether it is an animal that can make food of grass, or one that can make a nest of a hollow tree, or one which through its chromatic vision confers color upon the world. The symbolic process is no exception, and the difference it makes stems from the fact that it can control behavior through symbols for things not present and through symbols for possible but not yet actual things. If one reaches for the seen apple, then, indeed, vision is controlling his body, arm, hand, and fingers. We can say in general that distance receptors, such as receptors for sound, odors, and colors, enable us to control bodily behavior through "distance" sensations. But in such cases present sensations control human behavior even as they control the behavior of lower animals. And indeed the emergence of sense organs made a difference not only because sense qualities are by their virtue conferred upon the world but also because of the behavior of animals resulting from these sensitivities.

The function of the symbolic process is analogous, but not equivalent, to the function of a distance stimulus. Both control behavior. Although both the symbol and a distance stimulus control behavior, the method by which this control is effected is different. In cases where behavior is controlled by sense stimuli, the reaction (behavior) is to (or with reference to) that physical object which stimulates the organism. For example, one is stimulated by the color of an apple to reach for it, and the physical, manipulatable object, the apple, is colored. Similarly, we run from the physical, touchable rattlesnake because we are stimulated by the "sound of the rattlesnake." In these cases the stimuli received by way of sensory axons are temporally continuous with the responses effected by the motor axons, although intermediary neurones may be involved. But when in addition to afferent and efferent nerves, symbols are involved in behavior, the activity of the neurones of the cortex of the cerebrum lies between the sensory stimulus and the overt response carried out by the aid of motor axons.[12]

[12] *Ibid.,* Chapter VI.

THE PHYSICAL BASIS FOR FREEDOM

I have defined freedom in such a way that it is applicable to any organism that acts as a whole. Also, I have shown that the symbolic process is a characteristic of men, and that reflective thinking involves both a language and a calendar. The mechanism for the symbolic process and reflective thinking is found in the cerebrum, the frontal lobe of the brain, especially in the cortex of the cerebrum. Neither the physiological mechanism for reflective thinking nor reflective thinking itself is a superfluous appendage to the human organism; rather, both are integral parts of the organism as it adjusts and readjusts to the environment. In other words, the symbolic process is continuous with the activity of the form and with the environment of the form. It is an integral part of the ongoing life process. The organism is free to the extent that the symbolic process and reflective thinking are integrated with the behavior of the organism as it carries on the life process. If we answer the question: What specifically is the difference between the kind of behavior carried on by an organism in which the symbolic process is an integral part, and the kind carried on in behavior wherein symbols are absent? our answer will serve as the basis for distinguishing between kinds of freedom; i.e., freedom in human behavior and freedom in nonhuman behavior. Human behavior, integrated with the symbolic process, is a type of behavior controlled by symbols indicating actual as well as possible events or conditions that are posited hypothetically in a future. One predicts that a certain event or condition will take place in a future, and a symbol for that predicted event controls his behavior. Or, one acts as if something not here now will be there then.

Here let us make a distinction between two kinds of behavior integrated with symbols. First, the kind in which we adjust to events that are predicted but cannot be controlled; for example, adjustments made to earthquakes or tornadoes. Second, behavior which effects all kinds of changes conditioned by planning, such as the building of dams to prevent floods, or the simple acts of building houses. But whether we think of the first kind of behavior or the second, both lead to at least a partial determination of the future and therefore to a partial determination of the structure of the world through thinking, and this is the meaning of human freedom; i.e., self-determination, which results in an environment reconstructed and transformed by the aid of the symbolic process whose temporal dimension distinguishes it from all nonsymbolic processes.

Freedom of any organism means using the immediately present world to effect satisfactory, new surroundings. In man a foreknowledge of the effects of the laws of nature is a part of the conditions for a free act, yet such foreknowledge does not imply a fated future, for there are alternative possible ways in which we can act, as can be seen from a knowledge of physical objects and of the laws of nature. The physical world lends itself to being acted on in different ways, and these different ways can be symbolized prior to the act. As we shall see in the section that follows, our bodily movements are flexible and can act on objects in many different ways both in analyzing and in synthesizing them; and our bodies, unlike inorganic machines, can release stored up energy on objects at particular places and times and with reference to ends lying in a future. In general, freedom means getting away from a present by means of symbols, bodily action, physical objects, and an application of known laws of nature.

The Physiological Basis for Freedom

It is rather paradoxical that through a study of physical, chemical, and biological phenomena some have come to the conclusion that men are not free but, rather, that the behavior of every man is determined by his past. If we knew enough about a person's past, so the argument goes, we would be able to predict everything he will ever do and, therefore, no person is free. This is paradoxical, for it was only through our ability to set up *controlled* experiments that we came to the conclusion that events have histories or causes and that they are, therefore, determined and predictable. And yet when one says he can control experiments, he must assume that events that happen under his control would not have occurred at that time without control. Which is to say that a given spatiotemporal locus may be qualified by alternative possible events no particular one of which needs to take place, and that through control we can effect prevised ends only the symbols for which are present during the controlling period. This amounts to saying that, in some cases at least, we can predict and determine what will take place in the future.

THE PHYSIOLOGICAL BASIS FOR FREEDOM

Can one state the conditions under which an event will take place and predict when and where it will take place? Actually we can do so with regard to such things as the eclipse of the moon, the tides, or the summer solstice. But these are events over which we have no control, and they are said to be determined if not predetermined. If, however, a person's behavior can be made an integral part of the conditions necessary for the occurrence of a certain event, and if one has a knowledge of both the necessary behavior involved and the event following from that behavior, and if such knowledge controls that behavior and thereby enters into the process of effecting that prevised end, then one is free. But the control of behavior through a knowledge of the laws of nature (including behavior and the consequences of behavior) is possible only if the physiological structure of our bodies is such that energy can be directed, through our muscles, toward prevised ends.

It is easy enough to see that if the spatial position of objects in our environment were fixed and could not be changed there would be no sense in speaking of freedom of behavior. Similarly, if by means of our own bodily activities, such as walking, the manipulation of objects by the fingers or hands, we could not act on objects so as to change their relative positions, freedom would mean nothing. But freedom requires more than these two possibilities. It requires also that the rearrangement of objects take place by us according to a plan. And since a plan is a result of the symbolic process or reflective thinking, this means that the symbolic process must be continuous with both the physiological structure of the human body and the physical structure of the external world.

When the fingers and hands do work, they must act on some physical object. If, to an extent, the hands are responsible for the manipulation of objects so that their relative spatial positions are changed over a period of time, it is only because the objects will lend themselves to such manipulation. To say that one is free to act because he is unrestrained throws no light on the meaning of human freedom. Freedom involves the capacity to select and, therefore, determine beforehand both the place and the time at which certain events will occur, and this presupposes a temporal control over behavior, over the spatial direction of the movement of the body, and, consequently, over the movement of objects not the body. If one of my books falls to the floor, I can pick it up and put it back on the desk now or later. If it falls to the right of the desk, I can pick it up as easily as if it had fallen to the left. In either case my hands (as well as the book) lend themselves to the end of having the book on the desk. In the symbolic process the final stage of the act resulting in "the book on the desk" is represented, and it is this symbolized final stage that controls the act of replacing the book. The particular way in which I pick up the book will be determined, however, by the book's location and by the structure and flexibility of my body.

Indeed the physiological make-up of the human body must be such that energy can be released at particular times (and places) if one is to control his behavior so that it will fit in with processes in nature over which (for the time at least) he has no control. Practically all the energy exerted by us on objects is in the form of mechanical energy (in contrast to electrical energy, chemical energy or light). When we lift a stone, energy is spent against gravity. In that case, however, we should not say the stone stimulated us to lift it. The stone is a stimulus by way of our sense organs, such as our eyes and ears. But a stimulus presupposes a response, and the response can be expressed in terms of work done or in terms of energy spent. (Work = Force $\times$ Distance;

$$\text{Energy} = \frac{\text{Force} \times \text{distance}}{\text{time}}; \text{ hence: } E = W/T).$$ Every movement of the body can be expressed in mechanical terms or in terms of the amount of work done per unit time. If one's body acts on other bodies, it can do so only at the expense of measurable mechanical energy, and no such thing as mental energy, or spiritual energy, or will power can move or act on physical objects. Even reflective thinking requires energy, possibly in chemical or electrical form, but nevertheless physical energy is required to keep the process going.[13]

Before coming back to our main point, let us digress long enough to call attention to a serious but understandable error among scientists,

[13] A most peculiar emergent came about in connection with the chemical, electrical processes that take place in the cortex of the cerebrum; by means of that process one is able to present or represent to himself, so to speak, the physical, the chemical, electrical, biological, etc., processes that take place outside the brain, and it is hoped that through experimental psychology and physiology we will be able to understand the process in the brain which makes possible the representation of other processes.

including not only the physical scientists but psychologists as well. As a rule when scientists find the mechanism by which certain ends are effected, they proceed to assimilate these ends *to* the mechanism necessary for them. In other words, scientists identify ends with means, or assimilate effects to causes. And when this practice is applied to reflective thinking, psychologists show a tendency to reduce reflective thinking or the symbolic process to the chemical and electrical processes necessary for it. Operationalists and behaviorists go so far as to deny the existence of unobservables and are forced to identify the symbolic process with colors, sounds, or with operations. Their philosophy of science does not allow for the theory of evolution or, consequently, for the emergence of the symbolic process. This practice is a habit quite incongruous with a belief in evolution.

In this discussion I do not assume that a discovery of the mechanism necessary for thinking and for freedom puts in question the existence of these things, the means of which may be discovered. But a discovery of the natural mechanism by which thinking takes place does show that thinking has a natural cause and that it is not an unnatural (or supernatural) process. Thinking is continuous with the mechanical functioning of the body, and it is an emergent.

Now back to the nature of stimuli. Not everything in the external world within the range of our senses can be stimuli at the same time. We can "pay attention" to only one thing at a time. Behaviorists, Watson among them, are in agreement on this point, but they answer that we respond to the "strongest" stimulus immediately present. If "strongest" means the stimulus to which we respond, the statement "one always responds to the strongest stimulus" is, of course, tautological. If "strongest" means the stimulus exerting the greatest mechanical force on us, by way of sound vibrations, odors, light waves, etc., then we see at once that such a theory is not only false but silly. One may look for a lost diamond ring during a thunderstorm. If one's behavior is under the influence of symbols, physical objects become stimuli only if he believes that they fit into the planned act.

In general, objects stimulate us if they are either detrimental to the organism, as when one steps on a tack or stumbles over a stone, or if they release prepotent responses. A prepotent response is a process going on inside the organism, often referred to as a state or disposition such as hunger, anxiety, or fear, which can be completed or released only by an overt response to an environmental stimulus. At present let us confine our interest to stimuli in relation to prepotent responses. If reflective thinking does not enter into the behavior of an animal, stimuli, such as odors, sounds, and colors, release prepotent responses that in general answer to biological needs. The dog reacts to certain odors only if he is hungry, and in a hungry dog the process of eating and, consequently, digesting is already begun and can be completed through responses to odors and food. The presence of food will not make a dog hungry, and if "food" is to be a stimulus, it must enter into the completion of an act already begun; i.e., it must answer to a prepotent response. In general, for anything to be an environmental stimulus there must be inside the organism a process which is also the beginning of the response to the stimulus. Consequently, the internal processes condition the nature of the stimulus by determining the nature of the response. Stimuli, such as odors, sounds, or colors, serve as triggers in releasing a response; and we may call all distant stimuli triggers for releasing acts simply because the amount of energy involved in such a stimulus is by no means numerically equivalent to the mechanical response released by it.

Our physiological make-up is such that our bodies can store up energy and release it toward the fulfillment of biological needs. This process of storing and releasing energy is usually designated by the old-fashioned word "metabolism." All living things have the capacity to store up energy, and animals have the capacity to release stored up energy on objects that stimulate them. In most cases the objects that stimulate animals are also conducive to carrying on the biological process or, as we may say, these objects enter into the process of adaptation and the adjustment of the organism to the environment. H. Wildon Carr[14] is probably correct in his contention that this capacity to store up energy (independent of the relative temperatures of the body and the food assimilated and, therefore, in apparent contradiction to the second law of thermodynamics) is an emergent which marks the distinction between living and nonliving things. But most animals, in contrast with most plants, have the capacity of locomotion, which is

[14] See "Life and Matter," *Sixth International Congress of Philosophy* (New York, Longmans, Green & Co., Inc., 1927).

used very effectively in evading danger and appropriating food for themselves. They release energy in certain directions, so to speak, but only under circumstances which are in general conducive to the survival of the species or of the particular animal involved. For the most part responses made by lower animals take place automatically and are released by stimuli as if by a trigger. However, the trigger presupposes a prepotent response and a stimulus. This stimulus does not create or cause the response, but releases it; and the response, since it is prepotent, implies a future in which it can be completed and a direction for its completion. If an animal is free to act, i.e., if it acts as a whole, then usually the energy is released in a direction resulting in the fulfillment of an ongoing biological process.

If it were not for metabolism, the word "stimulus" would have no meaning, for the living organism would act as a machine and the energy that goes into the body would be released at a definite rate, in the manner that a warm body gives off energy to a cooler body at a certain rate. But the warm body does not select a particular cool body to which it gives energy, nor does it select the time at which it releases energy. In other words, in the nonliving world the rate of the release of energy and the time at which it is released can be stated in mathematical equations, but in some cases, e.g., radium, the rate cannot be affected by surroundings. It would be a misuse of terms to say that nonliving objects are stimulated to act as they do, for the actions of nonliving objects can be accounted for on the basis of efficient causes alone, whereas a stimulus implies both a direction of action toward a future end and a selection of the objects upon which the energy involved in action is released.

Suppose a person is hunting deer. During the hunt he is sensitized especially to brownish-gray colors and to antlers. The prepotent act (shooting) will be released under certain conditions, but the amount of energy received through light waves from that color and shape, in comparison to the energy received from the many other objects in the environment, is not responsible for the release of the act of shooting. Rather the hunter sensitizes himself to certain shapes and colors prior to the act of shooting, and this sensitization means simply that the organism is selecting the stimulus toward which energy will be released; the selection is teleological in character, for selection is always with reference to the completion of a prepotent act or an ongoing act, and these acts can be completed only in a future. An object becomes a stimulus only in relation to a response, and the responses of living forms are carried out with reference to the welfare of the organism as a whole or with reference to its species. What in the physical surroundings becomes a stimulus depends not only on the environment of the living organism but also, and primarily, on its biological state at the time. The physical object becomes a stimulus to the biological form only in relation to a future state of the form or, in general, only in relation to what biologists have called "survival value."

If we state the meaning of "stimulus" as applied in its widest scope, including sense stimuli as well as stimulation due to symbols, we may say that every stimulus directs the activity of a living form toward an end, and the end can be stated only with reference to value. The means to the accomplishment of ends is indeed expressible in terms of physico-chemical and electrical change, but the end cannot be expressed in those terms, and we resort to such terms as "survival value," or simply "value." No mechanical, physical, chemical, or electrical laws are ever "broken" but, rather, they are utilized in the achievement of ends (values). But we should not identify means and ends lest the basic purpose of science be jeopardized: namely, a study of nature in order to mold her to our purpose.

The lower biological form has the capacity to respond only to those objects in its surroundings which, in general, have survival value. In fact it is through the responses made by the organism that the particular nature and scope of the environment is determined. The squirrel responds to nuts and to the hollow tree. The ox responds to grass and hay. Survival value gives form and environment a unity such that each becomes significant, for both "form" and "environment" are abstractions, each apart from the other and apart from survival value. Survival value gives significance to (but not an explanation of) the capacity of an organism to store up energy and release it at certain times and places. Lower animals make no value judgments, and it may well be that they inherit general patterns of behavior from their ancestors (such as are carried out in the migration of birds or in nest-building activities), and biologists say these patterns of behavior have survival value.

THE PHYSIOLOGICAL BASIS FOR FREEDOM

Human beings are not only stimulated by sensed objects but they can stimulate themselves by symbols. To be accurate, one cannot act on symbols, but only on physical objects, and to say, therefore, that one is stimulated by a symbol means that a symbol determines both what particular physical object in one's immediate environment is acted on, and also the particular way in which one acts on it. For example, if an individual intends to pull a tack out of his shoe, he must first walk toward the tool chest, and he must walk on the floor, which is a physical object. Next, he must reach for the pliers, and, finally, he must pull on the tack. In every case there is something in the immediate environment to which a person responds. The symbols, then, determine the form of the act in relation to the nature of the immediate physical environment, or the symbol conditions one to respond in this manner instead of that, and to this object instead of that one.

Let us point out once more that if there were only one possible future state of an organism, freedom would be meaningless. Lower animals, unlike plants, gained their freedom because of their locomotive capacity. And although space is homogeneous (which means, among other things, that regardless of *where* an object, including living organisms, is in space, it makes no difference to *what* it is), objects in space are not homogeneous. An organism acts with reference to heterogeneous objects, not with reference to a homogeneous space. If an animal is falling down a cliff its freedom is limited, and if that animal is a man, he has practically no freedom; but if perchance it is a cat, it may still adjust its body so that it will land on its feet. Under freedom, then, the animal must be capable of responding to more than one physical object, or there must be alternative possible stimuli (with their entailed alternative possible responses), and the selection of the ones to which the organism actually responds is always made with reference to a future state of the organism. In many cases the responses of lower animals are in the form of patterns of behavior, but always with reference to survival value. Whether the bird picks up sticks, or strings, or straw will depend on whether these things are available, but the net result may be a nest in any case.

The capacity of men to think and to use symbols presupposes alternative ways of acting. One symbol stands for a particular future situation and another symbol for another. If a person could present to himself one and only one future situation, thinking would be meaningless. From our own experience we recognize that different symbols are competing, as it were, for control over our behavior. Finally one symbol (or symbols for a particular way of acting with reference to particular objects with the entailed consequence) has priority over the others, and we call the process by which this competition is resolved "choice." The physiological mechanism for choice is the same as the mechanism for reflective thinking and is located in the cortex of the cerebrum. *That* choice takes place we cannot doubt, but how it takes place we do not know. All evidence for the existence of choice is acquired through introspection. Choice is a process which results in an organization, a co-ordination, and a resolution of symbols whose possible referents are there as competing, distant, future stimuli; i.e., competing for control over immediate action. Freedom lies not in what has traditionally been thought of as static choice, a yes or a no, but rather in the capacity to organize action in order to resolve conflicts entailed in responding to alternative stimuli.

If we were to give a name to the intellectual side of this process by which we come to choice, we would call it "evaluation." The act that finally results from a resolution of conflicting attitudes (entailing alternative possible future conditions) is committed with reference to a preconceived possible future condition believed to be more satisfactory or better than the one rejected in the process of evaluating (judging) and reaching a conclusion. Our freedom lies in this capacity to co-ordinate the symbolic process with behavior and with the environment in which behavior must take place. But also the co-ordination of these processes must be effective if we are to remain free. Which is to say that in the last analysis our thinking and our judging must answer to the basic requests of nature—the biological process. This is not to say that nature will support the effects of one and only one kind of thinking and judging. Just as there are many different kinds of living organisms on earth (and presumably many more kinds are possible), so there are many different possible civilizations, cultures, and societies, and nature will be tolerant of the many different ways in which we carry on the life process.

The capacity to change external conditions by the aid of reflective thinking does not mean working against nature, but it means, rather, that the symbolic process is a part of nature and has entered into the process of evolution wherein, in the last analysis, lies the basis for freedom. For freedom involves instituting new processes, new forms, new cultures, new institutions, new habits, by means of old ones. The biological mutation uses dependable chemical and physical processes, as well as many of the patterns of behavior of the parent form, in carrying on the life process in the new form. Similarly, every newly instituted practice depends on some old customs and well-established habits. Under freedom the individual uses the laws of nature and his past to institute novelties,[15] new practices, which in turn tend to become habitual. In that sense he cannot get away from the past and the laws of nature, for they constitute the mechanism by which the new is effected and supported. Those who insist on identifying the end with the means of producing it will not be able to see anything in the world but repetition, and for them there will be neither evolution nor freedom. Unless one can employ symbols indicating future conditions not included in the status quo to control behavior in using the status quo to make those symbolized conditions actual, he is not free. Hence under freedom we use the status quo in order to get away from it, but our use of it is conditioned by a symbolic representation of those future conditions which will be instituted by means of it.

Human freedom is a different (if not a higher) type of freedom than the freedom of "freely falling stones" or the freedom exercised by lower animals. Insensitive bodies simply follow a law, and not much, if any, of the future is involved in such blind, mechanical behavior. Although much of the behavior of lower animals is mechanical, in general their life process has a direction and takes place with particular reference to the survival value of the species to which the animal belongs. Most behavior of a lower animal is carried out either through habits established through conditioning to stimuli peculiar to its environment or through "patterns of behavior" inherited from its ancestors. These patterns of behavior may apply to acts having either a long or a short duration, but they are native to the organism in that they are carried out automatically by every member of the species when the proper stimulus is furnished, e.g., migration of birds, ability to

[15] See G. H. Mead, *The Philosophy of the Present* (LaSalle [Ill.], Open Court Publishing Company, 1932), Chapter III.

swim, sexual intercourse, and hibernation. In a real sense Aristotle's conception of freedom applies to lower animals, for they are free only when they are not prevented from carrying out prepotent responses inherited from their ancestors or, in the case of a mutation, when there is something in the environment answering to the newly developed organs.

In *all* symbolically directed behavior men are conscious of, and, therefore, control by symbols, only certain stages of an act. These stages are usually of very short duration. The rest of the act takes place out of habit or because of some general law of nature. In driving the nail, the law of inertia is operative, and lifting the hammer takes place out of habit. One does not learn to act. We are active by nature. Men, however, can use native reactions and unlearned behavior in reorganizing behavior and in reconstructing habits that are new to that extent. But men must fall back finally on their native equipment and on predispositions for the reconstruction of behavior. Yet once a new act has been developed it can be used for reconstructing another. It will take considerable time to reconstruct many of our habits, for we must rely on old ones to develop new ones. We can reconstruct our "lives" (or our living practices) only piecemeal. Similarly, we must reconstruct our civilizations, our institutions, and our customs piecemeal, for we must use the old in developing the new.

A tool or an instrument of any kind increases the application of laws of nature. It is often said that there are six basic machines (wedge, inclined plane, screw, wheel and axle, pulley, and lever). These machines give us a mechanical advantage, but hand tools, nevertheless, require that we expend energy continuously while applying them. A higher type of human freedom is found when man enters into natural processes only here and there, at strategic places and times, but still directs these processes toward preconceived ends. To be sure, natural processes will take place even in the absence of all control. Men cannot create laws of nature, nor can they stop all processes. *Something* is going to take place *willy-nilly*. But since it is possible for a particular spatio-temporal locus to be qualified by any one of a number of alternative processes, the one which actually qualifies it will be determined by the particular conditions at that time. One may turn the key clockwise and lock the door, or if the door is locked one may unlock it. Unlocking a door may have wide implications regarding future eventualities, especially if it is a door to a prison cell. Again, one may close an electric switch and start a motor which in turn opens the gate at the dam. Water and gravity will do the rest, but the net result may be the irrigation of crops. Here we see that men enter into natural processes only here and there in order to begin or stop a natural process that takes place according to laws which can be neither prescribed nor annihilated by men or by anything they can do. It takes exceedingly little energy to effect the confluence of processes which makes future events different from what they would have been without the presence of man's body and the symbolic process.

Beginning with hand tools men arrived at a discovery of principles and finally laws of mechanics. By taking advantage of these things, human freedom has extended the time that natural desired processes will continue without human intervention. For example, cotton mills often run day and night, and they are started simply by turning a switch. As the cotton comes out of the mill it is woven, printed, cut in length, folded, wrapped, and stamped for shipping. Men are spending less time and much less bodily physical energy in making a living, and far more time in devising ways of using laws of nature to effect desired ends. Yet (in highly industrialized countries) there is more food per capita, and, in general, the standard of living is much higher than it was prior to the development of machines that operate automatically.

C. E. Ayres has attributed this growth of technological phenomena to a property of tools themselves. He writes:[16]

The diffusion of culture traits from one culture area to another is quite generally accompanied by innovation. Indeed, so striking is the stimulus which results from culture contacts that it has been called the "cross-fertilization" of cultures. But it is the tools themselves, not the people, that have been hybridized. Such innovations—and they include some of the most important technological advances in history—are not to be explained by any special excitation of the imaginations of the people among whom they occur. . . . We have here the explanation of the "inscrutable" propensity of all technological devices to proliferate. This "propensity" is a characteristic not of men but of tools.

[16] C. E. Ayres, *op. cit.*, pp. 118–119.

I think Ayres is mistaken in the belief that the cause of technological progress (which, he says, "increases very rapidly, by squares: x; x^2; $(x^2)^2$; . . .") is to be found wholly in the nature of tools. If this were true, it would shame our experimental laboratories and our educational institutions in so far as they pretend to treat of science and the technological phase of our culture. Ayres is saying in effect that if there are such things as the symbolic process and reflective thinking, they have nothing to do with progress in technology. It is, of course, tautological to say that our leisure time increases in proportion to the time natural processes can be left to themselves without supervision and yet yield the results desired by man. Witness the people of India and of the Philippine Islands, for example, and note that practically all of their energy is spent on getting food and other things necessary for continuing the life process. But the leisure of the American people has increased in direct proportion to technological developments. What do we do during this leisure time? Ayres leaves us with the impression that leisure time is spent in ceremonies and in all sorts of institutional practices which, when it comes right down to it, tend to prevent the tools from "proliferating" according to the law of squares. Actually more time and money is being spent on education in general and on laboratory science in particular than ever before.

But what is research science about? It concerns devising new ways of utilizing nature to the accomplishment of ends desired by men. And if it is true that technological progress tends to follow the law of squares, it is equally true that the time spent during leisure for scientific research tends to follow the law of squares. To separate these two phases of our civilization, namely pure research and applied science (technology), would be identical with separating reflective thinking and behavior.

The symbolic process, bodily activities, and the environment are continuous. This does not mean there are no distinctions among them, but it means that each phase of this continuous process enters into free human behavior. The symbolic process is being emphasized more and more in our industrialized, technological culture, which is to say that the freedom of man increases only to the extent that the symbolic process can be co-ordinated with nature, not tools. Tools, machines, the principles of mechanics, and laws of nature must lend themselves to being united and combined in ways first symbolized by men if we are to exercise freedom. But tools as such are sterile and will not cross-breed apart from that catalytic agent, the symbolic process.

The "lag of culture" or the so-called inertia of technology, caused presumably (according to Ayres) by institutions, is due rather to the stubborn fact that improvements in technology must first be planned by thinking men, and that these plans can be *instituted* effectively in the technological world of fact only when they become a part of our social practices—habits, customs—and it takes considerable time to condition our bodies to what the symbolic process has prescribed. The difficulty of making more rapid technological progress can be laid to institutions in the same sense that one can lay the difficulty of establishing new habits to old ones. But we must remember that we can effect the new only by using the old. Even new machines are a result of the use of old ones. Human freedom is based on our capacity to use the given, the status quo, to institute new practices which have been conditioned by symbols for their consequences.

Conclusion

Human freedom requires the co-ordination of symbols with bodily activity and with physical objects. In the process of evolution the symbolic processes emerged from the biological processes which, in turn, emerged from the physical world. The co-ordination of these three components is made possible by the capacity of men to condition themselves, and this amounts to the capacity to select the stimuli to which they respond. Selection means being prepared to act in a certain way when the proper stimulus arises, or it means establishing prepotent responses by use of symbols. When symbols are controlling one's behavior, that person is both restraining himself from responding to present possible stimuli and also conserving energy which will be released on selected stimuli. This capacity to store up energy and to release it upon selected physical objects distinguishes the living from the nonliving processes, and the capacity to select stimuli by use of symbols (or self-conditioning) distinguishes the human animal from all others.

To say the least, self-conditioning greatly extends the temporal dimension of a single act; which means an act controlled by symbols is committed with reference to events which, if they occur, can do so only in a more or less distant future. Controlling behavior by use of symbols by its very nature, then, implies what is ordinarily called *planning* or *planned behavior*. But planned behavior, as shown above, is of no consequence whatsoever unless one's environment lends itself to being acted on according to plans. To say that the environment lends itself to being acted on according to a plan becomes meaningful only if action according to a plan is instrumental in bringing about a circumstance (or circumstances) that would not have taken place at that time without planned behavior. In short, planned behavior must make a difference in the world, a difference that would not have resulted, at that time at least, without it. And when we follow the implications of "planned behavior" further, we find that it presupposes alternative possible future events and, correspondingly, alternative possible plans. Without these alternatives freedom would mean nothing. As explained earlier, pure science presents us with neutral statements that lend themselves indifferently to the accomplishment of alternative ends, and this, of course, assumes that alternative plans are possible.

By means of the symbolic process we both evaluate and co-ordinate various possible ends (with their corresponding means). And if an act is preceded by deliberation and choice, it will be committed with reference to a possible future that, for the time at least, has been "accepted." If one can justify the acceptance of a certain possible future, then it is not only desired but also desirable. Such justification leads to ethics, which is beyond the scope of this work, but it concerns the ordering (evaluation) of ends with reference to each other and also the construction of norms which consist of the co-ordination of technical means in such a manner as to assure the harmony of ends.

Freedom leads finally to responsibility, which gives rise to the problems of ethics and especially value judgments with regard to ends and norms. In this chapter I have shown that freedom is rooted in the physical world, biology, and the symbolic process. Morals have these same roots, and value judgments make sense only if men are free to act in various ways.

As a rule we think a person has achieved freedom to the extent that he can utilize natural processes and laws of nature in the accomplishment of desired prevised ends. This limited concept of freedom must be supplemented by adding that a person becomes freer to the extent that he can use nature to the accomplishment of desired, prevised ends *and* to the extent that he can decrease the amount of time and bodily energy spent in directing natural processes.

Machines that operate automatically have effectively added to man's freedom, permitting him more time to exercise the "art of living" and to improve technology, both directly and indirectly, through pure science. Short of the impositions inherent in the biological organism with its frailties and short endurance, there is no limit to such freedom. All that is necessary to allow a continuing increase in freedom is a peaceful, co-operative human society.

Index